MW00646991

THE WOMEN OF THE HOUSE

To the descendants

— living, dead, and to come—

of Janie and Van McKibben, especially to

the Mallet five of them for whom "Heritage" was truly home

and

with deep appreciation to Marcia Mallet Anderson

whose encouragement and assistance in the completion

of this book has been invaluable.

Prologue

January 1979

THE KEY WOULD NOT TURN. My cold hand and numb fingers could not lock the front door of Mother's house, and I stood shivering on the front porch, shaking as much from frustration and grief as from the chill of a gray January afternoon in Middle Georgia.

I remembered the frequent tantrums of my childhood when I had lain down on the floor of the porch and kicked the banisters as hard as I could. Now I could only mutter, "Damn the perversity of inanimate objects." Instantly I knew that I was quoting Grandmother's expression. I kneed the heavy door as I turned the knob and pushed. The old door, with a familiar grudging screech, allowed itself to be reopened, and I stood again beneath the high paneled ceiling of the wide front hall.

I did not want to be back here. All day I had worked in the unheated rooms, sorting and wondering what might become of things—the worn but still beautiful Chinese rug in the parlor, Grandmother's piano, the Tiffany lamp my sister had found in the attic and hung over the table in the huge kitchen. It was after four o'clock, and I was ready to escape the tyranny of tarnished silver and broken clocks and leaking, rusty plumbing. I could not face another family photograph or letter or diploma or any other rediscovered bit of treasure-trash.

Mother had said, "It's terrible that things outlast people. I've spent too much of my life taking care of things—this house and all these things of Mama's and Grandma's. I've fixed and painted and polished. I'm tired of things. It's people I care about."

We had been standing by the front steps when she indulged in that outburst so unlike her. Mother prided herself on cheerfulness and optimism. She was looking down at the granite millstone sunk in the lawn by the steps. After my father's death, she had the stone brought from an abandoned grist mill on property he owned. "I used to call this place Heritage," she said. "Now it's just The Old Grindstone."

Still Mother continued to cling to them all—her things, her house, her people. (She had ceased to separate the quick and the dead.) When we left her at the Living Center Nursing Home, she insisted, "I can go back home with you right now. There is not one thing the matter with me. Mama and the children won't know where I am. Who's taking care of the house? You know the pipes will freeze if it gets any colder."

The old arteries would not allow the brain to place her memories in order. Now we must order her house, her things, what remained of her life. She held and was held by the past—unwilling to let go, unable to break away. I could do both. I could close the door although I could not lock it; I could leave.

Instead, I moved down the hall to the stairs and walked up to the first landing before I stopped. (Could it have been so long ago that we chased each other up the front stairs, down the back stairs and round and round the dining room table?) I could see through the balustrade the massive chifforobe in the upstairs hall. (My sister Marcia now calls it an armoire.) Scraps of my great-grandmother Janie's turn-of-the-century elegance still remained in it. My sisters and I had played dress-up in a pale yellow outfit with high collar and whale-boned fitted jacket and in lacy blouses with leg-of-mutton sleeves. The waists were so small that we children had to suck in to fasten the tiny covered buttons.

I turned, refusing to step further into the past. Downstairs, I still could not turn the key, and I could not leave the house open and vulnerable. It held too much of us. Beginning with that first Janie, five generations of us have lived in the house (six if we count our children's children who have only visited.) We built it, lived in it, continued to change it. We have taken pride in it, cared for it and neglected it, been shackled to it, ignored it, laughed at it. We have cried and found sanctuary in this house. I could not walk away—not from our house, not from the women to whom it has belonged.

Here then are their stories—great-grandmother Janie's, grandmother Hattie's, and mother Mary's—twined tenaciously like honeysuckle in more than a hundred years of Middle Georgia.

Janie

Janie

PROP THE TORN PHOTOGRAPH OF THE THREE WOMEN on a marble topped table in the parlor. Look first at the oldest, the figure on the left, the stern, black-clad woman in her fifties—Effie Jane Fletcher McKibben.

Surround the picture with her cut crystal and china. Go up to the attic and scrunch back under the eaves. Pull out the old trunks and search. Find the rotting leather of her riding crop and a rat-gnawed farm account ledger. They fit into the picture. Like the pieces to start a jigsaw puzzle, they each have at least one straight edge. They begin to make a border. But the puzzle of the first woman of the house is not put together with easy pieces.

Look for the missing pieces, the hard pieces, the grotesque pieces that belong but will not fit. Piece together yellowed items from the *Middle Georgia Argus* before the turn of the century. Trace words carved into granite monuments in two cemeteries. Dig out a will from county courthouse archives and raise an eyebrow at the added codicil. Listen, listen to the stories told by an aged in-law and add them to the gossip from the shriveled lips of an ancient, surviving servant.

Most of all, remember, remember. Remember Grandmother. Remember her summer visits to us—her daughter and her grandchildren living in her girlhood home. Remember Grandmother's fan; remember Grandmother's crochet needle; remember Grandmother's stories. Remember Grandmother—talking, talking, talking. Remember hot July evenings, lit by lightning bugs and perfumed by the powder puffs of mimosa blossoms. Remember rocking chairs on the front porch and

Grandmother—talking and crocheting, talking and fanning, fanning and stirring the still air and threatening the humming mosquitoes, fanning and stirring ghosts and memory alive.

Now look again at the picture, at the oldest woman in it, Janie Fletcher McKibben. The steady eyes in the head held rigidly erect look directly ahead, not toward her daughter Hattie or her granddaughter Mary. Janie seems to stand austerely alone. Her eyes have been disciplined by the work, the gains, the losses of a proud woman. They may pierce in reproach or flash in anger. They may, on occasion, show approval. Those eyes will not now seek those of another, reveal adoration, or overflow with tears.

Effie Jane Fletcher (always called Janie) was nine years old in 1864. In November of that year, General William Tecumseh Sherman left Atlanta in smoldering ashes. His plan was to march his Union Army southeastward from that conquered, ruined city and cut a swath through Georgia to reach Savannah, the Atlantic, and supply and communication lines. His army would live off the land and demonstrate to Confederate rebels that War is indeed Hell. Janie knew nothing of General Sherman's plans, but their implementation was etched forever on her memory by the acids of excitement and fear.

The Fletcher farm, directly in Sherman's way, was little more than a long day's march from Atlanta. There Janie's mother had been left in charge of the farm, perhaps a dozen Negroes, and seven children.

Janie knew about the war, of course, but it had seemed something far off—in places called Virginia and Tennessee. For almost as long as she could remember, the talk of her parents and her older brothers had been war. Janie was not talkative, and she did not ask many questions; but she was perceptive, and she learned fast. She knew that Lee and Jackson were the best generals since Washington, that Jeff Davis and Alec Stephens were fine men, and that Abe Lincoln and Sherman were "damnyankees." Sometimes what she had heard sounded as if her father and brothers and the other men who came to their farm wanted to fight. "Ain't no Yankee yet can beat a Georgia boy." But that had been a long time ago, before her father had put on the gray Confederate uniform, taken the rank of lieutenant, and left home with a Georgia militia regiment.

"Molly, Molly, you'll have to manage," he had said. Molly (Mary Evalina Merritt Fletcher) had managed—even when Janie's older brothers, Richard Merritt and William Henry, both in their teens, had gone to fight the Yankees, too. They had looked like boys playing soldier, but Janie knew in 1864 that the war was no game and that it was not far away.

The summer and early fall of 1864 had been strange and tense. Her husband having come home on brief leaves, Molly Fletcher gave birth in June to their ninth child. As her husband had directed, she oversaw the remaining, bewildered Negroes in harvesting. She felt responsibility for them as well as the chickens, cows, pigs, mules, and horses they helped her tend. The children, including baby Johnny, were her primary concern and were never neglected.

She was accustomed to work. Her husband was listed in an 1860 census as owning fifteen slaves, but having farm hands did not give the Fletchers ease or luxury. They were working farmers, not leisured planters. Yet the work of that summer was different—hard and hurting and accompanied by news of battles fought and lost to the north and then as close to home as Atlanta and Jonesboro.

The Fletcher children worked, too. Mary Eliza was fourteen and old enough for almost all the tasks as was Julian Webster. His maleness combined with his eleven years to qualify him for work not usually assigned children. Janie could fetch and carry and rock her baby brother as well as keep a watchful eye on her little sisters, Laura, Emma, Sara, and Lula.

There was always enough to eat; the Fletchers had made their acres of red Georgia earth productive. Even before the war, they had owned little in cash reserve, and by 1864, what they had in paper Confederate money was already almost worthless. But here was food—corn and sweet potatoes, eggs, and milk. November was too early to butcher hogs, so there was only a little salted pork in the smokehouse. A tithe of their grain, like that of the other county farmers, was stored in the courthouse in Jackson, the county seat, for the "support of the Confederacy."

When word reached the farm of the approach of the Union Army, Mary Evalina Merritt Fletcher and her children buried or hid the family valuables and what food they could. They had been warned that what the

Yankees could not use or eat they would burn or shatter at will. Then there was nothing left for the woman and her seven children to do but wait and pray.

Two days later, the "blue horde" had left Butts County. Yankee soldiers had passed by and through Fletcher property, but the Fletchers were unharmed. They could see the flames and smoke as the county courthouse burned. Then the stench from carcasses of horses, mules, and cows mixed with the smell of ashes and smoldering timbers.

In the spring, the war so hard fought was lost and over. The dream of a new nation, the Confederate States of America, died hard. General Lee surrendered in Virginia, and the regiment in which Henry Baker Fletcher had served disbanded in South Carolina. In April, with his two older sons, Richard Merritt and William Henry, Janie's father returned to the farm. There were no slaves; there was no money. But in Middle Georgia there were rolling green acres of rich earth for a man, a woman, and a big, united family. They determined to plant, to grow, and to prosper.

Janie grew to womanhood there, absorbing her family's ideals of pride and determination and practicing its habits of industry and thrift. After all, Janie was only one of a long line of strong, active, intelligent women. She accepted, too, as part of her heritage a tradition that encouraged women to be useful and perhaps accomplished but also taught them to be subservient to their men—their fathers, their husbands, their sons.

Janie's immediate model was her mother. Years later, in a new century, Janie's daughter Hattie was to tell my siblings and me about our great-great-grandmother, Molly Fletcher. Our grandmother called her grandmother "Trit-n-Trot," she said, because she always seemed to be hurrying—trotting at her husband's call of "Molly, Molly" to do his bidding.

She was the oldest daughter of Mickleberry Merritt and his wife Jane Brown. Family histories state that Merritt was an "honorable and wealthy" Englishman who had settled in Georgia. He acquired respect and prestige and became a judge of the Monroe County Inferior Court. Jane Brown was described as a woman of culture and attainments. The couple evidenced their strong Protestant religious convictions by organizing a Congregational Methodist Church in their rural home. When their daughter Mary Evalina, at the age of sixteen, married Henry Baker Fletcher, she could lay claim to a respect for learning and religious faith as a part of her dowry. Twenty-one-year-old Henry, according to Monroe County deeds, was granted by his father "a horse, saddle and bridle, two cows and calves, one yearling also a bead stead and furniture" [sic]. Thus provisioned, the young couple could establish their own farm and household on the Towaliga River in neighboring Butts County, newly created from Monroe and Henry counties after treaties with the Creek Indians.

In 1843, Henry Fletcher and his bride possessed other assets for successful family farming—pioneer energy and a strong sense of family solidarity. The bigger the family, the better. Both had come from large families, Molly being the second of twelve and Henry, the youngest of eight. There were family names aplenty to be passed down to their own brood. When Janie (their fifth child and second daughter) was born on September 26, 1855, she was given the names of both grandmothers—Effie and Jane. When the war began, the Fletchers already had eight children; when it ended, there were nine.

In the years immediately following the war, the Fletcher family, like most throughout the rural South, knew hard times and hard toil. But they had all survived, and life was good. The two older boys, matured by soldiering and war experiences, were ready for early marriage and found brides among their neighbors. The younger children needed schooling.

Before the war, there had been a country school on the banks of the Towaliga River near the Fletcher farm and also an academy in Jackson. In the economic, social, and political chaos of the Reconstruction era, education was haphazard at best. Some parents taught their children whatever they knew themselves of reading, spelling, and ciphering. There were several one-teacher schools in the county. Set up by local scholars or by itinerant educators from the North, they were often short lived. The teachers were usually paid by the parents, the amount depending upon the number of students in a family and the subjects in which they received instruction.

The Fletchers were among the parents who paid tuition to a young neighbor who conducted classes in "English branches" and Latin (so his tuition account ledger shows). In Martin Van Buren McKibben, they found not only a teacher for their Janie but also her future husband.

"Colonel" McKibben's Good Lady

BORN IN 1840 AND NAMED FOR MARTIN VAN BUREN, then president of the United States, Van McKibben was well known to most of Butts County. In fact, he was already a kind of Fletcher in-law since Janie's oldest brother, Richard Merritt, had married Van's youngest sister, Hattie Clementine. McKibben family history and his own reputation preceded the entry of the soldier-scholar-lawyer-schoolmaster into the classroom where Janie Fletcher awaited instruction.

In 1832, Van's father, Thomas McKibben, had migrated from North Carolina to Georgia and the newly established Butts County. By the Indian Springs Treaty of 1825, the Creek Indians relinquished what remained of their Georgia hunting grounds. The land acquired from the Creek Nation was surveyed, divided, and distributed by means of government lotteries. The Cherokee Land Lottery of 1832 opened the last area within Georgia to white settlers. Thomas McKibben was part of a family migration, including his wife and several children, two brothers (one with a wife and children), and his widowed mother, Margaret Alexander McKibben.

Margaret McKibben, Van's grandmother, was the daughter of Abraham Alexander, one of the signers of the Mecklenburg Declaration of Independence, a North Carolina document announcing the independence of settlers of that colony before the great 1776 Declaration was signed in

Philadelphia. As the widow of Revolutionary War veteran John McKibben, Margaret had some advantage in the Georgia lotteries. She declared her personal independence when she sold her North Carolina property to finance for her sons, their families, and herself, a new life. The deed recorded in Charlotte reads "my home on Sugar Creek toward the sun rising." The McKibbens believed Georgia offered a fertile frontier opportunity for hardy pioneers. Margaret McKibben died in her promised land, and her sons prospered.

Her second son, Van's father Thomas, achieved remarkable increase in both family and fortune. His first wife, Elizabeth Duffy, who with many of her Duffy relations had trekked to Georgia with him, bore him four sons and seven daughters before her death in 1859. The census of 1860 records that Thomas McKibben owned thirty slaves in that year and that his oldest son, Van's brother Samuel, owned fourteen. McKibben slaves are credited with laying the stones of the low walls circling the cemetery of Fellowship Presbyterian Church near the McKibben farm.

When the War Between the States began in 1861, Thomas McKibben was sixty-one years of age, too old to become a soldier. Three of his sons, however, were among the more than nine hundred men from little Butts County to fight for the Confederacy.

Van's daughter and our grandmother, Hattie McKibben Lane, was to chronicle her father's military service—his enlistment in the 30th Regiment, Georgia Volunteers, his field promotion near Vicksburg after his captain had been wounded and his lieutenant killed, and his participation in fierce fighting in North Georgia and in Tennessee in 1864. He was wounded for the third time during General Hood's march in Tennessee, but he was later able to rejoin his company, which he commanded until the end of the war. Grandmother told us children that we must always respect and be grateful for Catholic nuns. The Nursing Sisters, she said, had saved her father's arm and possibly his life when the young soldier pled with them not to allow his shattered arm to be amputated.

With the South's final defeat in the spring of 1865, Van McKibben returned to his father's farm. He was twenty-five years old; his wounds were painful and would remain so for the rest of his life. But he was not defeated. He loved the land, but the Georgians he had come to admire most were more than planters; they were lawyers, politicians, statesmen.

Young McKibben knew he had a way with words, that he could persuade and lead men with them. Had not Robert Toombs, Alec Stephens, and Benjamin Hill, like Georgia Ciceros, talked their way to the halls of Congress and beyond? If he would follow them, he must have more education.

The University of Georgia—that oldest of the state universities—had reopened its gates even while federal martial law controlled Georgia. With the support and encouragement of his father, Van McKibben enrolled. He was graduated in 1868.

One of his younger classmates was Henry Grady, who, some years later, was to be editor of the *Atlanta Constitution* and a sought after speaker proclaiming the "New South" from Boston to Savannah. In 1868, when both Henry Grady and Van McKibben were studying in Athens, Georgia, a new South was already struggling to emerge.

In Butts County, Thomas and Samuel McKibben, Van's father and brother, and Henry Fletcher, Janie's father, were working through grand juries and their considerable personal influence to secure and maintain some order in the local government. In September of 1865, during some of the most chaotic days of early Reconstruction, Thomas McKibben served on the county grand jury. The courthouse had been burned, records destroyed, and civil law suspended and superseded by federal military rule. Nevertheless, the grand jury convened in an old tavern. Included in its presentments was the following statement:

> . . . the freed population . . . very few of them are employed in any business, but are strolling about at all hours of the night pilfering and stealing . . . We would solicit all persons . . . not to let the freemen and women have spirits . . . our court house and jail are in ashes . . . in view of the destitution of our county . . . we know not how long it will be before we can rebuild.

But the grand jury of 1868, the year of Van's graduation from the University of Georgia, reflected more optimism.

> The dark cloud of radicalism seems to be receding and giving way, feeling that we shall soon be relieved from its nefarious embraces and that order and good government be restored. We entertain the hope that the day is not far distant when we shall again be a prosperous and happy people.

An even brighter view was expressed the following year:

> The fears . . . engendered by the great change in our social system have been allayed, while the rights and privileges as defined by the laws and courts, have been granted without contention or direct antagonism. The result has been prevalence of peace and good order . . . the relation between labor and capital in telling the lands . . . has assumed a much more promising aspect.

Janie's father was foreman of the grand jury that recommended building a new courthouse to replace the one burned by Sherman's army. Van's brother later headed that body and congratulated all the citizens of the county on achieving peace and order and on the "Earnest efforts all classes are making to fully develop our agricultural resources."

Challenge, opportunity, and work packed the post-war years. The Fletchers and their McKibben neighbors were determined to achieve a better life for their big families than they had known before the war. Van McKibben, home from the university, was eager to be a part of the bustle and the building. His ambition would combine with his interests and talents in the practice of law.

He soon discovered that a young lawyer, no matter how popular or clever, could become rather threadbare between clients and court sessions. School teaching, with cash tuition paid by parents and guardians, offered a supplement to the small income produced by his fledgling law practice. He continued to be excited by learning and was exhilarated by the process of passing knowledge along. During his first term that love of learning and teaching extended particularly to one serious, reserved student—pretty Janie Fletcher.

Of course, he already knew her. She was the sister of his best friend, Merritt Fletcher. After the war, Van had been pleased when his sister Hattie Clementine and Merritt were married, bringing the families even closer. But Janie had been a child when Van joined the Confederate Army, and when he came home she was still young and too quiet to attract his attention. She had been taught that children, especially girls, should be seen and not heard.

In 1870, though, Janie was an appealing combination of youthful innocence and budding womanhood. Van liked her erect carriage and quick step, the tiny waist, the bright, steady blue eyes. He doubtless admired her logical, clear thinking and the diligence with which she attacked assignments. Perhaps he liked most of all her admiration for him and her willingness to be taught. Janie must have been flattered by the attention of her handsome, exciting teacher, a man who had gained respect for his bravery in battle and his scholarship at the university. Besides, her favorite brother considered Van McKibben his best friend.

On January 28, 1872, Effie Jane Fletcher was married to Martin Van Buren McKibben. She was sixteen, he was thirty-two. Her academic education was ended almost before it was well underway, but learning and living were accelerated and expanded.

The couple established a home in Jackson, and Janie put into immediate practice the domestic skills she had learned from her mother. On December 6, 1872, the girl-bride became a mother herself. Her husband was overjoyed at the birth of his firstborn, a tiny, perfect daughter. He named her Hattie Jane for his sister and his wife. As long as he lived he would see to it that she would have every opportunity within his power to provide.

The McKibben star was rising. Van's law practice grew, demanding his full-time attention; his teaching career was over. The year that began with his marriage and ended with the birth of his daughter held another occasion for pride. Van McKibben was elected for the 1873–74 term of the Georgia Legislature as representative from the Sixth District.

It was an exciting, important time in Georgia politics. Reconstruction was ended. When a Reconstruction governor fled the state, it was hoped that he took the turmoil and scandal of that era with him. Georgia was no longer conquered territory occupied by federal troops; its citizens were governing themselves again.

Janie, nursing month-old Hattie, received a letter from her husband from Atlanta, which had become the state capital after the war. The stationery bore the Georgia Legislature heading and was dated January 10, 1873.

> My dear Wife,
>
> I write you a short letter this morning not because I have any special news but because I know you are always glad to hear from me. I attended the Grand Inaugural Ball last night which was in truth a

> grand affair. The table was beyond description in elegance. The crowd was large and very much mixed, from the rustic to the farmer, with his grey jeans, to the fancy young man with his white kids and cravat . . . I have been appointed on the committee of privileges & elections . . . windy speaches [sic] from lawyers pressing the claims of their clients . . . It is useless for me to tell you that I am anxious to see you and Hattie. Be very careful with Hattie and teach her good manners. You must excuse this hasty letter & bad writing as I have no time to write with care.
>
> *Your devoted Van*

In the months that followed, "devoted Van" was caught up in more and more activities that did not include Janie.

In March of 1873, Van's brother Sam, again foreman of the county grand jury, reported that the new courthouse was "rapidly progressing toward completion." Erected on the site of the antebellum building in the middle of the town of Jackson and the county of Butts, it was the geographical, business, legal, and political center. It was a social center, too, especially during court week when men, sometimes accompanied by their entire families, came in buggies, wagons, or on horseback to convene on the courthouse square. They were magnetized by the prospect of local drama in and around the courtroom whether they were involved in the litigation or not. They met old friends and swapped jokes and war stories. They met old enemies or made new ones and swapped curses and blows. Pistols as well as fists were often in evidence, and duels were not unheard of, although they were more threatened or promised than realized. As the stories and gossip and political opinions circulated, so did corn whiskey. The chosen might sample special peach brandy in the legal offices around the square. For a quarter of a century, Van McKibben's office was the most popular gentleman's club in the county.

Like most southerners of their time, the McKibbens loved the land, and as his professional career prospered, Van continued to buy property. The first acquisition was about ten acres fronting on the main street, Third, only a short walk from the courthouse square. Here their home was located, a substantial but modest one-story frame house—long, low, with a hospitable porch stretched across the entire front. It stood directly across the unpaved street from the white steepled Methodist Church, separated from it by McKibben Presbyterianism and predestined dust or red mud.

These ten acres soon held, beside the house, orchard, vegetable, and flower gardens, four large barns and several smaller outbuildings, and a fenced lot for horses and mules. After what they called the "home farm" was added to their holdings, a row of little houses for farm hands bordered one side of the barn lot. The home farm was less than a half-mile from the Third Street property, and the farm implements, wagons and mules required for its operation could be kept in the barns and lot behind the house. Whenever it was possible, Van McKibben bought town real estate and farm land throughout the county. He knew when large pre-war plantations were being divided and sold; he knew when foreclosures offered bargains.

Although its price fluctuated, cotton was king. Except in the operation of the home farm, the McKibbens relied on a tenant system known as share cropping. The tenant, often a freed slave who signed the contract with "X" (his mark), received the use of the land and dwelling on it, farm implements, and a mule. He and his wife and children planted, cultivated, and picked the cotton and used a portion of the land for their own vegetable garden, pigs, and a cow. The tenant paid the landowner rent in the form of an agreed upon portion of the cotton crop. A century later, trunks in the attic disgorged scores of these contracts.

Sometimes acquisitions came as barter payment for Van McKibben's legal services. A mahogany table with a secret compartment in its massive pedestal base had once been in McIntosh's Inn at Indian Springs. The Varner family who bought the old inn and restored it paid their attorney's fee with it. By the time of my childhood when my family owned it, secret agreements half-breed Chief McIntosh of the Creek Indians may have made with his white cousins had disappeared. My siblings and I knew, though, that the treaties signed at McIntosh's Inn had cost the chief his scalp, and we valued the table. It stood in our side hall where we used it for card and Monopoly games and for an extra dining table at Thanksgiving and Christmas.

The *Middle Georgia Argus* weekly published the county news during the late 1870s and into the 1890s. Its columns mixed fact, flowery embellishments, flattery, gossip, and near libel in a wonderfully indiscriminate style. Words and deeds of Colonel Van McKibben were almost invariably included in them. "Colonel" was an honorary title automatically bestowed on lawyers of that time and place. He was "called upon and addressed" a May Day picnic between dinner and dancing in "his ever happy and pleasant manner." Another issue reported: "A jolly party began to assemble at the residence of Col M.V. McKibben, whose hospitality is unbounded and whose art of entertaining . . . is unsurpassed." Sometimes news of building on his rental properties was reported. His name led the list of those veterans gathered for the annual reunion of the 30th Georgia Regiment, Confederate States of America. He made the news when he accidentally discharged a shell from his gun through the flesh of his finger or when his horse was drowned during his attempt to ford a swollen creek. The *Argus* informed the county when he made hunting or fishing trips with his friends, when he bought especially fine milch cows or horses, when he grew and displayed in his office a superb vegetable or fruit, when he was elected or appointed to church and civic offices, when he addressed school assemblies. All was embellished and relayed by print.

Janie was seldom mentioned. In one social note describing a reception at the "residence of Col. M.V. McKibben," she is referred to as his "good lady." Cast in that role, Janie's hands and days were full. The girl-wife was no longer a teacher's pet. She must be a near perfect mother, being "very careful with Hattie" and teaching her "good manners." She must also be a model household- and estate-manager. Colonel McKibben's wife should present an image of virtue and dignity and, yes, elegance, too. There were rewards. She especially liked the fine horses in the back lot, and she took pride in her saddle and her riding ability. She liked good clothes. Jackson was booming and had stores whose buyers went as far as Baltimore and New York for dress fabrics and millinery goods. It was rumored that Janie McKibben had a room just for her hat boxes.

But Van McKibben was the family star.

Janie and Young Van

AT TWENTY-FIVE, EFFIE JANE FLETCHER MCKIBBEN was the wife of a successful, influential lawyer, the mother of a bright, healthy little girl, and the mistress of a house on the elm shaded main street of Jackson, the county seat. Were not these as many blessings as any woman in rural Middle Georgia during the 1880s had any right to expect?

At county social and religious occasions, especially the family gatherings of the ever expanding McKibbens and Fletchers, Van McKibben was invariably the center of any group he chose to join, dominating the talk of politics, crops, hunting, and fishing. Janie attracted eyes from the moment she stepped down from the surrey drawn by her own sleek mare. But she was not so warmly drawn into the women's circles. She added little to the exchange of kitchen, garden, and child rearing lore and even less to gossip concerning which young farmer was courtin' which young lady in a buggy "goin' mighty slow" or which wife seemed to be "expectin' again."

It may have been her own reserve that they could have interpreted as uppity aloofness or perhaps it was their envy of her clothes and small waisted figure which distanced Mrs. Van McKibben from other women. She could have overheard comments whispered discreetly behind fans or practical, hard working hands. "The trim on that hat was bought special for her in Baltimore; she'll always get the best. No wonder she can keep that figure—all the time she's been married, just has that one little Hattie. Van McKibben ought to have a son. Just goes to show you can't have everything."

After "meetin'" at the Fellowship Presbyterian Church near both Fletcher and McKibben home farms, Janie could have proudly announced in the summer of 1881 that indeed the Van McKibbens would have another child. She did no such thing. She was not in the habit of publicly spreading her personal affairs. They would find out soon enough when she no longer wore a fitted Sunday dress.

On February 19, 1882, her son was born. The news spread all over the county that there was another Van McKibben. The baby was named, of course, for his father. The initials were the same, but Janie named him Merritt, her mother's maiden name, instead of her husband's first name, Martin. Throughout his life, though, Janie's son would ever be Young Van.

No one could say Janie was not a good mother to her daughter. Hattie was not over-indulged, but she was well nourished and dressed and probably more meticulously taught than any other child in town. Janie saw to it that Hattie learned obedience as well as the "good manners" her husband had directed her to teach soon after their daughter's birth. Janie had little patience with Hattie's vivid imagination and impulsiveness and even less with her occasional flashes of temper. As for her early mastery of words and reading and her interest in music, Janie left all that to her husband, who, of course, knew more about such things. Janie was a dutiful, conscientious parent to Hattie, and her daughter respected her.

Being mother to her son was entirely different. If Janie was proud to present her husband with a son, what she felt for herself went far beyond pride. From the first time he was laid in her arms, Young Van charmed real smiles from his mother. Janie responded to the baby, the boy, the young man with a tenderness, a spontaneous joy that no other man, woman, or child could ever evoke.

Photographs, letters, McKibben legal and financial records, newspaper clippings, and the memories of my grandmother Hattie and her friends and cousins form a picture of the world of Janie McKibben in the 1880s and 1890s. The McKibbens must have added considerably to the business of local photographers.

One picture shows Janie posed with her two or three year old son. He is dressed in a little suit cut like a man's and wears a brimmed hat pushed back from his forehead. His mother also wears a dark suit with jewelry at the high collar. Her hat is a fabulous construction. Its trim is a bird, wings spread as if in flight, which seems to be swooping past the side of her head. Strangely enough, the woman looks not bizarre but handsome and happy. The little boy's legs are too short to reach the floor and dangle from the bench on which they are seated. His hand, as if to pat her, is on her lap. Her leather gloved hand on his arm is a physical assurance to her son as she looks down on his upturned, securely confident little face. Complete, serene love is in her smile. It is the only smiling picture ever found of Mrs. Martin Van Buren McKibben.

Other photographs show the McKibben family arranged and stiffly posed, often in an outdoor setting. Several include Fletcher and McKibben relatives, especially the Richard Merritt Fletcher family who lived at the Fletcher homeplace. He was Janie's oldest brother; she was Van McKibben's sister for whom little Hattie was named. Van McKibben had a namesake, too, among the Fletcher children. Their second son was Van McKibben Fletcher. The Fletcher and McKibben children, double first cousins, grew up together as playmates and friends. In the photographs, though, no one smiles. Janie usually is standing rigidly erect, looking stern, if not disapproving. Little Hattie looks exceedingly prim and proper as she had doubtless learned to appear if the occasion so required. Van McKibben, with gray hair and drooping mustache, looks older than his actual years. His little son Van is always the youngest in the family groupings. Whether as a toddler, secured between his mother and his pre-teen sister, as a child kneeling in the grass beside adolescent Hattie, or as a boy dressed reluctantly in his Sunday best (except for bare feet) and positioned with a pet raccoon between his seated father's knees, Young Van is the most appealing. Among all the posers, only the raccoon refuses to gaze solemnly into the camera eye.

The pictures suggest warmth and closeness between Young Van and his sister, but the ten year difference in their ages and Hattie's schooling would separate them.

Van McKibben, once a teacher and always a learner, prized education. He was somewhat ahead of his time in believing in and supporting liberal education for women—as much of it and as advanced as circumstances and opportunity provided. In one local debate he took the affirmative position of "Resolved that women should be given education equal to that of men." Such intellectual pastimes were sometimes arranged to augment the usual leisure activities of hunting and fishing for men, gossipy porch visiting and fine stitchery for women, and summer picnics and winter social gatherings to bring the sexes together. Whether the affirmative won or lost in the debate, the fact remained that in the mid 1880s, Jackson's fledgling academies offered only limited schooling for either male or female students.

Janie concurred when her husband decided to send Hattie away to school. Finishing schools were in vogue for young ladies, proclaiming the status of the families who could afford to send their daughters to them. The McKibbens wanted more than a "spit and polish" finish for their Hattie. Somehow the reputation of Mary Sharp College in Winchester, Tennessee, had reached them. Perhaps the young Confederate Captain McKibben had learned of the school during his war service in Tennessee. Hattie could receive there, her parents believed, a solid educational foundation as well as social graces. The East Tennessee, Virginia and Georgia Railroad had come to Jackson in 1882, so Tennessee did not seem quite so far away as Janie and Hattie, barely in her teens, packed for the girl scholar's first of many departures for the sake of higher learning.

No sooner had Hattie left home than Janie was to experience a more final loss, the death of her mother. Mary Evalina Merritt Fletcher, daughter of an English descended, highly respected country gentleman and an educated mother, mother of nine children by the time Sherman's soldiers invaded her Georgia farm home, and partner with her husband in rebuilding during the years of Reconstruction, died at the age of fifty-eight. Like many women of her time, she was old at that age, worn out by child bearing and unceasing, dutiful service to her family. Her husband, surviving her by more than a decade, died at the age of seventy-four.

Janie's own days were busy, especially with the care of her son, who daily became more active and adventurous. He was affectionate, too, and Janie, usually strict and undemonstrative with Hattie, showed limitless patience with Young Van's little boy mischief. The older Van was not so tolerant. He had been well pleased with every aspect of Hattie's growth and development. Perhaps he saw traces of his own shortcomings in the son so very much like himself.

Early Nineties Town Talk

AS THE LAST DECADE OF THE NINETEENTH CENTURY BEGAN, the McKibbens were more and more interested and involved in the town of Jackson and its growth. They had moved their church membership from the old Fellowship Presbyterian Church in the country to become charter members in 1887 of the newly reorganized Jackson Presbyterian Church. Van McKibben was made an elder. In December 1890, under the headline "A Liberal Donation," the *Middle Georgia Argus* reported that Col. McKibben had asked the church to allow him to give an organ as a Christmas present. Making this request before the assembled Sunday congregation, he also "asked to be allowed" to pay for new church carpet, hymnbooks, and all needed church literature. The editor commented that Col. McKibben was well known for generosity toward any cause in which he was interested. A hundred years after this publicized Christmas giving, a tattered hymnal was found in an old trunk filled with Janie McKibben's keepsakes. Inscribed on the flyleaf is "To Mrs. E.J. McKibben from her husband, December 25, 1890."

Another story still circulating within the family gives further evidence of Van McKibben's staunch and flamboyant support and defense of the Presbyterian faith of his Scottish ancestors. One evening after imbibing more than usual, he was enjoying the lingering twilight from a chair on his front porch. He watched many of his friends and neighbors gathering at the Methodist Church across the street and knew that a "revival" service was about to begin. He strolled over and took a seat in a Methodist pew. Unfortunately the preacher had chosen that evening not only to lead his congregation in the warmed heart way of John Wesley, their founder, but also to denounce errors of the ways of other denominations. As the preacher warmed to his subject, Van McKibben became hot under the collar. Rising to his feet, he interrupted in his well known courtroom manner. "Sir, I must object. I hope you will not proceed further, certainly not to an attack of my own Presbyterian persuasion." When the preacher did exactly that, McKibben, despite efforts to restrain him, rose again. "Sir, you are very like the turkey buzzard. The higher you fly, the brighter only your backside shines." The popular lawyer was forcibly escorted from the church.

The next day the irate offended and offensive preacher brought a charge of disturbing public worship against Van McKibben. The foreman of the grand jury happened to be Henry Baker Fletcher, Janie's own father. Amid more chuckles and knee slappings, religious toleration and peace returned to the community, and the charges were dropped. Janie remained discreetly silent and aloof throughout the entire episode. She might have wished that her Fletcher relatives had not taken such gleeful delight in spreading and embellishing the story.

Van McKibben could be counted on to be in the forefront of efforts to improve and expand end-of-the-century local education. In 1890, he was listed as a director of the Jackson Institute. Established by a stock company of city fathers in 1887, the Institute was envisioned as a means by which the youth of Jackson, Georgia, could share in the cultural and economic wealth the New South seemed to offer. Serious local scholars could also be prepared to enter any college or university in the land. The new school building was erected just across the road from the back of the McKibben property. The school bell could be heard from the McKibben porch. The Jackson Institute came too late for Hattie, but it was just in time to benefit Young Van and all other white boys and girls of the town whose parents could afford the modest tuition.

During the ceremonies at one of the Institute's commencements, Van McKibben awarded the prizes for excellence in composition, declamation, and music. It was just the kind of occasion that often gave him opportunity to expound, usually with humor and eloquence, on his favorite topics which included education for women. Before the announcement of the winners, who were girls, McKibben challenged the boys:

> Well, Boys, I have been a little uneasy for our sex for he last few days. We have claimed that men were the Lords of Creation & entitled to rule. Why we have thought that it was assumption for women to dare compete with us in the higher sphere of literature and the fine arts, that they were only suited to the low grades of literature, and to have a few foolish notions about dress & the like, but they have woke us up. They have walked out on this stage with the grace of a Chesterfield, the self possession of a Bob Tombs, the eloquence of a Cicero, and plucked from your brows the laurels which you had expected. Be ye men and suffer such dishonor, men and wash not away this stain upon your manhood? Arouse ye. Why if you let this thing go on, before another commencement, they will not only take your prizes, they will take your breeches . . .

The subject of the prize essay was prohibition. In 1887, Jackson prohibitionists had lost to a wet majority in a local option referendum, but strong and prominent voices continued to cry out against the sale of alcoholic beverages. Many Jackson women, unable to vote themselves, strongly influenced their men to unite (at least in public) to drive liquor from the city limits. Van McKibben had great respect for them, but he knew his own desires and weaknesses as he delivered the essay award.

> Your subject is one that at present & likely for the future will be the great political issue of the age. Statesmen and patriots are divided on the question as to whether the sale of intoxicating spirits should be prohibited by law. Great societies have been organized to put it down. What will be the result no one can now tell. One thing however is sure, that if female suffrage is ever adopted then prohibition will sweep the country & I shant blame the women. The great bulwark that now prevents the flood of intemperance from overflowing our country . . . is our women, is our WOMEN. God bless our women. Forbid that she should ever relax her efforts of stoop so low as to indulge in intemperance. O Woman, take our places on the forum, behind the lectern, at the counting desk, at the legal bars, in our pulpits, but for heavens sake don't take from the man his inalienable, his self assumed right to drink whiskey & smoke segars . . .

His own wife Janie never considered taking a place behind lectern or pulpit, in the "legal bar." Although she evidenced rigid disapproval of intemperance, she was never able to take from her husband "his self assumed right to drink whiskey."

There had been no Jackson Institute for Janie; there had been no boarding school, college, or conservatory such as those her daughter attended. Janie Fletcher ended her academic education as a teenaged student of her future husband. Mrs. M.V. McKibben would continue practical learning. There had been no diplomas, no commencement prizes for Janie. She gained recognition and respect for skilled, efficient, disciplined management of her household. There is evidence that her husband came to depend on her judgment in business matters. One memorandum in his handwriting found in the piles of his yellowed papers begins "Janie says . . ." Another note added to a business record reads "Ask Janie." She might very well have filled any male held position "at the counting desk." Her neighbors, her relatives and in-laws, and her husband's associates would recognize that the fine millinery for which she was known sat on a good, steady head for business.

A New House

THE MCKIBBEN HOME ON THIRD STREET, Jackson's main thoroughfare, had been good enough. Its single story was simple, sound, and well maintained. For the family of four, the old house provided as much room, comfort, and convenience as did most of the town's homes in the late eighties. There were open wood-burning fireplaces in parlor and bedrooms in winter and hand-held fans on the front porch in summer. Oil lamps lit evening activities. Water came from a well in the backyard. Black hands and feet supplemented Janie McKibben's own in keeping fresh water in kitchen and bedroom washstands and in emptying washbowls and chamber pots. But the house was not fine. Jackson was prosperous and building. So were the McKibbens.

When Hattie returned from Mary Sharp College, bringing two friends with her, her parents entertained in June of 1887 with a reception for the visiting young ladies. The local press called the party a "gala evening" with "nothing undone which would in any way, add to the pleasure of those present."

Hattie, at sixteen, was as good looking and fine figured as her mother and as outgoing as her father. Like him, too, she took equal delight in books and study and in people and social occasions. Already she was planning with her best Jackson friend from childhood, Hattie Buttrill, to continue her education at Georgia's own La Grange Female College. Young Van, just ready for the three R's, gave early evidence that he was happiest and at his best in company. The McKibbens foresaw many gala evenings to be hosted for both their children. Expansive hospitality would require more spacious, more fashionably furnished settings. Plans for a new house were begun.

Jackson and the surrounding county had never boasted the magnificent white columned mansions of deep South myth and actual history. There were such homes in neighboring counties, but little Butts, carved from Henry and Monroe counties and established from territory just ceded by the Creek Indians in 1825, was too new, too raw. The Civil War interrupted domestic building, and Sherman's devastating march left some of what had been begun in ashes.

By the time of the Middle Georgia building boom toward the end of the century, the classic symmetry of Greek revival architecture had been replaced by an eclectic American expression of late Victoriana. New houses flaunted Gothic turrets, balconies, steep gables, and wrap-around porches whose roofs were supported by slender spindles rising from elaborate balustrades. Some of the houses were fancifully ornamented with so much carved gingerbread that the results were like giant wedding cakes. Stained glass was a token not only of taste but of affluence.

Van McKibben was a man of his time. He and his wife would choose from all the features of the new styles what they liked best and what they could reasonably afford. Van McKibben was considered well-to-do, but he was no spendthrift.

What the family liked best about the old house was its location on the northwest corner of the ten acre plot between Third and College Streets. The McKibben law office on the courthouse square was only a few minutes walk away. In good weather the walk provided opportunity to talk with townspeople along the way and was preferable to saddling a horse or hitching up the buggy. Where the old house stood was where the new one should be, but tearing down a house still sound went against good Scotch McKibben instincts. As conferences with architect and builders progressed, a better plan emerged. With much human sweat and horse and mule power, the old house would be lifted and rolled halfway down the McKibben Third Street property to stand intact again. Then the building of the new house could begin.

The entire enterprise required detailed planning, the inconvenience of moving to temporary living quarters, and many months. Van McKibben was involved in every step of the process. He himself selected the choice building timber. Much of it came from his own wooded country acres.

The completed house, not ostentatious or overly ornamented by end-of-the-century standards, was not a showplace. It was a well planned, well built, spacious family home. For more than a hundred years, so it has remained.

The two-story frame house rose tall with its steep slate roof pierced by four brick chimneys. Front and side doors opened onto the almost-required roofed porch. Above the front entrance was a small square balcony reached by a door from the second story hall. Boys and pet cats have also been known to reach it by climbing convenient trees and clambering over porch roof and banisters.

The plan of the house made practical use of the slope of the lot. The front porch and steps were only slightly raised while the side porch and back of the house were some ten feet above ground level. The space beneath was divided into several daylight basement storage and utility areas. A retaining wall topped by an iron fence extended from the corner of the porch to where the west side of the property ended at the sidewalk and divided the front lawn from the much lower side and back yards. The kitchen and back porch were high off the ground with no part of the second story built above them. Upstairs bedrooms would be spared heat rising from the wood-burning kitchen stove and, it was hoped, danger of fire was lessened. For the same reasons, earlier southern plantation kitchens had often been completely separate or connected to the main house by a breezeway. Beside the back steps and beneath the back porch was a covered well. Water could be pumped into the kitchen, but there would be neither a city water system nor electric lighting until well into the next century.

The front door with ornamented panels and beveled glass at the top was flanked by tall, narrow windows. It opened into a wide hall that ran the length of the first floor, ending at a door to the back porch. A staircase with two landings rose to the second floor. Stairs rising from the front hall and stairs from the back hall met at the first landing. Three bed (or sitting) rooms opened into the hall on one side. On the west side were two larger rooms separated by a side hall that led from the side entrance to the main hall. The windows of the front parlor opened onto the front and side porches. The door at the rear of the dining room opened into the passage connecting pantry and kitchen. Both parlor and dining rooms had great paneled double doors that could be slid into wall pockets to make parlor, side hall, and dining room into one open area for entertaining. With doors closed, the parlor could be a more intimate music and sitting room; the side hall, with a center table, a breezy game area; and the dining room, the setting for family meals. Upstairs were three more bedrooms, each opening from a large center hall. Under the eaves were several storage rooms. Each bedroom, unlike those of many other houses of the time, had a closet.

Middle Georgia summers are long and hot; keeping cool in summer was a greater concern than keeping warm during the much shorter, if occasionally severe, winters. High fourteen-foot ceilings, many windows, and doors, each topped with a transom that could be opened even when doors were closed, halls, porches—all were designed for air circulation or "catching the breeze."

Interior woodwork details were a significant feature throughout the house. Hall and parlor ceilings were paneled. Wooden panels also covered the walls adjacent the stairs and the lower portion of parlor, dining room, and hallway walls. Grooved and fluted door and window frames further exhibited fine carpentry. There were eight fireplaces, each with a different mantelpiece. Each was unique, but they all consisted of a shelf supported by sidepieces ornamented with little brackets, knobs, and spindles. The front panel beneath the shelf became a display area for the woodworker's skill in rendering stylized flowers, birds, fish, and a variety of curlicues. The mantel in the parlor was the most formal and elegant. The fireplace and hearth in that room also boasted colored, intricately laid tiles.

After the architectural features were decided, Janie and her family set about selecting new furniture needed for a house twice the size of the old one. Following trends of the time, they bought massive pieces of oak and walnut. High bed headboards were carved or adorned with burl inlays and panels. Dressers, washstands, and occasional tables, already heavy, were topped with marble. Janie chose dark tapestries and velvets for parlor loveseats and chairs.

Janie, always the good housewife, tried to combine style with practicality in accessories. The washbowl, pitcher, and chamberpot for each bedroom washstand could not be too fragile, but they could be hand painted, maybe by a local lady. With a fine eye for quality, Janie would take pride in setting her oak dining table for company with china imported from England and France and crystal from Bohemia.

The Colonel's Good Lady well knew the work that preceded serving her home grown, well seasoned vegetables and meats and her hot biscuits and pies on china platters and in cut glass dishes. Her kitchen and pantry must be well equipped with iron kettles and frying pans, a big wooden bread-mixing bowl, sharp knives, heavy cooking tools, and plain crockery.

During much of the time of planning, building, and furnishing, Hattie was away at school. After graduation from college in La Grange, Georgia, she had continued the study of music at the New England Conservatory in Boston. She had been home enough, however, to make her preferences known and to influence her parents' choices. She had been home enough, too, to make for herself the most important choice in her life.

A young man, Andrew Lane, from neighboring Jasper County, just across the Ocmulgee River, had come to Jackson to attend school. He gained recognition and popularity and began "reading law" (standard preparation for a legal career at the time) in Van McKibben's law office. The association between the seasoned attorney and the would-be lawyer continued throughout Lane's college years at Mercer University in Macon and the study of law at the University of Virginia. Andrew Lane, called "Major" by his friends, extended his admiration for his mentor to the entire McKibben family. Hattie soon ranked Major Lane as her favorite of all suitors. He charmed Janie, too. In fact, both her parents and her little brother agreed with Hattie that Andrew Washington Lane would be a welcome addition to the family.

Under the headline "A Brilliant Wedding," the *Middle Georgia Argus* reported that on October 27, 1892, following the marriage ceremony uniting their daughter and Mr. A.W. Lane "invited guests all assembled at the residence of Col. and Mrs. Van McKibben where an elegant reception was tendered the bride and groom." It was the first important family social event to be held in the house.

Carved into the façade of the porch gable over the front steps and repeated above the beveled glass of the front door is a pineapple. It was intended and came to have more significance than mere late Victorian gingerbread decoration. The pineapple is the symbol of hospitality.

Fair Time

IN THE AUTUMN OF 1892, THE TALL NEW HOUSE on Third Street filled and swelled with new life. From the biggest upstairs bedroom where newlywed Hattie and her "Major" were ensconced to the backyard where ten-year-old Van could be found at the center of a moving circle of boys and balls and dogs, Janie managed a lively household.

She seldom knew from one day to the next how many would be seated at noon at her dinner table. Her husband and their new son-in-law usually walked home for the mid-day meal from their shared office on the courthouse square. They often brought with them out-of-town clients and associates or McKibben and Fletcher kin in town for the day. Occasionally Major Lane's family from Jasper County across the river was represented in dinner company.

Table talk was male dominated. A November sporting trip to Florida supplied Van McKibben and his accompanying local friends with enough hunting and fishing tales to last for months. The men, especially genial and considerate Major Lane, also brought Hattie and her mother items of interest to them from what was heard and seen around the square. Shiny new bicycles were reported passing buggies in town traffic. The buggies made right in Jackson in Mr. J. R. Carmichael's factory were being admired and purchased throughout the state. The manager of the millinery department of "The New York Store" had been seen boarding the northbound train. The ladies could expect her to return with a fine selection of the latest styles. There was much discussion, even argument, about the upcoming liquor referendum. If the county voted to prohibit the sale of whisky and outlaw saloons, one gentleman predicted that bootleg sale of "corn squeezin's" would be the most profitable business for miles around. He foresaw a moonshine still or "blind tiger" hidden in every thicket. He warned that "a huntin' feller'd have to be mighty careful and real sure which woods critters he was aimin' at."

Janie, busy with seeing to it that every diner was well served, seldom took active part in the conversation. It was her way to stiffen and draw her lips tighter into a disapproving line at references to liquor. She well knew that drinking was much of the sport of her husband's hunting trips. At least Young Van was too young to be a regular member of those expeditions.

The piano in the parlor was the center of the evening entertainment. Major Lane enjoyed music and had a pleasing singing voice. His bride happily accompanied his rich, true baritone in "Listen to the Mocking Bird" and "Hand Me Down My Walking Cane." Guests joined in, adding harmony to the popular melodies of the nineties—Stephen Foster ballads, folk songs, airs from the best known operas, and hymns—until the party ended with "Good Night, Ladies." The practice rooms of the New England Conservatory of Music and Boston concerts were miles away. Hattie expressed no longing for them.

Young Van celebrated his eleventh birthday in February of 1893. For months his parents had been engrossed in the affairs of his older sister. If the boy had been allowed more freedom for play and pranks and been subjected to less criticism, discipline, and direction from his father, that situation was soon to change. If his school year had been less than distinguished, Young Van could, at least, gain work experience and good habits from a job after school and during vacations. His employment in a general merchandise store on the square merited comment in a *Middle Georgia Argus* column: "Van McKibben, the eleven-year-old son of Col. McKibben, who is cashier at Fennell, Thompson, & Company, is an expert at making change. He never makes a mistake and is always at his post."

Knowing her husband was disappointed in the lack of interest the little boy exhibited in achieving academic honors, Janie could be silently gratified. It was hard to escape comparison of the double-first cousins, Van McKibben and the several years older Van Fletcher—both namesakes of her husband. The same issue of the paper that included the item about her son also gave high praise to her nephew: "Van Fletcher, who graduated at Jackson Institute last summer, has made the highest possible mark at the State University at Athens, Ga."

Throughout the summer of 1893, Janie's own responsibly filled daily schedules included preparation for the arrival of another family member. Andrew Wade Lane was born August 26, in the front downstairs bedroom of the McKibben house. Janie, a mother at seventeen, became a grandmother at thirty-seven—and a proud one, too. Andrew, the first child born to Hattie and Major Lane was a beautiful, happy baby; he seemed to know that he was welcomed. Other Lane grandchildren would follow, but Janie made little effort to conceal the fact that her first grandchild remained her favorite.

Young Van had no cause for jealousy and seemed to feel none. His place was secure. Besides, the baby and his parents would soon be in their own home forty miles away.

Neither the young couple's residence in the McKibben house nor the Jackson law firm of McKibben and Lane was intended to be permanent. With ever growing reputation in legal circles and the support and approval of his father-in-law, Andrew Washington Lane was ready to move on and ahead. Macon, the city to the south, where the young attorney had friends from college days at Mercer and where he was cultivating professional ties, offered opportunity for establishing a thriving practice and a home for his family. Van McKibben pledged funding for his daughter's new house to be built in Macon's fashionable Vineville area.

While the nation as a whole was suffering through a financial crisis, the Panic of 1893, the McKibbens continued to prosper. They could and would have their children benefit from whatever the times and their good fortune made possible. A great world's fair, the World's Columbian Exposition, opened in Chicago. Its planners, in the face of deepening national depression intended to show the world what the United States had accomplished in the arts, the sciences, industry, and agriculture. The time had arrived for Young Van to be given a special, eye-opening, educational experience. Chicago's fair was exactly the kind of celebration and exhibition that Col. M.V. McKibben would be expected to appreciate and attend. But the "Around Town" news column of September 21, 1893, announced that "Mrs. M.V. McKibben and son, Van, left on Saturday for the World's Fair." Col. M.V. McKibben was not mentioned.

Perhaps he had pressing court schedules; perhaps the incoming cotton crop demanded his attention; perhaps the old war wounds that were becoming increasingly painful argued against the discomforts of a long trip. Perhaps for leisure outings he preferred the company of his sporting companions to that of his wife and son. Certainly he approved and financed the journey and probably participated in plans and arrangements. This experience, though, belonged to Janie and Young Van.

Anyone at the Jackson depot that September day in 1893 would have seen a slender, well-dressed woman and a handsome obviously excited pre-adolescent boy board the northbound train. If Janie had any doubts or misgivings about this journey to a distant great city, she hid them well. As usual, erect posture and steady eyes seemed to indicate confidence and control. The exposition would show the world what progress Chicago had made since the fire of 1871. Janie Fletcher McKibben would show herself and anyone else who cared what progress she had made since 1872 when a Middle Georgia country girl of sixteen years became the wife of a wounded Confederate veteran, just getting started in the practice of law.

The city of Chicago was itself a wonder. There were new buildings so tall Janie and Young Van had to crane to see the top stories. No wonder they heard them called "skyscrapers." The tremendous Marshall Field and Company occupied an entire city block. That one store was bigger than all the courthouse square of Jackson, Georgia.

The exposition offered more than Janie's ambitious determination and Young Van's almost boundless energy and curiosity could take in. Enclosed in the gleaming white colonnades of the World's Fair buildings, designed as modern adaptations of classic Roman style, were promises of a brand new world just being created, made of steel and concrete, and energized by dynamos.

Other sights and sounds just as marvelous were within their range of understanding and interest. Outside a twenty-four foot high flour barrel, a former slave demonstrated making pancakes from a new mix called "Aunt Jemimah." An amazing machine brought from Germany made delicious chocolates. A Mr. Hershey saw that one, bought the apparatus, and had it shipped to his Pennsylvania address. Included in the concerts was a new "ragged" music played by a young Scott Joplin. Mr. Charles Tiffany, the New York jeweler, had a glittering display. His son Louis also showed in it some of his work made of colored glass that was becoming the rage, Janie knew, in houses being built and decorated back home in Georgia. From the American arts and crafts, Janie bought to take home to her husband an oil painting, very realistic indeed, of hunting dogs flushing quail in a field of wild grain.

Young Van could tell his less traveled friends about the grand fireworks exploding over the midway into stars and fountains of light. He could boast of firsthand experience with the most exciting attraction of all—the world's first Ferris wheel.

The McKibben Will

AT HOME AGAIN, JANIE RETURNED TO FAMILIAR ROUTINES. With her usual competence and increasing confidence she daily faced and dealt with old situations and new developments within her household and family.

Only weeks after she and Young Van had marveled at the spectacular midway fireworks of the Chicago World's Fair, they saw flames engulf a Jackson street. Late in an autumn afternoon a blaze issued from the roof of the building housing a printing establishment, the post office, a restaurant, a meat market, and living quarters. The fire leapt to the shops of the town's foremost industry, the Carmichael Carriage Factory. Jackson had no water system in 1893, no fire hydrants. The *Middle Georgia Argus* reported that "despite the heroic efforts of hundreds of men with buckets of water the whole establishment, consisting of four large buildings, was burned to the ground." The fire continued down the street into the residential area before it could be stopped.

Characteristically Van McKibben was in the center of the action. According to the *Argus* ". . . Col. McKibben was painfully hurt during the fire on Tuesday by a piece of timber falling on his left shoulder. During the war he was shot through the left arm and shoulder and this accident rendered the member even more painful and it may be some time before he will be truly well again."

Janie knew better than anyone else whether he was ever "truly well again." Actually, he soon returned to his office and to the courtroom. Whiskey, for him and for many of his associates, lubricated sporting and professional occasions. For a long time it had also been his medicine, his painkiller. Now his self-prescribed doses were massive and frequent. Disapproving and concerned, Janie still heard of no complaints from her husband's clients. A year after the fire, the *Argus* editor included in his comments, along with observations of the popularity of chin whiskers with the town's young dandies and the excellence of the exhibition of Carmichael buggies at the Macon fairgrounds, the assertion that "Col. M.V. McKibben is called upon to represent more clients in the courts of Macon and Atlanta than any attorney outside of those two cities."

He continued to receive and regale longtime friends and companions in his office. His jokes and his pranks still enlivened the courthouse square. He proposed a bicycle race around the square with prominent businessmen as the contestants and one of them, Mr. L.J. Ball, as umpire applying Queensberry rules. He instigated a mock trial of the editor whom he charged with placing too cheap a price on town and county news.

In his own home, though, Janie and Young Van lived with a pain-wracked, alcohol-dependent aging man. Van McKibben's well known high spirits and his patience were sorely tried by his son, already exhibiting many of his father's characteristics. At twelve, Young Van liked horses and dogs and guns. He noticed pretty girls. He attracted friends easily and obviously enjoyed having them around him, generously sharing whatever benefits were his simply from being Young Van McKibben. He was bright and quick witted. His father, however, saw little evidence of high academic achievement in his school grades, which never reached the level of excellence attained by his sister. But anyone with eyes could see that Janie McKibben's sun rose and set with the boy. It was easy to blame any faults and shortcomings in the son on his mother's doting over-indulgence.

Janie concurred in the decision for Young Van to leave home for a boarding school that offered the strict discipline of military training along with traditional subject matter. Barnesville, a town less than twenty-five miles to the southwest, had just such an academy. Gordon Institute, named for Confederate General John Brown Gordon, was gaining recognition as a fine training ground where boys became men. Janie was not eager to be separated from her son, but she wanted every advantage for him. Had not Hattie in her early teens benefitted from leaving home for a boarding school much father away? Gordon was close enough for Janie to visit and for Young Van to spend weekends with his parents.

The prospect of a uniform much like that of a real soldier and the opportunity to parade with a rifle must have been appealing to the boy. He doubtless had no objection at all to swapping the orders that came down from his father for those from an "officer" who was actually a student, too. He could be one of those officers soon himself. An old photograph shows Young Van posed in Gordon's full dress uniform. He is parade ready, eyes front, white-gloved hand holding a rifle, which with its bayonet tip extends at least a foot above his head.

The McKibben house on Third Street was no longer the setting for bustling conviviality. The shouts, the games, the laughter, the music seemed to have moved away. Hattie was in Macon where her life was filled with her handsome husband, their new house, their new babies. They all visited, and Young Van was home for holidays and an occasional weekend; but it was Janie, Janie alone, who was left to watch, with no power to stop, the day by day deterioration of the man, the vital force so long the center of McKibben life.

Janie had never been a complainer or confider. She was reserved, and she was proud. It was best that Young Van was away at school. Janie had no desire to burden her daughter with her beloved father's worsening condition. Hattie and Major Lane surely saw it for themselves. Merritt Fletcher, Janie's brother and her husband's closest friend, would help if he could. Janie knew there was nothing any of her family could do. With jaw set as firmly as her determination and head held high, Janie Fletcher McKibben made necessary arrangements. Just inside the barn lot fence a little one room house was built for a trusted, dependable servant. It was his job to attend the "Cun'l," accompanying him every time he left the house and assisting as he stumbled home.

Van McKibben knew what his condition had become. In the spring of 1897, during hours of a painful sobriety, he talked seriously with his most trusted friends, Merritt Fletcher, David Spencer, and Levi Ball.

In April he drew up a new will: "I, M.V. McKibben, being of sound memory but of feeble health do make this my last will and testament." In May, he added a codicil. Both will and codicil were dated and witnessed.

On September 6, 1897, less than a week before his fifty-seventh birthday, Martin Van Buren McKibben—Confederate veteran, teacher, planter, lawyer—died in the house he and Janie had planned and built. Hundreds of his friends and relatives from miles around called to pay their respects and offer sympathy to Janie, Hattie, and Young Van. Again guests thronged on the porches and in the halls, parlor, and dining room. The house had been built to welcome them. The mourners followed the body in the horse drawn hearse eight miles out into the country to the cemetery of Fellowship Presbyterian Church. There, as he had requested, Van McKibben was buried near his Scotch-Irish kin and within the low walls whose stones had been set in place by his father's slaves.

Janie and Hattie clipped and saved the obituary comments that appeared in the next issue of the *Jackson Argus:*

> The death of Col. M.V. McKibben, which occurred on Monday, was no less sad because of the daily expectation of his demise.
>
> "Van" McKibben was a household name in this county, a name well known throughout the State, and a familiar name in many parts of the nation. He was a man who had the courage of a lion, with a heart as tender and sympathetic as that of a 16-year-old girl. Some years back he was a power for good in the church of his choice, the Presbyterian, but because of misfortune, he has not figured in society to any great extent for several years, and the world lost the good it would have gotten by his influence. But as it is, many men and women are better citizens than they would have been but for his magnetic touch, which gave them the strength to ascend the scale of human existence . . . He has kept a young man or young woman, and at times both, in some good college. There are many today . . . who feel they are men and women . . . of learning through the kindness of M.V. McKibben. . . . many in Butts County today . . . realize his death as a personal loss. For, when crops were short, and they asked for the matter to "stand over," they knew Col. McKibben would say: "Yes, let it go over." At the time of his death, he was the leading tax payer of our county, being a good business man . . .

Van McKibben's family appreciated and treasured the overblown prose of the tribute. They believed it was sincere. They knew the man who had dominated their lives had been successful, that he had been generous, that he had been "a good business man."

The following week, under the heading of "A BIG ESTATE—COL. McKIBBEN'S ESTATE IS ABOVE $100,000," the *Argus* printed the provisions of Van McKibben's will and the appraisers' estimate of the value of his holdings. Regardless of whether Janie would have preferred that personal family matters and finances remain private, wills are a matter of public record. No sooner had the will been filed for probate than its contents were known by avid courthouse watchers who wasted no time in circulating every detail. The *Argus* corroborated what county gossips already knew. Van McKibben had willed that all his assets, after several special bequests, be divided equally among his wife, his son, and his daughter. His brother-in-law Merritt Fletcher and his friend David Spencer were named executors. His son-in-law A.W. (Major) Lane was to serve as their attorney.

Young Van was bequeathed his father's gold and silver watches and his guns. If he should become a lawyer, he was to have the law library. A special sum, not to be included in calculating his son's third of the total estate, was set aside for the exclusive purpose of his schooling. "I do this because of having expended quite a large sum on the education of my daughter." To further ensure fair and equal treatment, the will provided that the amount given for Hattie new house be deducted from her share. She was to "agree" with her mother on her portion of household goods. For her and her son's support, Janie was given use and control of all Jackson tenant houses for her lifetime. Before the estate was divided, Janie was also bequeathed all the cattle, two mules, and one horse of her own selection.

The *Argus* described the document as a "common-sense will, and one which shows that Col. McKibben was a thoroughly practical, and a thoroughly fair man."

Janie neither objected to nor disputed any stipulation of the will. She knew that her husband had taken care to provide well for her and for both of their children. Good business woman that she was, she knew also that the value of the estate considerably exceeded the conservative appraisal. She could recognize that her husband had tried to give his children equal treatment—at least as far as wealth was concerned. Her son, at fifteen, could not be expected to handle his own property, and a legal guardian was needed. Janie approved the choice of the highly regarded Levi Ball to serve in that capacity.

But the Widow McKibben had to regret the wording of Item 5 of the will, which was quoted throughout the county to the accompaniment of knowing smirks and nods:

> My son Merritt Van McKibben being reckless and without discretion and thinking he would be entirely incapable of taking charge of his interest in my estate, I hereby appoint and it is my will that Levi J. Ball shall be his guardian and shall have charge and control of the entire interest in my said son's estate, to be used in the discretion of the said Levi J. Ball for the benefit of my said son . . .

It was obvious that her husband had intended to set limits to what he saw as Janie's over indulgence of their "reckless" son.

The codicil added in May was also a subject for comment and speculation. In the April will, Item 2 had provided that the McKibben house in Jackson and the ten acres on which it was located go to Janie and Young Van "to have and to hold" until Van was twenty-one. If Janie did not remarry, she should have the "use and control" of the homeplace for life. Only if she remarried was it to be sold and proceeds divided among the three legatees. The May codicil, however, stated: "I revoke Item Second not through any personal feeling or any animosity, but because I think all my legatees ought to have an open fight for the property I know they will all love."

Indeed! There would be no fight concerning any McKibben property. Young Van returned to school. With Hattie and Major Lane and the executors and guardian, Jane completed post-funeral tasks and set business and farm affairs in working order. The house had been built for the McKibben family, and it would continue to belong to them all. It would remain the home of Janie and Young Van and the second home for Hattie and her growing family. Janie would conscientiously insist and see to it that the Lanes received as much of the garden, dairy, and orchard production as they wished or could use. Open fight? The very idea!

Janie had carried out every expressed desire of her husband in his funeral rites and place of burial. There remained only the selection of a fitting grave marker. When the granite shaft she chose arrived some months later, it proved to be the tallest monument in the cemetery. Van

McKibben's widow carefully checked every word and every number engraved in the stone. It was exactly what she had ordered.

M.V. McKibben
Born Sept. 11, 1840
Died Sept. 6, 1897
With us his name shall live
Through long succeeding years
Embalmed with all our hearts can give,
Our praises and our tears.

Clad in mourning of fine fabric and fashionable cut, the wealthy Widow McKibben could take the reins of the horse of her own selection and go home.

One Widow's Priorities As a Century Turns

THE NINETEENTH CENTURY EXITED WITH GENTLE GRACE in Jackson, Georgia. In the summer of 1899, the Widow McKibben and her son were well placed to observe or to take part in the social life of their town and the surrounding county. Janie was too serious, busy, and reserved to be much interested in the tea and card parties that often occupied the leisure of other comfortably fixed matrons, but she nodded proud approval when Young Van was sought after for the activities of the younger set.

He not only pursued pleasure; he spread it. Schools and colleges were out, and young people were looking for fun and finding it. Male companions abounded for ballgames and almost any other sport that called for water, horses, dogs, or guns. Van's good looks and charm guaranteed his inclusion, too, in the entertainments planned to bring young ladies and young gentlemen together. Croquet matches set up on front lawns and well chaperoned picnic outings to nearby ponds and groves enlivened long, lazy summer days.

Indian Springs, the resort community five miles south of town, was a favorite destination. The mineral water from the spring was touted throughout the state as good for any ailment. The Springs hotels were filled in summer with guests who came for the waters and a spa vacation. The medicinal value of the water was not the attraction for the young. A pretty girl, flattered by an invitation to ride anywhere beside Young Van

A young Janie Fletcher McKibben. This hand-tinted photograph has long hung in the back hall of Heritage.

A young Martin Van Buren McKibben, about 1875.

Janie Fletcher McKibben poses happily with her young son Van, c. 1885. Known for her stylishness, Janie is wearing a hat trimmed with a bird, wings spread as if in flight. Although there are many pictures of Janie, this is the only one ever found in which she is smiling.

The McKibben family c. 1886. Janie McKibben stands at top left beside her three sister-in-laws. Her husband, Martin Van Buren McKibben, sits with their children, Hattie and Van Jr., in the foreground.

Janie with her husband and son, c. 1886. Hattie may have been away at school at this time.

An early photograph of the McKibben house on Third Street, c. 1891–92, shows the original color scheme, steep roof, and wrap around porch. M.V. McKibben is seen standing on the porch steps, Janie stands on the porch. A barn is seen in back of the house to the right.

Mature trees and shubbery partially obscure the architectural details from this angle today. The lone tree seen at left is the "rain tree," which survived for nearly another century.

Martin Van Buren McKibben late in life.

A newspaper photograph taken in Jackson prior to the funeral procession for Colonel Van Mckibben shows townspeople gathered on the sidewalk in front of the McKibben law office and the New York Store.

A young Van poses in his uniform at Gordon Military School, c. 1896.

Janie McKibben, pictured c. 1880s, enjoyed fashionable clothes.

Two photographs of Van McKibben reclining in his room at the University of Virginia where he studied law in 1901. The decor includes several weapons, a photograph of his mother displayed alongside numerous photographs of young women, and fabrics suggesting the exotic East.

Van McKibben appears to be deep in thought amidst his carefully arranged books and personal items. A sign designates the bed "For Ladies Only."

The charismatic Van McKibben made the town news with his Locomobile, which he filled with friends and christened the "Red Devil."

Van poses between two friends in a photo originally captioned "United We Stand."

Janie McKibben at middle age, in the late 1890s, about the time of her husband's death.

in the McKibben buggy, might hold her nose and decline to sip what she said smelled like rotten eggs, even if it was supposed to be good for her.

There were other attractions. Clear water splashed over and around big rocks in the creek bed, and shady paths led through wooded hills. Long dead Indian warriors and raven haired maidens still roamed beneath the tall pines and great oaks. At least, so went the tales of those who claimed to have sighted their ghosts. One trail ended at a massive rock, the legendary site of the deaths of a Creek Romeo and Juliet separate by tribal warfare. Turn-of-the-century pale faced beaus and belles embellished the old stories and lived their new ones of flirtation and whispered intrigue.

What chaperone could be so deprived of all romance that she would object when a lass, dressed in her best ankle length sheer voile frock, required a strong arm around her waist to steady her step from rock to rock in the shallow creek? What maiden aunt could possess a heart so hardened or so bound by propriety and a stiff boned corset that she would not look elsewhere when a soft feminine hand was held by a firm, strong masculine one as a couple walked the trails? Treacherous outcroppings of roots and jagged stones could trip a dainty foot and endanger a shapely ankle. Young Van could be counted on for gallant attention. The prettier the girl, the more gallant he became.

Rumors circulated that Young Van and other bold boys sometimes slipped away to investigate what was happening behind the hotel doors that led to back game rooms. But boys would be boys.

Talk of the exploits of daring seventeen-year-old Van McKibben served to enhance his popularity with his peers and never caused gracious, ambitious Jackson mothers to strike his name from a guest list. He could be assured of the invitations to all the best parties as the ladies seemed to vie with each other in entertaining for their daughters. Young Van was one of forty guests of Miss Mary Will Brown at her home on Second Street where entertainment and refreshments flowed from the palm decorated parlor onto porch and lawn strung with Chinese lanterns. Music, "both serious and comical," was provided by several of the "talented" young people. The weekly society columns described it all. Summer nights in little Jackson in the decade preceding the coming of electricity could be lit by more than lightning bugs.

Janie did not herself figure prominently in the town's social whirl. She had pursuits of her own. From childhood she had been biblically taught that a good woman "looketh well to the ways of her household and eateth not the bread of idleness." The ways of her household meant keeping a big house in good order. It meant supervising or often doing herself the work of preparing and preserving the produce from garden, orchard, and dairy. She had been taught and had learned well the virtues of thrift and good business management. When there was more than the household in Jackson and her daughter's in Macon could use, she sold from her abundance. One neighbor sniffed that no matter how well-off Janie McKibben was, she would walk the entire length of her hall from front door to back just to sell a nickel's worth of buttermilk.

Janie could not have been unaware of the speculations concerning the possibility of her remarriage. She was known to be the best catch for miles around. Any man who married her would get a handsome woman and a share in a sizable estate. Janie ignored such talk and tended to her own affairs, but she did not shun male attention. One of her husband's friends and sporting companions had been J. H. Ham, a well known courthouse figure who had become Butts County Ordinary or judge of the probate court. Janie accepted Judge Ham, a widower, as a frequent caller and often went riding with him. If he were more than a family friend or if there were other gentlemen whose calls were more social than business, Janie kept her own counsel.

It was no secret that the most important male presence in her life was her son. It may have been that despite the attention he gave and received from young ladies, he preferred not to share his mother with another man. His older cousin, Van Fletcher, enjoyed telling and retelling how Young Van demonstrated that he had no intention of allowing Judge Ham to feel comfortable in the McKibben home.

The Fletcher boys, always welcome in their Aunt Janie's house, often spent several days at a time there when town activities attracted them from the country. On a Saturday evening during one of Van Fletcher's visits, the two Vans were together in an upstairs bedroom where Young Van was showing a pair of pistols to his cousin. Downstairs Janie had just received a guest. When Young Van heard the voices below and recognized that one of them belonged to Judge Ham, he directed, "Watch this, Van."

With no further warning and a pistol in each hand, Young Van ran down the stairs as noisily as he could, stomping hard on the landings and brandishing the guns. Town talk had it that Judge Ham's exit was remarkable, that the clatter of his feet could be heard all the way to the courthouse square. He never stopped or looked back, it was told, until he reached that familiar hub. If Janie's son actually fired the pistols that night, he must have shot into the air from the doorway. There are no bullet holes or any other evidence of gunshots in the paneled ceiling or the woodwork of the front hall.

Young Van's reputation for derring-do was enhanced. Many remember what the elder Van had said of his son in his will— "reckless and without discretion." As for Judge Ham, he married another lady—happily, it is presumed. Representatives of both families maintained that he and Janie had never been more than friends.

Janie would not be long distracted from what she evidently considered a primary duty—that of maintaining the McKibben house for the purposes for which it had been built. The house was meant to be a comfortable setting for her family's pursuits and pleasures and their shelter and refuge in times of distress.

Young Van temporarily moved his pleasures, his charm, his pranks, his unquenchable thirst for new experience to Athens and the University of Georgia. His student pursuits there were highly successful if not entirely or even primarily directed toward academic goals.

Janie and the big house were soon to be otherwise occupied. Hattie and her family needed the refuge of her home and strength. Janie had never lavished outward shows of affection on her daughter. But Hattie knew and had known from as far back as she could remember that her mother was as never failing in support as she was sparing in praise. When young wife and mother Hattie and her family confronted crisis, they turned to Janie.

In September of 1900, scarlet fever attacked the Lane household on Macon's Hardeman Avenue. By then Hattie's near idyllic marriage to Major Lane had produced four beautiful, healthy children. After the Lanes moved to Macon, the baby Andrew, born in Jackson, was followed by a brother, named Van McKibben for his maternal grandfather. Then in quick succession, two girls, Mary and Lucia, balanced the little brood. Lucia, only two, fell victim to the highly contagious disease. Antibiotics were unknown in 1900. The best medical science their city could offer, the most constant and loving care, the most fervent prayers were not enough. Before September ended, pretty little Lucia was dead.

Hattie was distraught. Terrified that the other children might be infected, she scarcely allowed herself time and tears to mourn the loss of her youngest. From the beginning of Lucia's illness, she had tried to keep the older children completely away from their little sister. She had anxiously watched each of them for the slightest flush or telltale rash that could signal the onset of the dreaded killer. No symptoms had appeared, but she could not relax her vigilance for a single hour. Her doctor and Macon health authorities advised that all Lucia's clothing, bedding, and toys be burned and the entire house thoroughly fumigated. Decisions and plans had to be made at once. Major would remain in Macon to oversee what had to be done there. Hattie, seven-year-old Andrew, five-year-old Kib, and four-year-old Mary would leave immediately for Jackson. Janie and the McKibben house meant sanctuary.

Jackson residents knew of the outbreak of scarlet fever in Macon and of the death of the Lane child. They felt sympathy for the family with its deep roots and close connections in their town and county. When they learned, however, that Hattie and the three surviving children had arrived at her mother's home, fear was their controlling emotion. The sad little group was still settling in when a municipal official arrived to fix a quarantine sign on the McKibben house. His task completed, he was still on the front walk when Janie, indignant and determined, tore off the offensive poster from the front door and slammed it shut. She would care for her own kin in her own house without contaminating any other family. She would scrupulously observe every health precaution she knew to prevent contagion. And she would do it without a sign from the city hall on her own front door.

The Lanes remained in Jackson throughout the early fall. Major came by train from Macon for weekends. No symptom of scarlet fever appeared in any of the children. They ate their grandmother's food; they slept in her beds. After days of unnatural quiet stillness, they began to play again. The boys, followed by Mary, raced through the halls and up and down the stairs so noisily that they were allowed outside—only in the backyard and with prohibitions against shouting invitations to other children they might see. Hattie let them briefly out of her sight when she knew her mother or a servant was with them. She continued to get up throughout the night to feel foreheads and listen for breathing, but she gradually could sleep and wake without panic and guilt. When weeks passed with no sign of illness and the Macon house had been rendered as disinfected as possible, Hattie and her children returned to their home with Major Lane.

Janie, satisfied that she had provided adequate refuge for her daughter and grandchildren, turned primary attention again to her son, the education planned for him, and his merry comings and goings.

A Shining Mark

YOUNG VAN MCKIBBEN FOUND A NEW STAGE and a new playing field in the university town of Athens. Not so seriously intent on his studies as his father had been in the grave years just after the war, he still exhibited his father's inquiring, often humorous turn of mind. He seldom let pass an opportunity for new experience. Like his father, too, he possessed a kind of magnetism—part vitality and physical attractiveness, part generosity, and part genuine interest in and liking for people. Making new friends while keeping his old ones was easy and natural for him. He often invited the new ones to come home with him where Janie made welcome the young males who filled her house with laughter and talk of sports and girls.

"Van McKibben has bought a brand new Locomobile and he and his friends are enjoying it to the fullest extent." So reads a tidbit in the *Jackson Argus* of May 10, 1901. It was a marvelous machine, one of the first automobiles in the county. Young Van christened it "Red Devil." Old photographs show him posed proudly with his new possession. It looked like an open horse drawn carriage—without the horse—in which driver and rider sat perched over shells similar to those of a bicycle. In one picture, the car is parked below the side porch of the McKibben house. Nattily dressed in a suit and sporting cap, Van lightly holds the steering stick. Beside him sits a young lady, obviously wearing her Sunday best, complete with hat and a serene expression. Grouped around them in an admiring circle are four young men and another young lady. The men all wear suits, ties, and straw hats with flat tops, narrow brims, and wide bands. The second girl's summer chapeau is adorned with an enormous tulle rose. In another picture, two girls, one of them strumming a banjo, sit on the Red Devil's high seat. Young Van, in protective, proprietary manner, stands beside them and his prized contraption. An open umbrella to protect fair complexions from the sun is abandoned on the grass.

In a third Red Devil photograph, Van, with a man beside him, is driving along Jackson's unpaved main thoroughfare, Third Street. The entire front panel of the Locomobile proclaims the July coming of a Chautauqua series to Indian Springs. Butts County, like hundreds of turn-of the-century communities throughout the nation, was to have an entire week of entertainment and enlightenment dispensed under the great tent of the traveling Chautauquas. Young Van McKibben, heir to many of his father's ways as well as his means, would be pleased to engage his time and energy and his newfangled vehicle in advertising and promoting high culture in his community.

At that summer's end, Janie McKibben was engaged in preparation for her son's departure for still another school. He would study law at the University of Virginia. Janie was in complete accord with the decision. She could face the long months and the hundreds of miles separating her, alone in the big, still house in Jackson, Georgia, from Young Van, in the midst of new friends and activities on a college campus in Charlottesville. What she wanted, what she had wanted most for twenty years, was the very best for her son. In 1901, a law course at the University of Virginia seemed the best. So did his own choice of the profession of his father.

In leaving the University of Georgia where the first Van McKibben had studied, Young Van was following the recommendation of his brother-in-law. Andrew Lane, Hattie's husband, had capped his liberal arts education at Mercer with law study at the University of Virginia. Now his Macon law practice and reputation were growing admirably. Janie's son would do well to follow his legal preparation route. Van liked the idea of travel and residence for a while outside his native state. He was eager for independence at the university founded by Thomas Jefferson himself.

Perhaps students such as he, exuberant and interested in everything his world could offer, were what Jefferson had envisioned when he wrote of a university "based on the illimitable freedom of the human mind." Van could look to his nation's capital for another model. In 1902, a young progressive with boundless energy, curiosity about everything, and a distinctive flamboyance ascended to the presidency. Theodore Roosevelt seemed the mature embodiment of the very qualities many found attractive in Young Van McKibben.

At the end of the century so promising at its beginning, an attic cleaning uncovered the photographs Van brought home from Virginia. Stained, brittle, and fading, the pictures can still reveal glimpses of an earlier university life to a new generation of family students.

They show his living quarters in Charlottesville crammed with the trappings of his activities and current enthusiasms. Doorways, study table, mantel, and couch are draped with fabric suggesting the exotic East. Three masks, turban wrapped heads of Arabs, hang over the fireplace. An Oriental hookah is the most prominent object in the clutter on the mantel. This was a pipe for smoking tobacco by means of along flexible tube passing through a glass container of water for cooling the smoke. Beside the hookah is a human skull or replica of one. Crossed swords, pistols, and other guns are arranged on an adjacent wall. Pictures of girls, however, dominate the decor. Framed dancers and models in a variety of costumes and poses mix with the real women of his life. One of the latter is honored by placement at the center of a fanciful heart. Another sits proudly beside Young Van in a fine open carriage. He holds the reins of the sleek, dark horse. Contrasting with the weapon display, two fans, prettily tasseled and painted with flowers, hang near pictures of charmers who perhaps gave them as flirtatious souvenirs. Attached to one side of the head of the bed is a hand-lettered sign: "RESERVED FOR LADIES ONLY." A long study table bears a weighty burden of books. One is open, and the others are arranged at the back in an impressive row. Van himself appears in two of the photographs of his Charlottesville room. In both he is posed in an almost trance-like state of meditation. Whether he is pondering pursuit of the law or the ladies or some other chase cannot be known. At the center of the pictures of pretty girls propped along the length of a shelf above the mantel is a photograph of Janie. With impassive dignity she surveys it all.

Van brought home from Virginia a trunk filled with memorabilia. His family trusted he had also acquired sound preparation for the practice of law. But he was in no hurry to settle down to any regular routine that might demand hours of desk work. There were too many other choices, beginning right in his own hometown. Old friends welcomed him back to local athletic teams and sporting events. He was elected an officer in the Knights of Pythias. Again he enlivened the social scene of town parties and entertainments at Indian Springs hotels; again his Locomobile, the Red Devil, brought excitement to Jackson streets. In fact, the Jackson weekly *Argus* of July 3, 1903, under the heading "BAD ACCIDENT," reported in disapproving tone:

> Yesterday afternoon while Van McKibben was speeding along the public square in his automobile, two horses, which were hitched to a new surrey . . . became frightened and ran away, tearing the surrey all to pieces and injuring one of the horses.
>
> Two drummers were in the back seat and both jumped out, one of them succeeding in getting the reins which had been laid over the dashboard, but the horses were then beyond control and he relinquished his hold . . . they were going at breakneck speed, tearing the carriage to pieces. The damage was about 150.

Conversations around the square and on front porches included remarks that the McKibben boy was just as reckless as ever, just would not grow up. Sterner moralizers expressed regret that he had come home only to continue extravagant pleasure seeking. Ignoring or oblivious to his critics, Young Van felt no pressure from his financial situation, his mother, or his own inclination to concentrate on the serious business of earning money rather than spending it. A sign, "VAN MCKIBBEN'S LAW OFFICE," was affixed over the entrance to one of the buildings on the square, and later, it was assumed, there would be clients and court cases.

In the meantime, his interests and personality continued to attract and hold admirers and real friends. Many years later, an old man who had been one of them said to my sister, "I'll never forget your uncle—your great uncle—Van McKibben. Julia won't forget him either. Van lent me the money to buy her engagement ring."

Another elderly southerner, known and respected throughout the region, was introduced to my Atlanta aunt at a party in the 1960s. He was extremely interested in her background and family connections. "Why you're Van McKibben's niece, then. I never knew another like him. I was one of the lucky young fellows invited to go with him to Mexico. That was a trip I'll never forget." As memory led him, he described a journey that was no rough camping expedition. Young Van and his friends made their way West in luxury; he had engaged an entire railway car for them.

What his party saw, did, and learned across the Mexican border can only be imagined. Some time after their return, the *Jackson Record* included an observation that "Col. M.V. McKibben is feeling badly this week because of the loss by death or otherwise, of his little Chihuahua terrier . . . brought from Mexico in his overcoat pocket." Although Young Van's actual legal career may not have occupied him to any great extent, the local press had prefaced his name with the honorary "Colonel" designating a professional lawyer.

What was occupying him was the Jackson Rifles, a volunteer military company. Formed as part of Georgia's State Troops, it became a member of the National Guard in 1904. Van McKibben became its company commander in 1905. His boyhood training at Gordon Military Institute, his interest in weapons, and his natural leadership ability were assets in his new post. He took pride in it; it meant more to him than weekly drills and target practice with his friends. In 1906, he commanded the unit in a training camp at Chickamauga site of the bloody Civil War battle.

Later in the same year, the governor called the company under Captain McKibben to Atlanta for a four-day tour of riot control duty. Those days of racial tension and violence are dark pages on the history of a great city rebuilt and growing on the ashes of Sherman's burning. For the young men from Butts County who had grown up with role models whose best tales had been of wartime courage, they were opportunity to prove that they, too, were ready when duty called. Perhaps Young Van McKibben returned home with satisfactory proof that he was, indeed, worthy of his father's name. His mother had never needed proof.

Then it was all over. He had flamed briefly over his little Middle Georgia world like a shooting star. On a Sunday morning, November 4, 1906, Merritt Van McKibben, at the age of twenty-four, was found dead in the bed of his upstairs room in the McKibben house on Third Street.

Shock and disbelief were followed by the almost paralyzing pain of grief. Fifty years after that awful Sunday, ancient Sallie Berry, who had been a McKibben servant, stopped by our house for a front porch visit with my mother. Sallie often was confused. Sometimes she thought my mother, who by then owned the house, was my great-grandmother Janie McKibben. Sometimes she thought my brother Hugh was our great uncle Van. Sometimes she was able to sort out the generations and her memories fairly accurately. "I was right here," she recollected. "I was here with yo' grandma when we found Mr. Van. I be hearin' her till I die. Ain't no way to forget it. Po' Miss Janie." Sallie shook her head and drew the back of a gnarled black hand across her watery eyes. "Po' Miss Janie. She couldn't never be the same after that. I knowed her. I knowed Miss Janie when Mr. Van was here, and I knowed her after he passed."

From the McKibben house, the tragic news was spread like a pall over the county. Merritt Fletcher and his wife had expected his sister Janie for Sunday dinner. Instead of her approaching buggy, they heard the pounding hooves of a galloping horse. The messenger of death had covered the miles from town at breakneck speed. In a matter of hours other messages carried by foot and horseback, by telegraph and recently acquired telephones notified relatives, friends, neighbors, and acquaintances.

What was the cause of death? No one seemed to know. Questions were multiplied by rumors. There were few answers. Van McKibben's general good health had been assumed; he had appeared to be the picture of strength and vitality. Only the day before, it was reported, he and several friends had used lengths of heavy pipe, intended for the new municipal water system that was soon to bring modern plumbing to Jackson, as weights in a contest and demonstration of physical prowess. Could that exertion have triggered a fatal heart attack? No details were circulated, if they were known, of his exact whereabouts or activities during the evening hours preceding his return home to bed and death. Romantic commentators noted that on the very day Young Van was found cold and lifeless, the Atlanta newspapers announced the engagement of a Georgia belle he was known to have squired. The only certainty was that the warm heart would beat no more. Death—unforeseen, swift, inscrutable—was fact.

Janie, controlled and efficient, made necessary arrangements and moved through the ceremonies of death and burial. The town was his home; her son would be buried in the Jackson city cemetery rather than beside his father in the country graveyard of old Fellowship Church. After the Masonic funeral rites, when the scores of mourners and sympathizers had left the flower covered grave, a photographer made pictures of the elaborate floral offerings. They show Masonic symbols shaped from roses, carnations, and lilies. One wreath is a great horseshoe. Other flowers form crossed rifles.

During the following weeks, Janie surrounded herself with scores of pictures of her son. After critically examining every one, she chose a photograph bearing the imprint of the University Studio of Charlottesville, Virginia, in which he stands between two friends above the subscript "United We Stand." She commissioned a full-length oil portrait to be made of Young Van, showing the same features, expression, and posture. On the back of the photograph she penciled "blue eyes, light brown hair, fair complexion." When the painting was completed according to her directions, she hung it in the home he had enlivened. There he would remain, always young, always near her, as long as she lived.

Two generations later, when the house was my childhood home, Great Uncle Van was almost as real a presence in our lives as our living, breathing Mallet and Lane uncles. His portrait hung then in the side hall above our game table. He seemed to stand, looking over our shoulders at clever or foolish plays, at luck and losses. Hat pushed back from fair forehead, hands in his pockets, he focused steady, confident blue eyes on the scene to which he belonged as much as we. Were not the poker chips his? We had retrieved them from the attic where his saddle, his books, and his pictures still molded and faded. From the portrait he looked down at us as if assured we knew that our house was still his, too, and he had every right to be there.

My mother once decided that the parlor was a better place for Uncle Van's portrait. Soon after she moved it, Dude Bell, our town's skilled black tinsmith, was working on the gutters of our house. When he missed the picture of the young man who had hosted barbecue feasts for his black companions as well as his white, he demanded, "What you done with Mr. Van?" My mother led him to the parlor where an open door temporarily concealed the portrait. "That ain't no place for Mr. Van," his old friend declared. "Not behind no do'!" My mother returned Uncle Van to the side hall.

Old Sallie Berry was right. Janie McKibben could never be the same after her son's death. She managed her house, her business affairs, her family concerns. Her kin knew that her home was open to them and her assistance available. One of her nieces, herself past ninety, remembered and remarked, "Aunt Janie was always good to us." But the purposeful energy was gone. Janie had Van's Red Devil moved to the back lot. Clip, the fast, beautiful horse both she and Van had raced, was retired to the barn lot, too. One Jackson merchant later recalled being chased from the fence by a stern woman dressed in black. "You boys, you leave my horse alone."

Hattie and her Lane family were frequent visitors. The older grandchildren—Andrew, McKibben, and Mary—came often enough to have a circle of friends in Jackson and to know their Fletcher and McKibben relatives. Andrew, born in her house, remained Janie's favorite and was singled out for special gifts. For her sixteenth birthday, Mary received from her grandmother a crescent shaped diamond pin. Janie was partial, but she wanted to be fair. She let it be known that her will would include separate bequests for each of her six grandchildren. In 1913, Hattie and Andrew Lane had four sons—Andrew, McKibben, Louis, and Harry—and two daughters—Mary and Margaret. There had been another daughter, Eugenia, who like little Lucia, died as toddler. If Janie made the will, it was never probated. She did not know that another grandchild, whom she did not live to see, was expected. Virginia, the youngest, would have been left out.

When Janie McKibben developed a serious kidney disorder, doctors and medicine could do little. There was no treatment for loss of will as well as strength to survive. Her death in December of 1913 was not unexpected and was marked with the mourning rites befitting an admirable woman of her time, place, and status. She had asked to be buried beside her son in the town plot rather than in the country with her husband.

In the older part of the Jackson city cemetery, beneath a granite headstone marked "McKIBBEN," two graves are side by side. The stone covering one of them is engraved simply with identification.

JANIE FLETCHER,
WIFE OF
MARTIN VAN BUREN
McKIBBEN,
SEPT. 26, 1855,
DEC. 14, 1913.

Seven years earlier Janie had ordered the inscription for the stone beside it:

MERRITT VAN McKIBBEN,
FEBRUARY 19, 1882,
NOVEMBER 4, 1906.
Death loves a shining mark.

When Janie's oldest granddaughter, my mother, Mary Lane Mallet, was herself an old woman spending what remained of her life in a nursing home, I visited her, taking with me the recently discovered photograph of Janie, posed with her daughter Hattie and her granddaughter Mary. For a long time, my mother had been unable to manage the simple routine tasks of living in the present and had withdrawn into a world of overgrown, tangled memories we could not enter. When I showed her the picture, though, immediate recognition and pleasure lit her face. "Why it's Grandma and Mama and me! I was fourteen."

For moments lifted and suspended above the drab, apathy laden hours of her days, my mother was alert and interested again. She studied the photograph intently and smiled.

"What do you remember most about your grandmother, Janie McKibben?" I asked.

"Grandma?" Her fingers gently traced the faces as she replied. "Grandma . . . She always stood tall."

Hattie

Under the Rain Tree

THERE WAS NOT A CLOUD IN THE SKY, but Hattie heard the sound of rain. The hot July air seemed still, but there must be enough breeze to stir and touch together the big, dry, fan-shaped leaves of the enormous tree towering above her. She knew exactly what she heard. She even remembered that Papa had said "Vaisyamaglia" was the botanical name for the unusual poplar tree beside the house.

The woman smiled. The child Hattie McKibben could have been tricked by the rain tree, but the fiftyish Hattie of Macon, widow of Andrew W. Lane, in Jackson again for a summer visit, was not deceived.

A few hours later in the upstairs bedroom, made ready for her, Hattie looked out on the tree again. Then the scene, the sound, and memory became quatrains in the notebook she tried always to keep handy.

THE RAIN TREE
Dedicated to "little" Mary Lane Mallet

The pecker-wood high in the poplar tree
Makes thunder, as of old, for me,
And, as in days of yore, again
The leaves, wind-stirred, resound like rain.
'Twas in that old tree's dappled shade
My first mud-pies and cakes were made.
Oh, how I loved the long rope swing
Where Mother Gooses's rhymes I'd sing.
My first tea set it saw out-spread.
My table-cloth its leaves when shed;
A dozen dolls at tap of bell
Came to the table by the well.
What changes that old tree has seen

Since from primeval forest green
It stands today beside the lane
And soothes us with the sound of rain.
Youth's bark with sails of hope is sped,
But age's craft is memory led
Along the winding years that flow
Back to the Isle of Long Ago.
'Tis joy to live those scenes once more,
For, standing in her play-house door,
My wee grand-daughter calls to me
To come play near the old rain tree.

H. McK. Lane
July 20th, 1926
Jackson, Ga. (My home for 20 years)

Her craft was often memory led when Hattie, my grandmother, visited Jackson during my childhood. When she joined us grandchildren with her crocheting, we knew a voyage to her "Isle of Long Ago" was about to begin. The oars—her shining crochet hook and seldom still tongue—were ready for rowing. If we preferred not to risk drowning in deep streams to the past, we could and sometimes did flee her presence to seek solitary escape with a book. But usually we embarked with her.

My parents set the example of welcoming and accepting our unique grandmother. We all understood why, every time she came to see us in Jackson, she came just as much to visit the setting of her childhood and youth. Vocabulary builder that she was, Grandmother taught us the meaning of nostalgia.

Our house had been hers first. It was ours because she gave it to our mother when she married our father, a Jackson native.

Grandmother never finished giving. Our house still holds many of her belongings—her pictures and books, her piano, her father's desk. More than half a century since her death, we still have not finished sorting the contents of trunks and boxes filled to bursting with letters, notebooks, photographs, newspaper clippings, and keepsakes defying identification. She wanted us to know her Past, and she continues to draw us to it.

"Heritage," she told our mother, "is a good name for the house." Maybe it is. But the house is only a part, the shell, of our legacy. Grandmother left us her Past. That is our heritage.

Early Lessons

HATTIE MCKIBBEN WAS A VERY FORTUNATE LITTLE GIRL. That must be true. She heard it often enough from kin and her parent's acquaintances. The words weren't exactly the same, but Hattie sensed the same idea when a playmate or one of her cousins admired her dress or a new doll. She suspected that it had much to do with her parents.

Everybody liked her father. No wonder. He let people know he liked them. And nobody could know as much, Hattie thought, as her Papa did. Sometimes he laughed at her questions, but it wasn't the kind of laughing that made her feel bad. Papa made her laugh, too.

Hattie had been afraid of the dark. Confident and daring by day, she was no match by night for the terrors created by her own imagination. She dreaded having to go alone to any unlit part of the house. Even worse, she could not conceal the fears she was ashamed to confess. But their revelation came after supper one evening when her father asked her to bring his papers left in a chair on the porch. It was already dark, and Hattie dawdled suspiciously. Recognizing his daughter's problem, he took her hand. Hattie would remember what he said. "Don't ever forget who you are, Hattie McKibben. My Hattie will not be afraid of anything there is no reason to fear." From the front porch, he pointed to the thin sliver of a new moon surrounded by a scattering of the first stars of evening.

It was the beginning for Hattie of a new interest—the skies. Papa suggested that they pay close attention to the moon and begin counting the nights to see how many it would be before the curve of light swelled full and round and bright enough to light a walking path. He told her that the stars had names and began to point out some of them and show her how to find and recognize them. Before they went inside again, Hattie learned the word astronomy and had her first lesson in it.

Hattie McKibben Lane was to teach us Mallet grandchildren a line that we rarely fail to repeat when we see a new moon: "a scarcely perceptible curve of light, yet it makes the whole sky smile."

Hattie's mama had lessons to teach, too. Janie Fletcher McKibben, only seventeen when her daughter was born, took very seriously the responsibility of motherhood. That the child would be well tended, fed, and clothed was taken for granted. Her more demanding and challenging task was teaching and requiring good behavior and proper manners.

This is how my grandmother remembered her upbringing in the 1870s and early 1880s. First, Mama and Papa were to be obeyed and respected. Among Hattie's first words were "please," "thank you," "ma'am," and "sir." She must come quickly when called and speak when spoken to. She was not to interrupt when grown-ups were talking.

More important, Hattie must conduct her little girl life by moral and religious rules. Papa was an elder in the Fellowship Presbyterian Church some miles from town where the vast McKibben clan worshiped and in whose churchyard were buried. Hattie went to services there with her parents, but it was their precepts and examples that were immediate and ever present.

Her Mama would have Hattie distinguish very early the absolute difference between Right and Wrong. Right were God's commandments and Mama's Rules. It was Right that meals began with a "blessing" because God must be loved and thanked for all good things although it was Mama who got the food on the table. Since God commanded that parents be honored, it was Right that Mama's rules about table manners be obeyed. It was Right to "do unto others as you would have them do unto you." Hattie could recite that golden rule before she knew what it meant. She knew it was in the Bible where God's commandments were written down. Mama's rules did not have to be written down.

Wrong, Wrong, Wrong were lying and stealing. Hattie loved hearing and telling stories. Papa read and told wonderful tales. Mama stuck to unembellished facts and directions and corrected exaggerations in Hattie's chatter. Janie McKibben's daughter must learn the difference between "true" and "made-up" stories. Any attempt to pass off the latter as the former was lying. Hattie wondered about the stories in the Bible. In the very same book with God's commandments, they must be "true." But what about the talking snake in the very first story? And could any boat be as big as that one called the "ark"—big enough to hold two of every kind of animal in the whole world? Maybe those stories were like Papa's tales, which weren't lies either.

There was no question about stealing. That meant taking something that belonged to someone else. The person who did such a thing was a thief. Stealing was no temptation. Why would she want to do that?

What the child Hattie did want was her Mama's and Papa's approval. She knew that she pleased her Papa; she was not sure about Mama. Her mother, going about household responsibilities, was a model of efficiency, neat grooming, and handsome carriage. Bending down for spontaneous shows of affection was not her way. Her smiles and praises must be earned and deserved.

One late afternoon as Hattie made her way home after a visit with a schoolmate, she saw what she believed would surely please her mother. Hattie had been allowed to walk by herself all the way across town. She had progressed to the square, passed her father's office, continued on Second Street, then turned right. Just a hop, skip, and a jump away was the home of her friend, Hattie Buttrill. The two little Hatties had the same first name, the same age, and the same first school classes. They already shared, too, the knowledge that they would be best friends forever.

Now Hattie McKibben was returning the way she had come. The hours just past had been spent in games and giggles and whispered secrets, all sweetened by company tea cakes and lemonade. Walking again along Second Street, turning over in her mind every detail of the afternoon, she suddenly was aware of beauty she had not noticed before. A front fence was completely covered with pink roses. Branches and tendrils bearing hundreds of blooms—some just opening, some full blown—climbed and wound every post and railing. Here was a present for Mama.

Nobody watched from porch or dooryard as a pretty child picked a bouquet. The project was not easy. Sharp green thorns pricked her fingers as she pulled and tore at stems hard to break. Decapitation was easier. Many buxom blossoms were seized without steams or leaves. Finally, the little flower girl, leaving a trail of pink petals behind her, continued the walk home.

Mama was on their front porch, waiting and watching for her return. "Did Mrs. Buttrill send these to me?" she asked as the flowers were thrust into her hands. Hattie smiled, shook her head, and proclaimed, "Not Mrs. Buttrill. They came from a fence on Second Street, and I picked every one for you by myself."

The mother's lips pressed together in the firm line the child knew all too well. It had never occurred to her that taking roses from the cascade flowing over the fence onto the sidewalk was stealing and that she had broken a commandment. Tears of disappointment and shame washed pale the rosy pink memory.

Further humiliation followed. Mama knew the house where the roses grew, and she knew who lived there. Hattie would have to walk back there, confess the theft to the lady of the house, and return the flowers, already drooping, to their rightful owner.

When our grandmother, the grown-up Hattie, recounted this memory tale of wrongdoer brought to justice, she never told just how the encounter went with the lady behind the fence. But more than once, she told us, "I always loved my father; I respected my mother."

School Days

HANDWRITTEN ON THE FLYLEAF of a worn little blue volume proclaiming itself to be *McGuffey's New Fourth Eclectic Reader: Instructive Lessons for the Young* is

> Hattie McKibben
> Jackson,
> Ga.
> April 1st, 1880

Its owner would have been seven years old.

Hattie had learned early and easily to read for herself; she did not remember exactly how or when. By spring of 1880, she was enrolled in the Jackson Academy. She was deemed ready for the instructive and morally edifying stories and poems selected for the young by the renowned Dr. W. H. McGuffey.

The first story in Hattie's reader was entitled "Where There Is A Will There Is A Way." Exemplar of the title is young Henry whose widowed mother cannot afford to buy the book he needs for his grammar class. The enterprising lad takes advantage of a snow storm to earn money by clearing paths for his neighbors. The story ends with these lines:

> He knew no such word as fail, but
> always succeeded in all he attempted.
> Having the will he always found the way.

Interspersed with tales in which a Ned, a George, or a Susan learns the rewards of honesty, industry, thrift, and a good nature are stories from the Bible and history. There are pages and pictures featuring animals, too. Rural and small town children who had never seen them could read about monkeys, elephants, giraffes, and lions.

The "Poetical Lessons" were Hattie's favorites. She liked the sound of words; she was glad when she was called upon to stand beside her desk and read aloud. And just as the worthy Dr. McGuffey had intended, she absorbed practical, ethical, and religious precepts more easily when they were versified in rhythm and rhyme. She knew she would not follow the ways of Lazy Ned who

> . . . would never take the pains
> To seek the prize that labor gains
> . . . And died a dunce at last.

When she was tempted to give up on a baffling arithmetic assignment, she remembered more rhymed advice:

> Tis a lesson you should heed,
> Try, try again;
> If at first you don't succeed,
> Try, try again.
> . . . All that other folks can do,
> Why, with patience, should not you?
> Only keep this rule in view:

Try, try again. Little Hattie, quick and bright and often impatient with her slower schoolmates, needed much more the concluding moral of the fable-poem of the tortoise and the hare:

> . . . plain, plodding people, we often shall find
> Will leave hasty, confident people behind.

The narrative poems, following the tastes of the times, were often overloaded with melodrama and sentimentality. Later educational psychologists would find such selections as "Casabianca," a regular inclusion in Friday afternoon show-off elocution recitals, inappropriate for children. That popular example of poetic pathos tells the story of a boy on the burning deck of his father's warship during a long ago battle on the far away

Nile. Faithfully carrying out his father's orders to remain on deck to await further orders, the boy would not join the sailors deserting the doomed ship. Unaware that his father had already been killed, he was obedient (Dr. McGuffey italicized the word in his commentary) to his fiery end.

> . . . The boy stood on the burning deck,
> Whence all but he had fled,
> The flame that lit the battle's wreck,
> Shone round him o're the dead.
> Yet beautiful and bright he stood,
> As born to rule the storm;
> A creature of heroic blood,
> A proud, though child-like form.

Hattie, a Georgia child of the 1880s, was more personally moved by the tragedy in yet another poetic tale, "The Dying Soldiers." Among the dead and wounded on a Civil War battlefield are two soldiers, one from New Hampshire and one from Georgia.

> ". . . Our time is short," on faint voice said;
> "To-day we've done our best
> On different sides: what matters now?
> Tomorrow we shall rest!"

After learning that both have wives and little girls waiting at home, the young men, their warfare over, die with their hands entwined.

Hattie knew about that war. Suppose her own dear Papa had been killed instead of wounded in it. Suppose he had not lived to come home to marry Mama and be her Papa.

Dr. McGuffey and his blue texts demanded much of readers. Accompanying each selection were questions, exercises, and drills. Young scholars were required to learn definitions and spellings. Hattie's childhood vocabulary came to include such words as amiss, woeful, alacrity, and ludicrous. She spelled vengeance, perseverance, dialogue, anecdote, and many other words longer and harder. She cheerfully submitted to drills on correct pronunciation, articulation, and rising and falling inflection. She became good at reading aloud and was a willing participant in the Friday afternoon programs.

She liked the companionship of other children, especially the daily opportunity to be with her best friend, Hattie Buttrill. What a pair those two Hatties were—almost inseparable, usually laughing and calling each other "Hat."

For Hattie McKibben, an only child for the first ten years of her life, Hattie Buttrill was the sister she never had. Hattie B. had a little sister, Mamie, only a year younger, and two younger brothers, too, but Hattie McKibben occupied a place in her life no member of her family could fill. The girls had much in common. Both were children of families of long and respected county standing. They were the same age. Both were fair and petite. "Little" usually prefixed "Hattie" when either was mentioned. Hattie Buttrill was not so devoted to books, so entertained and fascinated by them as was her friend. She would leave striving for highest school achievement to Hattie McKibben. The latter found Hattie B. clever enough, loyal, trustworthy, and fun. The girls were not competitors; they were friends.

Both girls earned favor with their teachers. In the early 1880s, the Jackson Academy was served by a professorial family, the Becks. J. W. Beck and T. J. Beck, ministers as well as teachers, and Miss Leonora Beck, too, considered moral and religious instruction as basic as the three Rs of Reading, 'Riting, and 'Rithmetic. In Hattie Buttrill's little leather bound autograph book, "The Ideal Album," the Reverend T. J. Beck wrote:

> My dear little Friend,
>
> Your little heart is doubtless already busy with many aspirations, plans, & purposes, but let me commend to you the counsel of the wisest of men. "Get wisdom, get understanding; forsake her not, and she shall preserve thee. Wisdom is the principal thing; therefore get wisdom; and with all thy getting, get under-standing. Exalt her, and she shall promote thee; she shall bring thee to honor. A crown of glory shall she deliver to thee.

Miss Leonora, on another album page, recommended virtues perhaps more attainable for the child than Solomon's exalting wisdom:

> Be gentle and unselfish, pure and true, my dear little Hattie; "And, spite of all the lies of creeds, hold fast the truth that God is good."

As wise as were the words and as noble as the examples of those teachers, Van McKibben was not satisfied that his daughter was receiving instruction as wide and deep as he envisioned for her. In the fall of 1885, his Hattie did not return to the local academy. The McKibbens had decided to send their daughter to Mary Sharp College in Winchester, Tennessee, to which a number of Georgia families had entrusted the molding of their daughters' minds and characters.

So before her thirteenth birthday, Hattie McKibben would leave the Georgia home she had known since her birth, her parents, her three-year-old brother, and her best friend to go to school in Tennessee. Getting there meant a major train trip. Between Jackson and Winchester, and between September and Christmas vacation, Hattie measured miles and months of separation.

Hattie Buttrill gave her departing friend a little autograph book as pretty as her own and on one of its pages wrote "Into each life some rain must fall/Some days be dark and dreary." Hattie B. had good reason to quote Longfellow's doleful observation. She had already known dark days. Her mother had died the year before, and now her best friend was leaving.

On another page, one of Hattie McKibben's many aunts wrote the centuries old advice to "Gather ye rosebuds while ye may." Hattie meant to do just that. She would study and make Papa and Mama proud; she would have fun, too.

When Mary Sharp College opened in 1851, its first president wrote that the school would offer to young ladies "the same knowledge, literary, scientific, and classical, that has for so many generations been the peculiar and cherished heritage of the other sex." He wrote further that education should offer a woman what "she was designed to be by her creator, a thinking, reflecting, reasoning being, capable of comparing and judging for herself and depending upon none other for her free unbiased opinions."

One Tennessee versifier of the time expressed entirely different views regarding education for women:

Boys go to school to learn hard names,
To spell, and play at grammar games,
The girls they learn to draw and paint,

Primp up their mouths, speak fine and faint:
This is fashionable learning.
When boys have learn'd that they are made
To heave the earth with plough and spade;
And girls, that they must toil for man,
Make clothes, wash pots, and frying pan;
They're then prepar'd for learning.

Scorning such narrow opinions, the McKibbens would have their daughter prove the worth of the "literary, scientific, and classical" learning promised by Mary Sharp College. Hattie would excel in her studies. She also possessed at thirteen the social skills and graces required for adjustment to living with other select southern girls in the Bledsoe House dormitory. She soon made friends.

Hattie anticipated giving a glowing report of her activities when she returned to Jackson for Christmas vacation. But sad home news was waiting for her. Mary Evalina Merritt (Molly) Fletcher, the beloved grandmother Hattie had nicknamed "Trit-n-Trot" had died in early November. Hoping to shield their daughter from the trauma of grief experienced without the comfort of family and familiar surroundings, the McKibbens had not written of the death.

Hattie felt left out. How could she look forward to visits to the Fletcher country house again if her grandmother would not be there? Her grandfather, the uncles, the aunts, the cousins who played with her and called her "Chatty Hattie" were still there, but they could not make up for the loss of her sweet "Trit-n-Trot."

That grandmother, no matter how busy, always seemed to make time for her McKibben granddaughter. It was she who told Hattie of the great-grandmother, Jane Brown Merritt. Hattie's whole name was Hattie Jane McKibben. Hattie learned that Jane Brown had been a "woman of parts." That meant that she knew and could do many things. She could even paint pictures of woods and ponds or fruit and flowers. Hattie wanted to be a "woman of parts" herself, but the painting part must be missing. Now the grandmother who had connected her with that Jane of her family's past was missing, too. Mary Evalina Merritt Fletcher had kept her mother's paintings. Hattie would keep memories of her grandmother Fletcher to be unwrapped for her grandchildren. They would be as treasured, as real as the landscapes and still lifes of Jane Brown Merritt.

There yet remained present pleasures to be enjoyed during that first vacation from school in Tennessee. There were Papa and Mama, of course, and little brother Van, who was already playing with a puppy under the raintree where she had served tea to her dolls. It was good to be with Hattie Buttrill again, to feel and know that their friendship was as strong as ever. The Hattie who returned to Mary Sharp College was more experienced, more grown up, and somehow stronger that the excited girl who had boarded the train that took her there for the first time.

The woman little Hattie became was to look back happily, proudly on the school years at Mary Sharp College. In that small, sheltered nineteenth-century school for southern girls, she learned that she could master any academic discipline that was required or that she desired. Fine embroidery was a pretty accomplishment, but Latin and algebra were just as firmly within her grasp. She began learning, too, as she chose for herself how and with whom she would spend precious leisure moments, just who Hattie McKibben was growing up to be.

Only words and dates engraved on a marker in Winchester, Tennessee record where the old school once stood. Only fading signatures elaborately inscribed in her autograph album ("Maggie" from Cartersville, Georgia; "Bridie" from Sevierville, Tennessee; "Fannie" from Pembroke, Kentucky . . .) above variations of "Forget me not" record the friendships. Only a few tattered texts are tangible evidence of her studies. Mary Sharp College endured for Hattie as a recognized stepping stone toward a liberal education.

The next step would be located in her home state. For more advanced studies that were to lead for her to a baccalaureate degree—not a common attainment for women in the 1880s and 1890s—Hattie enrolled in the Southern Female College of LaGrange, Georgia. Hattie Buttrill was enrolled, too, as was another friend, Mamie Ellis, daughter of a prominent Jackson physician. Grandmother said of her best friend's studies at LaGrange, "Hat took a kind of eclectic course."

In her own course of studies, music claimed much of her schedule. Piano and voice lessons required hours of practice. A lover of music and a serious student, she demanded more of herself than did her teachers.

In the "chit-chat," of the *Middle Georgia Argus* of June 17, 1890, it was reported that "Misses Hattie Jane McKibben and Hattie Buttrill returned home from LaGrange, Ga. on last Thursday where they have been attending school. They graduated with highest honors."

Two weeks later Hattie's reward for academic achievement made further local news, this time under the heading "A Beautiful Gift."

> Col. Van McKibben has purchased for his accomplished daughter, Miss Hattie, one of the most elegant pianos ever sold in Georgia. It is of the famous Weber make, in a most elaborate case of French walnut, with beautiful carvings, forming indeed a charming present for a most worthy recipient. Miss McKibben graduated with great distinction at the LaGrange Female College a few days ago, taking the medals for excellence in all departments.

Hattie, at eighteen, possessed a diploma declaring her to be a bachelor of arts. She also owned a fine instrument on which she could practice one of those arts.

What lay ahead? Hattie was not sure. She knew she had only sampled the surface of academic and musical knowledge. Would she dive deeper? She had listened intently to lofty, traditional speeches, all sacred stuff of graduation ceremonies. She had heard learned educators expound the significance of "commencement," its meaning as "beginning." What was she ready to commence?

A Major Key

"DON'T GET MARRIED UNTIL YOU KNOW YOU CAN'T LIVE WITHOUT HIM." Fifty years after her own marriage, that was my grandmother's advice. In the 1940s, her granddaughters chose to ignore it. In the 1890s, Hattie McKibben, college graduate, did not find it the common wisdom of Jackson, Georgia. A woman could be considered an old maid at thirty. Rather than be delegated to that pitiable female category, many chose an early "I do" to a promise to love, honor, and obey almost any available and reasonably suitable male. A hometown friend wrote popular sentiments of the time in Hattie's autograph album:

> In the tempest of life,
> Each needs an umbrella.
> May yours be upheld
> By a handsome young fella.
>
> Your true friend,
> *Pearl Carmichael*

Hattie was not looking for an umbrella. She had never known and did not fear the "tempest of life." The only daughter of Van and Janie McKibben was not looking for security because she had never been without it.

She did not need to turn her education into a salary, but she had been taught and she believed that all talent and training as well as time and money should be put to good use. She played the piano for church; she taught Sunday School classes; she helped her brother with his lessons.

She attracted and enjoyed male attention. She contributed bright smiles and brighter chatter to social occasions. If there was singing, she could accompany it on the piano or add a clear soprano. But she seemed to feel no necessity to turn every carefree gathering of young people into husband hunting. Hattie Buttrill and other close observers of blushes, special smiles, and the like were soon aware, however, that young Andrew Lane, called "Major," was favored above all the young men of Hattie's acquaintance.

Not actually a local lad, he was already known, liked, and admired in Jackson when Hattie returned from college in LaGrange. Major Lane lived on his family's plantation just across the Ocmulgee River, which separated Butts and Jasper Counties, and had attended Jackson Institute. The East Tennessee, Virginia and Georgia Railroad had transported Hattie to boarding school in Winchester, Tennessee. Major had depended on a horse and a ferry to take him to learning nearer home.

His education had begun earlier with his father's tutoring. Augustus Washington Lane, planter and lawyer, had fought in the Creek and Seminole Indian Wars with the rank of major. "Gus" Lane gave this third son, Andrew Washington, his own "A. W." initials and, as a nickname, his rank. Andrew Lane was called "Little Major" and then "Major" for as long as he lived.

Intelligence and a will to learn earned Major an enviable institute record; good looks and good manners made him welcome in Jackson society. His interest in law brought him to the attention of Van McKibben. The older man became his mentor, and the student was often in the McKibben office and home. Although Hattie was away during the school year, the entire McKibben family considered Major Lane their friend.

Ties to Jackson and the McKibbens remained strong throughout his college years at Mercer University in Macon. In May of 1890, while Hattie was in the midst of preparation for graduation from LaGrange College, her parents received an invitation to another commencement event. Carefully addressed in Major's best penmanship, with its formally engraved pages tied together with a tasseled silk cord, it requested the presence of Colonel and Mrs. M. V. McKibben at the Academy of Music, Macon, Georgia, for the Anniversary Exercises of the Delta and Ciceronian Literary Societies of Mercer University. The second page included the information that A. W. Lane of Monticello, Georgia, was an "Anniversarian." The McKibbens were pleased to attend. Whether they understood a word of his address or not, both the Colonel and his wife were impressed that their young friend delivered it in Greek.

In the early summer weeks of 1890, Major and Hattie were often together. He was one of the first to hear her play the new piano that was the graduation gift from her father. He was present when the family discussed its placement in the parlor of the almost completed new house. Hattie came to look forward to the frequent appearance of his tall, slim figure in the McKibben doorway with another of his mock serious announcements: "Again, I have braved the raging waters of the Ocmulgee to be at your side, Hattie."

The flow of leisure hours Major could spend with Hattie was interrupted by the necessity of earning a living. His big family, always generous with genuine affection and encouragement, could offer little financial assistance. His father had died some years before. His younger brother James would maintain the family home and farm, and an older brother Tom was just establishing a law practice in the south Georgia town of Americus. Major decided to accept the teaching position offered him in the south Georgia town of Blakely. To become a lawyer and to claim the hand of Hattie McKibben would require more planning and study, more work, money and time.

His departure left Hattie with an emptiness she was too proud to acknowledge. She could and would fill her time. There were decisions and tasks for her in the completion and furnishing of the new house. She could count on Hattie Buttrill for companionship and confidences and on another Jackson friend, Mamie Ellis, for the piano duets that were becoming popular features of social evenings. Hattie played her treble part and told none of the group gathered around the piano that she would rather be listening to singing that included Major's baritone. No other male voice or presence could substitute.

Weeks stretched into long months. Hattie never admitted to boredom, a condition her family considered a silly complaint of the idle and self-centered and a sure sign of moral and intellectual weakness. But she wanted stimulation. She missed the challenge and the sense of achievement she had known as a student. She loved learning, and she loved music. Her liberal arts education had supplied only an introduction to serious music study. She would become a student again, a student of music.

The "Local and Personal" column of the *Middle Georgia Argus* of October 6, 1891, included the following item:

> Col. Van McKibben left on Thursday, with his daughter, Miss Hattie, for Boston, where the latter will enter the New England Conservatory of Music to complete her musical education.

Boston was farther from home than Hattie had ever been before. New England was like another country, known only from reading. Her father, as sophisticated as he seemed to her, had never traveled there and knew little more about the area than did she. The Civil War was over, lost, and past. But to a Confederate veteran, even after twenty-five years, Yankees were Yankees. Van McKibben thought it wise to escort his daughter into what had been enemy territory. He approved what he found there. So did Hattie.

A long letter to her parents, dated October 18, 1891, records events and impressions of her first weeks in Boston. A small swatch of the grey material she had selected for a new dress is still pinned to the first page.

> My dear Parents:
>
> I received Papa's letter last Wednesday and was so delighted to hear from home. A letter from Hattie last Tuesday was the first I had gotten since I came. I also had a letter from Mamie Ellis Thursday. She is anxious to come here in January. I have spent another very pleasant Sunday in Boston . . . services at the new Old South Church . . . an excellent sermon . . . singing also was very fine . . .
>
> I am getting more and more interested in my studies and I believe with earnest work and careful practice I shall make fast progress. I am well pleased with all my teachers, and, of course, I am delighted with my work. Papa asked how long a vacation we have Christmas. They give only one week; that time I expect to spend reading and practicing. My room-mate will visit relatives . . .
>
> . . . two girls from Tennessee next door . . . Very nice . . . at Mary Sharp the year after I left there . . . we have been talking over the places and people familiar to us. I have been very close at work all the week, have been out very little except for a walk which we are required to take every day, and Wednesday afternoon I went down

town and bought me some winter clothes. Mama, I sent a sample of the dress I bought, hope you like it. It will be trimmed in silk to match and big pearl buttons. I have not bought my cloak yet, have been trying to decide what kind I want. They have every kind imaginable. I am sorry I have so little time for reading, for they have such a fine library in the building, but I shall make use of that during the Christmas holidays, and then there will be so much to be seen here in Boston . . . only 15 minutes until the lights will go out. The warning bell has already rung, so I must hurry to a close . . . I find so little time for correspondence. You may be surprised to know I have written only five letters while I have been here. Hattie wrote me a long sweet letter. I also received two copies of the *Argus*. I suppose the hanging took place. I hope you will write to me real often. Much love to all.

Goodnight,
Hattie

In subsequent letters Hattie continued reports of satisfaction with both study and leisure. Mamie Ellis did join her at the conservatory in January, and the two Jackson girls came to know other young women from Georgia who, like Hattie, were exploring new and distant opportunities for women.

Miss Annie Blalock from Barnesville, Ga., who is teaching at the Emerson School of Oratory where she graduated last May, called on Mamie and me, also on Miss Ada Brown, a student here also from Barnesville, Monday aft. Miss Blalock's visit was very much enjoyed, and yesterday morning we received tickets from her to a recital at the college there.

Mamie couldn't go as she had a lesson, but Miss Brown and I went, and as it was something different from our entertainments here which consist only of music, we enjoyed it . . .

Sunday was such a delightful day here we were out most of the day in the morning to hear Edward Everett Hale and in the afternoon a party of us took a very long walk down to the Public Gardens and up Commonwealth Ave. where the elite of the city reside.

. . . I believe I am making progress with my studies . . . trying hard to complete the 4th grade in piano by June; it is considered the hardest grade to pass as it includes such a list of exercises and studies . . . I have a lesson in dancing every Friday night. Am glad you have

> no objections to my taking lessons. We have an excellent teacher . . . I hope to dance well by the end of the term . . . just half over now.

More excerpts from the faded letters reveal glimpses of a student, a Southern woman not yet twenty, in the city of Boston in the spring of 1892.

> Mamie and I count the weeks very grudgingly . . . flying so fast, not that we don't want to see you all soon but opportunities are passing which probably will never again return, and we are so anxious to make the most of them . . . almost forgot again to tell you my weight. A week ago I weighed 109 lbs. . . . next opportunity I have will go down and have my picture taken. will write to Brother before long . . .

> . . . and this afternoon Miss Brown from Barnesville and I went out to see Miss Blalock who boards at Roxbury, a suburb . . . She also had some of her gentlemen friends out and we spent an hour or so very pleasantly. . . . disappointed in our trip to Plymouth . . . faculty thought it best to postpone the trip till some weeks later . . .

> . . . Only ten weeks more and we go home! How short the time is beginning to seem . . . My studies are all going nicely . . . I can do a great deal more in ten weeks.

Jackson parents in 1892 preferred that their unmarried daughters be chaperoned. Plans were made for Mame and Hattie to be met in New York by the Wrights (Mame's older sister and her husband) to be escorted home. Hattie wrote that she and Mame were hoping that the journey would include an excursion to Niagara.

Hattie's letters always included comments and questions about family and events in Jackson—the completion of the new house, her father's business and sporting trips, her little brother's school work. One letter answered a question her parents must have asked about a Butts County gentleman who had inquired about her and asked her father for her address.

> Yes, a week or so ago I received a letter from J.R.L. Smith which I'm just going to answer . . . He wrote a very nice letter asking for a correspondence, but I have not the time . . . toward the close of school I will be if possible more busy than ever.

The author of the "very nice letter" was president of the stock company that operated a passenger railway between the Butts County village of Flovilla, a regular train stop, and the popular resort of Indian Springs. Familiarly called "The Dummy," it was said to be the shortest incorporated railroad in the world. During the season, the little train and its waiting platforms were crowded with excursion groups and pleasure seekers on their way to the hotels and health giving waters of Indian Springs. Until the automobile usurped its function, the Dummy was a significant part of county business and recreation.

More than the pressures of time and studies, however, prevented Hattie from encouraging the attentions of its president, the enterprising Mr. J.R.L. Smith. She sometimes consulted a volume owned by her friend Mame, *Our Deportment or The Manners, Conduct and Dress of The Most Refined Society.* Correspondence with Mr. Smith was precluded by advice from this authority.

> . . . a young lady should not allow special attention from anyone to whom she is not specially attracted because, first, she may do injury to the gentleman in seeming to give his suit encouragement; and secondly, she may keep away from her those whom she likes better, but who will not approach her under the mistaken idea that her feelings are already interested. A young lady should not encourage the addresses of a gentleman unless she feels that she can return his affections . . . It is only the contemptible flirt that keeps an honorable man in suspense for the purpose of glorifying herself by his attentions in the eyes of her friends. . .

Hattie was no contemptible flirt. Besides, although no letter to her parents has been found that mentions him, Hattie and Major had evidently corresponded often. She had reason to believe that Andrew Lane could soon be acknowledged as her most favored suitor.

He was coming to the end of his second year as teacher and principal in the Blakely Institute. He had made a success of his job and friends in the town. But he had never forsaken his primary goals—claiming Hattie McKibben as his wife and law as his profession. For two years he saved his money and spent much of his free time in independent law study. He made plans to resign at the end of the 1892 school year and enroll in summer law courses offered by the University of Virginia. He was waiting for Hattie's June homecoming to tell her his plans and gain her participation in them.

Meanwhile, Hattie was seizing and enjoying every opportunity offered her by the conservatory and Boston. She and her father had arrived the preceding autumn with no definite limits as to length or extent of her studies beyond the 1891–92 school year. The students she met often expected to follow their piano, violin, and singing lessons with teaching them. Some cherished dreams of the concert stage. Hattie had no music career plans.

Her music study was not, however, the insignificant pastime of a privileged, indulged southern girl. Music, as a source of joy, deserved from Hattie McKibben her best. She gave it. And she received, too, the satisfaction of playing choice bits of Beethoven or Chopin well and mastering concepts of harmony and music theory. She was pleased and flattered when a faculty member in whose harmony class she excelled urged her to return for the 1892–93 school year. If she continued through the advanced program leading to graduation, her teacher was assured that Miss McKibben would be offered a teaching position herself.

Hattie whirled through weeks of May and early June as if they were compositions marked vivace. She prepared for examinations for the Solfeggio Certificate awarded for satisfactory completion of first year academic and performance instruction. Days of practice and study were often followed by evenings of faculty and senior student recitals in Sleeper Hall—appropriately named, according to some audiences. She saved the programs, which listed the hometowns of the student performers along with their names. In a spring recital program in 1893, would Miss Hattie McKibben (Jackson, Ga.) appear?

Finally, on Monday afternoon, June 20, 1892, she was seated in Tremont Temple where commencement exercises for the New England Conservatory of Music were about to begin. End of term examinations, packing, dormitory confidences, and teary goodbyes had been mixed in an exhausting jumble. She could compose herself for an orchestral concert followed by the commencement address to be delivered by the distinguished R. H. Dana, Esq. Hattie read the names of the graduates, most of whom she had come to know, listed under the headings of Pianoforte, Organ, Voice, Violin, Oratory, or Elocution. At the bottom of the last page was the announcement: "Next School year begins Thursday, September 8th."

After nine months in Boston, Hattie found Jackson and herself not at all the same as when she had left. She was glad, of course, to see Papa and Mama and Brother and Hattie Buttrill. She listened as they brought her up to date with happenings in her hometown, and she regaled them with tales of her recent doings in Boston and on the long trip home with Mame Ellis and Mame's chaperoning sister and brother-in-law. She did not tell them that Jackson seemed much smaller or that the new McKibben house, although very nice, did not yet seem like home to her. She did tell them—not to their surprise—that she expected the arrival of a gentleman caller they knew well, Major Lane.

Arrive he did. In the lingering light of a June evening, Hattie could watch for his coming from the window of her upstairs bedroom in the new house. She could see him open the iron gate and stride up the front walk. How could she be ready for the excitement, the pure joy of seeing him again when she had not yet unpacked what she had brought home from Boston in her bags and trunk and in her head? Hattie was to keep the next hour polished and stored in her memory to hand down to her granddaughters.

His letters—as long, as frequent, as revealing as they were—had not prepared her for Major's actual presence. His good looks had not much changed; his charm was still part wit and part courtliness. But she sensed subtle differences. Still natural and unaffected, he was now more confident, more in control, but without the slightest taint of arrogance.

Politely waiting for Hattie to rush through only a brief account of the last conservatory weeks and her homecoming excursion, Major enthusiastically launched into his plans for the two of them. His letters throughout the spring had promised that he would make them complete and clear to her as soon as they could be together. She did not know how complete and clear the plans already were for him. Seated beside her on the tapestry covered loveseat, he took her hand in his and proposed marriage—not an engagement to be culminated in some happy, hazy future but marriage as a definite event. He had worked out to his satisfaction how their lives together could begin with a wedding only a few months away.

Hattie heard how he had managed his money and his time for two years to make possible his enrolling in summer law classes at the University of Virginia. He would leave within days and remain throughout the summer in Thomas Jefferson's town of Charlottesville. Hattie learned that Major had already talked with her father about the Virginia law course. Colonel McKibben had done more than approve. He had offered Major the opportunity to continue learning while he began his practice in the McKibben law office in Jackson. If Hattie's father were also considering the likelihood of other McKibben and Lane connections, they were not a part of their professional discussions.

Major said he would, of course, leave the exact date and other arrangements for the wedding up to Hattie and her mother. He requested only that the ceremony take place as soon as possible after his return from Virginia. An October date would please him well.

For moments Hattie was speechless. Then ideas and plans of her own poured out. Perhaps she did not know they were her plans until she heard them fall from her lips. She did want to marry him. She loved him! There. She actually had said it. But were they ready to pin down dates for a wedding? Why not wait until Major had completed the law course and settled into association and practice with her father? She could return to Boston in September. She was making good progress; her teachers had encouraged her to return. One more term could make a real difference. Why not wait until. . .

Major let go her hand and walked across to Hattie's piano, sat down, and began to thump an accompaniment to his song:

> The jig is up, and I am flung
> Sky high, and, worse than that,
> The girl I love and thought loved me
> Said NO. I'll get my hat.
> Said NO, said NO, said NO, said NO,
> And so I'll take my hat.

When he stood up, Hattie was standing behind him, laughing. She reached up and threw her arms around his neck. She would not return to Boston, and he would not get his hat. The jig was far from up; it was just beginning. Hattie Jane McKibben could not choose to live without him.

Inseparably Interwoven for Weal or Woe

HATTIE LOVED LETTERS. She never begrudged the hours she spent writing and posting them or reading and re-reading those sent to her. As a thirteen-year-old student, miles away from home in a Tennessee school for girls, she had depended on letters to keep her connected to family and the life she knew in small town Middle Georgia. Throughout her teen years, whether she was at home or away at school, Hattie kept old friendships alive and nurtured new ones through letters. She learned, too, the uses of letters for flirting, for encouraging or discouraging suitors.

In the summer of 1892, the last year letters would be addressed to "Miss Hattie McKibben, Jackson, Georgia," her correspondence became more important than ever before. When she saw that address, written in Major Lane's handwriting, on envelopes with "UNIVERSITY OF VIRGINIA" printed in the upper left corners, Hattie's moods, appropriate for mere mundane matters, could swing in seconds to anticipation of bliss. The contents of those bulging envelopes gave assurance that Major awaited her letters just as eagerly.

July 22nd, '92 University of Virginia, Charlottesville, Va.
Friday night

My dear Hattie,

You can imagine how happy I was to receive your letter this afternoon . . . How is it that it takes your letters such a long time to reach me?

> . . . I confidently expected a letter by Thursday's early morning mail—however it came this afternoon and brought such pleasure and happiness. . .
>
> My dear, your expressions and assurances of your devotion to me awaken the tenderest feelings of all that is noble and cause me to know that I love you with all the fervor of a manly nature. I am sure . . . that your destiny is inseparably interwoven with my own . . . we are constantly separated . . . each time only to fully realize how much the happiness of my life depends upon you . . . How much better it would be if I could talk to you even for a little while instead of writing . . . which interprets so slowly . . . one's real feelings . . . in the absence of a closer and better means of communication I truly realize that the United States mail service is a great institution.

In that summer of 1892, it was. Major complained of the long time it took Hattie's letters to reach him. However, he expected a letter Hattie wrote on Monday night and mailed on Tuesday to be in his university box on Thursday. He was disappointed that it was Friday before he received it. He wrote his answer on Friday night, mailed it on Saturday morning, and hoped Hattie would find it in the McKibben box on Sunday morning. Mail trains between Georgia and Virginia were fast for that time and dependable. So were postal workers. Major and the McKibbens picked up their mail twice daily and also on Sunday morning. A bill, a wedding invitation, or news of a great aunt's demise, as well as a love letter, could receive first class attention when each bore a two-cent stamp.

Major's letters, often more than fifteen pages long, contained more than declarations of love. He wrote enthusiastically about his law courses and participation in class activities.

> . . . our class now numbers over 120 members.
>
> We had the class election on last Tuesday night. Truly the enthusiasm, the "Parliamentary Tactics" and the noise would have done credit to a National Democratic Convention . . . I was chosen one of the Executive Committee . . .
>
> . . . I have decided to spend tomorrow in Washington. The boys are busy making preparation for our departure in the morning at 6 o'clock. We will be there to witness the closing exercises of this session of Congress and also "take in Washington" generally. We will return Sunday and thus miss but one day from regular class.

In responding to Hattie's questions and concerns, he wrote of his certainty of the rightness of his choice to study law and make its practice his profession.

> . . . It is true that the Goddess of Justice is a jealous Goddess and demands almost the entire time of her votaries, and I conclude therefore that a lawyer should preserve an air of seeming busyness, even in total idleness. I do not need this artificial air just at present however for really I am very much devoted to my Blackstone. However this may be, My Dear, I have ample and sufficient time to read and enjoy your letters and answer them promptly however frequent. I truly appreciate your interest in wanting to know how I like the study of the Law. In short, I not only like but love it. As a profession it opens up to a man a world of study. He may study and practice it for a lifetime and then die without having mastered the science at all. While I am ambitious to know as much of it as possible, still the fact that the more you know about it the more you are able to see that you don't know does not discourage me but rather gives this study a fascination . . . I have no doubt but that I will love my work very much when I get actively engaged in the profession. It is a source of constant pleasure to know that you like the Law as a profession for me . . . I know in my lifetime work I could have no greater stimulus than a knowledge of your full sympathy.

Hattie and Major agreed that they would not announce their engagement until he returned from Virginia. She had no ring to flaunt, and there were still practical matters, including the wedding date, to be settled. Her parents knew and approved; other confidences were restricted to lifelong best friend Hattie Buttrill. Anyone else who was interested could guess and gossip while she went about her service and social routines just as though the love of her life were not hundreds of miles away. She knew that the letters to and from Virginia were the true center of her life, and secrecy added intrigue and excitement to their romance by mail.

The letters Hattie wrote during that summer of separation do not remain. His copious replies found among her keepsakes suggest their contents. In mid July he wrote:

> . . . I am glad Miss Mamie has returned for it is so pleasant for you two to be together. . . As for Miss Hattie B., I feel that I must love her a little for your sake and a good deal for my own . . . I so much appreciate that trait of character in you that causes you to make your-

> self useful to the "home folks"—especially in Sunday School and church . . . This disposition to serve those where you live even though many of them never attended "New England Conservatory of Music" is an . . . illustration of what few people possess—"Good Common Sense." I am glad the social world of Jackson is so pleasant—leaving it to you to be as bright and happy as possible this summer for I know you need nothing else than your own good judgement to aid you in adapting yourself to all the exciting circumstances. Yes, Thompson is especially thoughtful . . . if he can add any to your pleasure during my absence I will think all the more of him.

An August letter thanked her profusely for tuberoses she had sent him from her mother's garden. They may have had special meaning to him because the lily white fragrant blossoms were often used in bridal bouquets.

> . . . You have never shown me any little remembrance that I appreciated more than the little box of lovely tuberoses, received on last Saturday. They were wrapped and fixed so nicely that they were as fresh and beautiful when they reached Charlottesville as when they left Jackson.

In the same letter Major wrote that he had acted on Hattie's request and called upon a young lady of Charlottesville whom Hattie had known in Boston.

> . . . I went to see Miss Lyons on last Saturday afternoon. I wore a tuberose of course . . . I found her as pleasant, genial and entertaining as could be . . . She leaves for the Conservatory on September 1st . . . She seems to be a great admirer of you and expresses sincere regrets that you will not return to Boston this fall. I explained to her in a very innocent kind of way that I hardly thought you would return in as much as you had been away so constantly for the past five or six years that I thought your parents would want you at home for a little while at least. You know I can evade matters with a great deal of composure sometimes. Do you affect innocence any these days? I am sure if you meet Miss Eva Sasnett you will be put to the test.

Hattie had evidently reported that at a party Major's older brother Tom, who was often a part of the Jackson social scene, suggested to their companions that Hattie's real interest was not present.

> . . . I am not surprised to hear that Tom was teasing you. It is nothing new for him. . . Truly Tom is a great tease but I am glad his teas-

> ing is usually harmless. No, he is not aware of the situation further than that there "has been a renewal." I suppose however that he very correctly anticipates the results . . .

He also commented when Hattie wrote of traveling with a family group to adjoining Monroe County to visit the old plantation house of Mickleberry Merritt where her beloved grandmother had grown up.

> . . . I know that your visit to the old home place of your great grandfather must have been full of pleasure and interest. There is a silent grandeur about those old antebellum settlements that is almost inspiring. I am glad that you were so fortunate during your recent visit in renewing old acquaintance . . .

Throughout the summer Hattie's letters kept Major happy and assured of her loyalty and devotion. They also made him aware that neither she nor her hometown was pining in a state of suspended animation while awaiting his return. In a late August letter, he commented:

> . . . The Gypsy Party must have been a grand affair . . . from your description I know entertainment must have been pleasant . . . Jackson is showing itself to be an enterprising little town generally— in the business, social and baseball world.

Major's approval of the enterprising little town doubtless reflected his own plans. He anticipated being married in Jackson, living there with Hattie, and entering the legal profession through the portals of her father's law office.

> . . . as the time of my return draws near the more anxious do I become, it seems, to see you. Do let me hear from you real soon.

Plans and dreams were soon to be realized. The *Middle Georgia Argus* of November 4, 1892, in its customary full blown style, described the marriage of Hattie McKibben to Andrew Lane.

> On Thursday evening, October 27th, at half-past eight o'clock, one of the most brilliant weddings ever witnessed in Jackson occurred at the Baptist Church. Mr. A.W. Lane, the groom, graduated with high honors at Mercer, afterwards took a law course at the University of Virginia, and is now a rising lawyer in our little city. Of the fair bride he has won, too much cannot be said, for Miss Hattie McKibben has friends innumerable who admire her not only for her many accomplishments and charming manners but for her pure Christian charac-

> ter and nobility of soul. She graduated at LaGrange and returned only a few months ago from Boston, after spending a year at the Conservatory of Music. Our whole town turned out en masse to witness the ceremony which united these two for weal or woe.

Subsequent paragraphs did not describe the autumn weeks of "bustle and busyness" that preceded the ceremony. Hattie wanted a wedding with meaning, beauty, and distinction, but she had never imagined the multitude of decisions and details necessary for its production.

First, arrangements were made for the marriage ceremony to take place in the sanctuary of the Baptist Church just a block up Third Street from the McKibben house. Baptists, who at one time had shared facilities with local Presbyterians, had built their separate and larger church on the main street while the building of a new Presbyterian Church was still being planned. Besides, Major and the Jasper County Lanes were Baptist, and Hattie would worship with her husband. Dr. Quigg, the Presbyterian divine so loved and respected by McKibbens and Fletchers, would perform the ceremony.

Those ecumenical arrangements taken care of, Hattie and Major selected their attendants. There would be ten of them and also four young men chosen from among their friends to serve as ushers. As this granddaughter-chronicler read again the account of "A Brilliant Wedding," names of several bridesmaids and groomsmen attached themselves to actual men and women—respected, dignified, old when I knew them. I saw them young and costumed in wedding finery of a Georgia past preserved no longer in the memories of the living.

Hattie Buttrill, the maid of honor, was not the white-haired spinster-of-means of our childhood—a kind of extra grandmother. I saw a young "Hat" of twenty summers—blond, petite, and escorted by her best beau, R.L. Etheridge. I remembered Mr. Bob Etheridge as the funny old fellow who owned the fertilizer, feed, and seed store. He and Miss Hattie never married. Grandmother said that Mr. Buttrill was against the match.

The bride asked her best friend's younger sister to be in the wedding, too. Miss Mary Buttrill was escorted by Mr. E. L. (Lee) Smith, whom she married several years later. He was to become one Jackson's wealthiest citizens. Miss Mary died before I was born, but I knew Mr. Lee and his New York Store. The biggest enterprise on the square, it sold everything from bacon to buttons, from sofas to shoes. I knew his fine house, too, built just across the street from the Buttrill house. Hat was to help "Brother Lee" rear her sister's three motherless children, whom I knew as millionaire adults, two of them suicides.

The bridesmaids were all Jackson School friends. One was Mame Ellis, the companion who shared LaGrange College and New England Conservatory student days. Years later, as the widow of Atlanta attorney John Moore, she was "Miss Mame" to us little Mallets. On her visits to Jackson, especially if Grandmother were visiting from Macon, Miss Mame would have her chauffeur stop at our house. Childless herself, she occasionally brought presents to her old friend's grandchildren.

Another bridesmaid was Cleora Gibbs, who became Mrs. John Lyons. We Methodists of the 1930s could expect to see her—a tiny, brittle old lady with jet black hair in which no strand of gray was allowed to appear—seated every Sunday beside her tall, white haired husband in their regular pew. They were pillars of our church. Mrs. Lyons was also a prime force in the local unit of the Women's Christian Temperance Union, whose mission was to rid society of the evil of strong drink. Her activity in the WCTU was appropriate, for there was no hiding the fact that several Lyons were indeed intemperate drinkers. Sorely tempted by liquor, they sometimes succumbed.

Major's brother, Tom Lane, and Hattie's cousin, Henry Fletcher, were among the male attendants. The best man was John Wade from Blakely. One of Major's letters to Hattie from Virginia told her about a visit from his "good friend and cultured gentleman, John Wade," who would succeed him as superintendent of Blakely schools. During an 1892 summer vacation jaunt to Washington and historic Virginia, Wade swung west to Charlottesville to see Jefferson's home and the university he founded and also Major Lane, his old friend and companion studying there.

Hattie arranged for music to be played softly throughout the ceremony. One of the melodies must be that of "Juanita," a popular ballad she loved to hear Major sing to her. She knew that he meant the bride of the song to be his Hattie and not some Spanish "Nita." On the fortieth anniversary of her wedding Hattie wrapped her memories in rhyme.

October 27, 1892–October 27, 1932

Nita! Juanita! Ask thy soul if we should part!
Nita! Juanita! Lean thou on my heart.

Sweet and low from long ago,
Tender strains are stealing;
Fair young faces all a-glow —
Holy vows are sealing.
"Nita! Juanita! Let me linger by thy side;
Nita! Juanita! Be my own fair bride."
Smiles to brighten tears that flow,
Youth with love a-gleaming —
Was it forty years ago?
Let me go on dreaming.

Hattie never made a poem of it, but she did tell us grandchildren what followed the "elegant" McKibben house reception, reported in the *Argus*. The couple had decided to postpone a honeymoon trip. They would spend their wedding night in Hattie's room in her parents' house, which was to be their home, too, for a while. When the last guest departed, she and Major mounted the stairs.

"Sex" was a rarely used word in Hattie's vocabulary. The subject, by whatever current euphemism, was almost as rare in the social conversation of the 1890s. Janie McKibben's dutiful facts-of-life instruction had placed most emphasis on what a young lady should not do. Girls' dormitory talk on the topic was more giggles and gasps than information or actual experience. The heavy book Hattie consulted that treated human reproductive anatomy seemed to have little relevance for the way she and Major felt about each other. She knew they were in love; whatever followed their wedding would have to be joy just because she was she and Major was Major. But neither of them was prepared for the prelude of their first night together.

They pulled down the window shades and were about to turn down the oil lamp that dimly lit the bedroom in those years before electricity came to the municipality of Jackson. Then more noise and commotion than they had ever heard before rose from beneath them—from Third Street and the front lawn, from the narrow McKibben Lane which bordered the side yard. Instead of whispers of lovemaking, blaring cacophony assaulted their ears.

Whether Hattie and Major had ever heard of the ancient custom of shivaree (or charivari as the prank is sometimes spelled) or not, they were now the couple for whom that mock wedding night serenade was performed. Their very best beloved friends—girls who just an hour before had been sweet and demure, pretty and daintily gowned in ruffles and lace and well groomed young men who had just displayed impeccable manners—had reassembled as hoydens and rowdies. They wailed, they hooted, they roared. An orchestra featuring pots, pans, washboards, mallets, broomsticks, saws, and any other utensil or tool capable of contributing clangs, booms, and screeches accompanied the vocal renditions.

The whole town—at least according to the local press—had turned out for the ceremony that united Hattie and Major. Their friends arranged that the whole town could and would have to hear the riotous celebration of consummation of the marriage they had witnessed—for weal or woe.

Beginnings: Marriage and Motherhood

A PROUD WIFE FOR ALMOST SIX MONTHS, Hattie was pleased but not yet accustomed to receiving letters addressed to Mrs. Andrew W. Lane. One of them, postmarked April 14, 1893, Johnson City, Tennessee, was from a former fellow student and friend at New England Conservatory.

> My dear Hattie,
>
> I will not call this answering your letter of some months ago—but if you will not be mad with me for this long delay I will write you awhile tonight. I hardly know what to say to you tho—'cause you are married. You don't know how very odd that does sound to me. I can't think of you as anything but Hattie McKibben. I have before me now three letters—one from you saying "Major is the dearest man on earth," one from Clara saying "He is sweetest," and one from Irene Gregory saying "Albert is the dearest, noblest lover a girl ever had." Such foolishness! See me turn my nose up at you silly girls. I think music is very best and I don't like boys anyway . . . Mr. Clayton, my old flame of Blue Hill—you remember—is married—boo hoo!!. . . I think everybody I know is getting married. I have averaged two wedding invitations a month since I came here in Aug. I believe you asked me what I was doing in Johnson City—now don't become disgusted when I tell you I am teaching. . . Johnson City is a beautiful little city of 6000 inhabitants situated in the mountains of East Tennessee. The scenery is grand and the climate is delightful. They have eleven churches, three schools, three or four R.R.'s, electric

> lights and cars—in fact is quite citified. I just love to teach . . . I am in the midst of Commencement preparations. Our school closes the 26th of May and I get home the 29th, my birthday. I tell you I wish time in her flight would not go so fast. I'm going to be an old maid before I know it. Now to tell you something of the Con—or do you care to hear anything from that all important place? Clara has just left there. She worked herself sick again this year. I think she did it on purpose tho because she wanted to see her sweetheart . . . She writes me she heard Paderewski just before she left and that "he never played so well or appeared so handsome" altho he is going to marry a New York belle . . . Now my dear I know I've waited a long time to write to you but it isn't because I don't love you for I have no friends I think of oftener . . . write really soon—the first time Major leaves home as I believe that's the only time you devote to your distant friends. With lots of love and best wishes for your continued happiness, I am
>
> Lovingly,
> *Ura Wrinkle*

Hattie read and remembered herself in the Boston conservatory scene of just the year before. If she had chosen music over matrimony she would have been in the audience of that amazing young Polish pianist and composer. She could imagine that. But suppose that she, like Ura and several other classmates, had needed to turn music to a means of earning her own living. Hattie folded the letter, returned it to its envelope, and placed it with keepsakes to be discovered by a granddaughter at the end of another century.

In that spring of 1893, Hattie would not dwell for long in memories—even happy ones. No one, not ever in her life, would hear a word of regret for the choice she had made. She had not been part of Paderewski's spellbound audience, but that very evening she could play her own piano in her mother's parlor. Major would stand beside her and sing the melodies he loved—concert enough for now.

There was more. Hattie had not written her Tennessee friend the news that hardly needed announcing in Jackson. She had put away her fitted trousseau dresses and was already wearing loose, flowing gowns with shawls draped in front. There was no concealing, though, from interested close observers that Major Lane and his bride were expecting an heir.

Although Hattie may not have anticipated that married love would result so soon in pregnancy, she and Major wanted and expected to have children. An only child for ten years, Hattie knew the advantages of undivided attention and possessions. The arrival of her little brother had not usurped her place as only daughter or diminished her privileges. She loved him, but the difference in their ages prevented the kind of companionship her numerous cousins seemed to enjoy with their brothers and sisters. Major had been part of a big, loyal, affectionate family and intended to head such a family of his own. This baby would be the start.

With Major quite happy about the coming event and her mother ready to advise and assist, Hattie made preparations. Janie McKibben could and did help her daughter stitch and assemble what was needed for a new baby. But Hattie had fears, concerns, and questions she could not bring to her mother. A wall of reserve had always stood between them; there were no passages for personal, intimate confidences. Janie, only thirty-seven, had become a mother herself at seventeen. She conscientiously taught her daughter high morals and good manners, but she passed along little of what would later be called "sex education" and almost nothing of the physical process of becoming a mother. Even as the two women prepared a front, downstairs room for the approaching lying-in, Hattie had no idea how the new life she felt move inside her could emerge. Perhaps, she thought, Dr. Ellis would perform an operation—cut her open.

At seventy, my talkative, frank grandmother told me how she remembered August 26, 1893. With the doctor, her mother, and a servant experienced in such matters in attendance and with Major and her father waiting on the porch, Hattie gave birth to a son—perfect, beautiful. He was born in the way babies usually are—no cutting was necessary. She and Major had already agreed that if the baby were a boy, he should be named Andrew for his father. He would have the same initials—A.W.— as both his father and his grandfather, the late Major Augustus Washington Lane. But the baby's "W" would be for Wade, Major's good friend in Blakely.

Baby Andrew was no sooner clothed and in her arms than Hattie heard her Papa give orders that the buggy must be hitched up. "We'll have to send for Miss Hattie Buttrill. She'll want to see what we have here!"

The house Van and Janie McKibben had built was a home now. The first bride had walked down its stairs, and the first baby had been born in it.

The Major Years

BEFORE BABY ANDREW WAS BORN Hattie knew that the law partnership of McKibben and Lane would not be a permanent arrangement. Her husband had received and learned much from her father. They both possessed sharp intellects, wide interests, outgoing personalities. They respected each other. But the small office on the square with the massive oak partner's desk where they daily faced each other would not long hold both of them. Van McKibben encouraged his son-in-law to take advantage of opportunities a bigger town could offer. In one short year Major Lane had demonstrated, not only to his highly esteemed partner but throughout Middle Georgia legal circles, that he was an asset to a firm or a client and an opponent not to be underestimated.

Macon was the little city that beckoned. There Major had attended college; there he already had friends and a growing reputation. It was only some forty miles south of Jackson and closer than that to Major's childhood home. The Ocmulgee River was like a muddy-red Georgia cord tying the Lane plantation to Macon.

Hattie did not know Macon as well as did Major, but she liked what she was learning about it. It was a beautiful town. Sherman's march to the sea had left it, unlike little Jackson, intact. Antebellum mansions gave evidence of a prosperous past, and big new houses and charming cottages built in late Victorian styles showed continuing growth. Higher learning flourished there at Mercer University, Major's alma mater, and at Wesleyan, a liberal and fine arts college for women—the oldest anywhere actually chartered to grant degrees to women. A college town suited

Hattie. Colleges to her meant good companions, interesting conversation, ideas, music. She and Major and their children could have it all in Macon.

Hattie possessed a mind and spirit of her own; she was better educated than most women of her generation. But men—no doubt about it—shaped and moved her world. Choosing to marry Major Lane meant that she chose him, not Van McKibben, to decide where and how their life would be. That was the way it was. Hattie would spend little time or energy fighting the generally accepted male control of the society into which she had been born. Why should she when the men in her life were Papa and Major?

Van McKibben gave the money for building a house in Macon appropriate for his Hattie and her husband. The Lane's new address, 316 Hardeman Avenue, seemed just right. Where Vineville Avenue, a major and fashionable thoroughfare, ended and branched, Hardeman Hill sloped down and up again to College Street. The downtown area and Major's office, Wesleyan College and Mercer University, and the First Baptist Church were all easily accessible by street car, buggy, or strong young legs. The architectural plan of the Lane house was similar to that of the McKibben house in Jackson. The newer house had slightly lower ceilings and fewer wide halls, but it was spacious enough and just as ready for family living and easy hospitality.

Hattie brought love and enthusiasm to her roles of wife and mother. The domestic skills required for household management were another matter. She brought determination to those as she scribbled the beginnings of a rhyme about her situation:

> Woe is the woman who cannot cook,
> Domestic science never took.
> Manage she must by hook or crook . . .

Ellen Green became the hook. Hired as cook-housekeeper soon after the Lanes occupied their new house, she was to remain with them for more than twenty years. The kitchen was her special domain, but her efficiency permeated every room. Colored Ellen Green came every morning to make it possible for fair Hattie McKibben Lane to be the virtuous woman described in the Bible Proverbs she had learned in her Presbyterian upbringing. "She looketh well to the ways of her household."

Hattie did that as had her mother and grandmother, and Janie McKibben continued to help her daughter follow their example. What Ellen Green cooked and Hattie served her family often came from Jackson. Each week Janie took eggs, butter, and fresh vegetables and flowers from her garden to the Jackson depot. In a matter of hours they would be in Hattie's Macon kitchen. From the McKibben farms, too, was sent a man-of-all work. Quartered behind the Lane house, over the barn-like structure that later became the garage, he took care of horse and buggy and outdoor work. He never became a polished butler, but sometimes he did appear in the dining room when Hattie's toe pressed the bell set in the floor beneath her place at the table.

Hattie had much to make her happy, and she was. A second son, Van McKibben Lane, was born before little Andrew was two. In less than three years of marriage, Hattie had produced a namesake for each of the two men she adored. The demands of toddler Andrew and infant Kib controlled and rearranged her days and sleep-interrupted nights, but Hattie could manage. Best of all, Major's devotion and unfailing good humor could bring relief and often laughter to kitchen and nursery crises.

Major had warned her before their marriage that practicing law meant serving a jealous goddess of justice. Hattie did not intend to be jealous, too. Accustomed to praise and prize winning herself, she was willing to shine in Major's reflected light as he achieved remarkably early professional success. When the governor of Georgia appointed him solicitor-general of the Macon Judicial Circuit in early 1896, Major received a letter of congratulations from Dr. Henry Quigg, the Presbyterian minister who had performed their wedding ceremony: ". . . I rejoice that you stepped in at the 11th hour & took the prize. I am so much gratified at reading the tall compliments you are receiving on every hand. I am rejoiced to see that you are in every way worthy of that beautiful and very sparkling wife I gave you. . ."

The birth of their first daughter in December of the same year was to them more reward. The big family they expected and wanted was well begun. The new baby was named Mary for Major's mother. With his sons, Major had already proved that he was as fitted to be a father and as happy in being one as any man could be. Her own father's pride and joy, Hattie could not have been surprised when her husband showered affection on his first daughter. When he spoke of her, it was "Mary, bless her heart."

In the midst of bright bustle in Macon, Hattie was distressed by changes in the McKibben home in Jackson. There was no hiding her father's increased drinking and declining health. With her brother away at military school, her mother was assuming management of more business as well as household affairs. Hattie Buttrill reported to her friend: "I try, Hat, to stop by your papa's office every chance I get. But usually he's already been too heavy into the peach brandy for us to visit very much." One piece of family wisdom passed down to present generations may have roots in such bleak times. "Don't speak anything but good of the family. The bad will be known soon enough."

Mourning had preceded her father's actual death. When that not unexpected event occurred in September of 1897, Hattie could receive with gratitude and pride every expression of sympathy, every word of appreciation and praise for the man Van McKibben had been. It was the memory of that man that remained with his daughter.

A second baby girl, Lucia, was born the next summer to the Lanes. Little Mary had a sister less than two years younger. The young parents enjoyed the prospect of their girls being playmates and companions as their boys already were. But at the age of two, Lucia died of scarlet fever.

Too grieved and exhausted to object, Hattie was persuaded that the first consideration must be protecting the other children from contagion. Following the doctor's advice, Major insisted that Hattie take Andrew, Kib, and Mary immediately to Jackson for refuge in her mother's house. He would remain behind to take charge of the affairs of death and the fumigation of the entire Macon house according to the best epidemiology of the time. Major wrote Hattie almost daily and joined his family as frequently as possible.

Oct. 3, 1897
Tuesday afternoon

My dear Hattie,

I reached Macon this morning feeling very much depressed of course, but hopeful. After getting some breakfast from Isaac's I went out home. Found Ellen there with the men who are doing the fumigating. Today they are fumigating the parlor, dining room, & kitchen and the lamps have been burning since about 10 o'clock . . . Tomorrow I suppose we will open up the house. I have just had a talk with Dr. Burnam. We have decided that it will be best for you not to return to Macon for some time to come. You & the children are safe in Jackson, and if no symptoms of scarlet fever appear within the next few days I shall be relieved. So for the present remain in Jackson with the children . . . Dr. Burnam says it will not be wise for you to make visits back & forth from Jackson & you couldn't be contented here without the children and besides you had best be there with them where you can give them your personal attention as well as be a great relief to Mother. It is hard for me to be here without you all but I believe it is best and will go to work to stand it the best I know how. It is now my intention to buy a new fall suit & leave it at the office & simply put it on here when I start to Jackson & then leave it at the office when I return. Mr. Park is out of the city . . . My intention is to come up Saturday & I will then talk over the whole matter with you. My mind however is fully made up on the proposition that for the present you & the children should remain in Jackson. I feel relieved that I have reached the conclusion because I believe it wise. Of course we will have no trouble in arranging details with Mother.

I don't know how we would get along without her. Dear, I know you intended to come Thursday and I do not want you to feel disappointed but to remain in Jackson as happily and contentedly as you can under the circumstances. We must not hurry. We should be careful and patient and trust God to lead us as we work and plan for what we believe, under his guidance, to be for the best. I have read some twenty-odd letters from various friends who have been thoughtful in trying to say something that would comfort us . . . I will try to bundle them & mail them to you. After reading them, you might make a list of them and destroy them or put them away where the children can't handle them. I suppose it would be proper for us to answer them some time. They have not been in the house. Ellen had some at

> her house. Others were at the office . . . I will go out home about 5 o'clock this evening, but before doing so will go out to the cemetery & spend a few moments at the last resting place of our dear little "Dolly." Precious little Lucia, our baby . . . Her little spirit still lives and will be a ministering angel to the little household that loved her so dearly, oh, so dearly. Take good care of yourself & the dear children. Watch them closely all the time. And Dear, be just as bright & cheerful as you can. Write me every day if only a few words . . .

Several weeks later, Major wrote of progress in getting the house ready for his family's return and of his lonely bout with grief:

> . . . I am so tired of my present surroundings here but I am glad it will not be long until you will be at home with me. My heart is too heavy at this hour to write much. While I want to be resigned to God's will, the separation from our baby for all this life is so hard. Yet, my Dear, we must not be dejected or despondent. We have great responsibilities upon us & God, our refuge & strength, expects us to meet them . . .

When Hattie and the children came home to Macon, she and Major found shared grief easier to bear. And as she had from girlhood, Hattie poured her feelings into written words:

> FOR LUCIA
>
> Into this, our happy household
> Came the stranger to us, Death,
> Claimed our precious one, our baby,
> Just a little sigh, a breath,
> And she'd gone from us forever. . .
> It is hard to know why thus
> God has let affliction prove us,
> But we bow beneath the rod,
> Trusting all to our dear Savior,
> For our baby is with God.
>
> *Her Mother*
> October, 1900

And life, Lane family life, returned to the house at 316 Hardeman Avenue as Hattie and Major were restored by each other and their children. When another son was born the next year, they named him Louis for Lucia, the toddler they had lost.

More Major Scales

"THE WEDDING TRIP—(12 YEARS DELAYED)" Hattie wrote above the picture of herself and Major and added "St. Louis and Canada. July & August 1904." Hattie is dressed and hatted for travel. Major, now without mustache, sits beside her and seems ready to lead the way. He wears the coat of his dark suit buttoned and holds a wide-brimmed Panama hat. By his crossed legs, Hattie wrote "Atlantic City, N. J." The couple is stiffly posed for a picture postcard of themselves, a popular souvenir, cheaply and readily available in the early years of the twentieth-century before tourists came to consider their own cameras almost required equipment. Hattie did not address the reverse side. Neither did she follow the instructions: "Place one cent stamp here." Hattie intended to keep this postcard herself. For the first time since their son Andrew's birth in 1892, Hattie and Major would be together, separated from children and the demands of domesticity and Major's growing law practice.

For almost an entire summer they would be traveling as far north as New York and Canada and as far west as the Mississippi River and St. Louis. That city in 1904 was the scene of a grand exposition to celebrate the centennial (a year late) of the Louisiana Purchase of 1803. The St. Louis Fair also attracted the Democratic National Convention whose task was to nominate a presidential candidate to oppose the popular incumbent, Theodore Roosevelt. Major planned to attend although, aside from a term in the Georgia Legislature, he had chosen not to mix politics very heavily into either his professional or his personal life.

Again the Lanes depended on the resources and help of the Widow McKibben. Andrew, almost eleven, nine-year-old Kib, eight-year-old Mary, and Louis, not yet three, would be in their grandmother's care in the big house in Jackson.

Good care it was, despite occasional incidents such as the one related by my mother, who had been the eight-year-old Mary. Few little girl pursuits were as appealing to her as whatever her brothers were doing. When they decided to explore their grandmother's barn lot, separated from the backyard by a fence whose gate was always closed, Mary followed. When the boys climbed the steep ladder steps to the loft of the biggest barn, she was right behind them. How was she to know there was a wide opening in the loft floor for throwing down hay? Her hay-cushioned fall resulted in no serious injuries, but grown-up Mary, when she owned the McKibben house, made the barn lot off limits for her children—officially, anyway.

Barn lot adventures were only one feature of that summer for the Lane children. They found playmates up and down Third and on nearby College and Covington Streets. They learned their way around the center of town, the Courthouse Square. Accompanied at first by their businesslike grandmother or their fun-loving, high-spirited Uncle Van, the Lane grandchildren were soon recognized by shopkeepers, shoppers, and the occupants of the business and professional offices. Beyond the city limits was the Butts County countryside where crops of cousins were as abundant as those of cotton and corn.

Meanwhile, their parents were traveling in style. While a smoke-belching steam locomotive swallowed up miles of America, Hattie and Major could watch their country slide by from the windows of a dinning car where both service and food were good. Their trains had Pullman cars, but they spent most nights of their "delayed wedding trip" in hotels in cities and resorts they had chosen for sightseeing and relaxation. At Montmorency Falls, Quebec, Hattie placed a stamp bearing the likeness of British King Edward VII on a picture postcard showing rocks, falls, and the hotel, all decorated with maple leaves. She addressed it to her mother and wrote: "Good morning: Greetings to all of you—Major and Hattie."

From St. Louis she kept a guest ticket to the Democratic National Convention of 1904 and memories of the Exposition that one melody and its lyrics would always revive for her: "Meet me in St. Louis, Louis. Meet me at the Fair."

Their American travels were far from the proclamation of financial and social status that the European Grand Tours often were in those early years of the twentieth century. But for Hattie and Major Lane, their long postponed honeymoon was just right.

So was the return to home and children. Hattie had experienced the longest separation from all of her children she was ever to know.

Eugenia of red-gold curls, the baby conceived during their happy journey, died before her second birthday. In October of 1906, she was buried beside little Lucia in Macon's old Rose Hill Cemetery whose quiet acres sloped down to the Ocmulgee River. The Lane plot was only one of many there with small graves. Marble cherubs, angel wings, reclining lambs, and tombstone instructions to "suffer little children to come unto me" were cold comfort for hard facts of those years: big families were common; so were the deaths of children in them.

Hattie needed no further lessons in loss to know that advantages, abilities, and a happy marriage could not insulate her from grief, but just two weeks after Eugenia's death came shocking, tragic news from Jackson. Hattie's twenty-four-year-old brother—promising, popular Van McKibben—had been found dead in his bed. Her own baby's death still an open wound, Hattie could offer her mother only a daughter's presence, no real solace when Janie McKibben had lost the son who was the joy of her life.

Always preferring the company of men to that of women, Hattie's mother turned more readily to Major. Janie could never be a leaner, but she liked and trusted the son-in-law who called her "Mother." There was some consolation, too, in her grandchildren, especially in thirteen-year-old Andrew, the oldest and her favorite.

Three more children were born to Hattie and Major. Margaret (born June 25, 1907), with Hattie's small frame and strong will and Major's brown eyes, was named for her great-great-grandmother, Margaret McKibben, the pioneer matriarch who headed the McKibben family trek to Georgia from North Carolina. Harry Merritt (born September 10, 1909) completed the quartet of Lane brothers. When Harry was almost four without a prospect of younger brother or sister, Hattie believed her baby-making years were over. Even when she experienced the familiar symptoms of pregnancy, she at first attributed them to what ladies called "change of life." The change was Virginia (born April 6, 1914).

My uncle Harry told me how he remembered learning a new family member was expected. He was sitting on the front steps at 316 Hardeman Avenue with his mother when she asked what he thought of having a new little brother or sister. My uncle said that he replied honestly that he had never thought of such a thing at all. Although Virginia's arrival meant his relinquishing the role of family pet, he joined in the welcome to the red-haired baby who was to be the sparkling treasure of them all.

Hattie's last pregnancy was not an easy time. Her mother, whose health and strength were taken for granted and depended upon, was seriously ill. Already worried, Hattie was further alarmed by sentences in a letter from her doctor cousin, Quigg Fletcher. Writing to urge the presence of the Lanes at his upcoming wedding, he told of a recent visit to the McKibben house where Mary was with her grandmother. "I saw Mary in Jackson," he wrote, ". . . Aunt Janie is looking very badly and it certainly distresses me to see it as I am afraid she can't live so very much longer unless a great change takes place."

No change for the better happened. Problems with her "delicate condition" prevented Hattie from being constantly in Jackson during all of her mother's final illness. Even if independent Janie McKibben had been willing to accept personal caregiving from her, Hattie was unable to give it. The mother whose help and whose home had been always available died in December of 1913. She did not live to see Virginia, the youngest of her grandchildren.

Hattie inherited more than property from her mother. There was something of Janie McKibben's strength in her determination to assume in her own way the new responsibilities that came with her material legacy. With Major's encouragement, Hattie stepped up to a new level of maturity.

The Home That Held It All

FOR MORE THAN TWENTY YEARS Hattie held a child in her womb, at her breast, or by the hand. She could have drowned, her very self washed away in a sea of domesticity. That could and did happen to women in her world—even to those with successful husbands and education of their own. But for Hattie, the processes by which her family was well fed, clothed, and housed were mere means to an end. She never mastered some of them. Always considering Major's preferences, Hattie could plan good meals, mainly from the meat, dairy products, and fresh fruit and vegetables from the McKibben farms in Butts County. Ellen Green cooked them and took care of routine housekeeping tasks. Hattie did put the needlecraft she had learned as a girl to practical use in family mending and darning. She joked that she was a faithful darner or, at least, darn faithful. A professional seamstress came to the house for an entire week in the spring and again in the fall. Major took pride in his own appearance; Hattie saw to it that his family did not fall beneath his standards.

The end of all housekeeping for Hattie was a home where she, Major, and their sons and daughters wanted to be. The Lanes had many concerns and interests besides Major's profession: music, reading, writing, involvement in their neighborhood, in the First Baptist Church where Major taught a Bible class, in happenings at nearby Mercer University and Wesleyan College. Always there were the varied and changing demands and pursuits of every one of the children. The Lane house could hold them all and be shared, too.

Relatives and friends from Jackson and Butts County, especially Hattie Buttrill, were frequent guests. Janie McKibben's visits could be anticipated until her failing health and subsequent death ended the duties she felt were hers. Her visits to Macon and her daughter were never long; it seemed she needed merely to see for herself that all was well, that members of her family wanted for nothing she could supply.

From the old homeplace, the farm on the Ocmulgee River in Jasper County where Major had grown up, his youngest brother Jim came occasionally to Macon for a mule sale or other farm business. He might be accompanied by his wife Lily and one or more of their children (finally twelve in all). Those Lanes could count on taking time out from their city errands for a mid-day dinner with Major and Hattie.

When young Jackson ladies came to Wesleyan, as they often did, especially if they wanted to study music, Hattie made it her practice to invite them to visit the Lane house, within easy walking distance from the college.

Small children at home or a baby on the way could prevent Hattie from being by Major's side at every social, religious, or cultural event he attended. Pleased when she could go out with him, he found greater satisfaction when they entertained in their own home. When he sat at the head of their massive oak dining table, she was the gracious hostess at the other end. Then in the parlor she was the accompanist for those who gathered around the piano. When she was pregnant, she wore long, loose tea gowns designed to be comfortable, concealing, and becoming.

The children learned hospitality and good manners by example. As soon as they could demonstrate acceptable dining deportment, young Lanes joined adult company at the table. Schoolboy Andrew deemed a riddle with a Biblical context appropriate for a guest prominent at both Mercer University and the First Baptist Church. "Do you know why Joseph didn't sleep with Potiphar's wife?" Without waiting for a reply from the astonished gentleman, Andrew gave the answer, "Cause he wasn't sleepy; that's why." Hattie and Major may have reconsidered their non-adherence to the popular dictum that children should be seen and not heard.

Lane progeny, like their parents, were all sociable, but each played a different, special family role. Andrew was the good-looking, popular family wit. McKibben, more beset with childhood illnesses, was the book lover, scholar, and quick, clear thinker. Mary's optimistic energy and caring good nature made her the willing help with the younger children. They turned to her sometimes more readily than to their mother. The deaths of Lucia and Eugenia left a wider age gap between Louis and an older or a younger sibling, but he could attract companions glad to join his quests for fun and pleasure as audience for his jokes and songs and players in his pranks. Constant parental surveillance and prodding were required to keep Louis on time and on task for school and home assigned duties. My grandmother Hattie confessed to me that she never prayed for patience although hers was in short supply. Louis tried what little she possessed. Attractive Margaret's flair for the dramatic was encouraged by lessons in "expression." Harry, with a larger body frame than any of the others, was not a "little brother" for long. His size and strength were assets when his older brothers and their friends introduced him to sports. He joined in, too, singing lead when they harmonized.

Major participated actively in the upbringing of his children. Both respected and loved, he was an accessible guide and model for his sons. Hattie and the children spent most of each summer in Jackson, with Major joining them for weekends. When Andrew and McKibben reached adolescence, they could, if they wished, remain in Macon with their father. One letter described how the three fared:

> . . . I received Mary's letter this morning . . . did not write yesterday as I had just left you . . . really no news here now. I am writing just to say I miss you . . . plan to come up Thursday or Friday afternoon & not return until Monday . . . McKibben will take supper with Roland Neel this evening. Andrew will be at Lakeside & I will be at home alone. It would be much more pleasant at Jackson.

While Major was serving as municipal judge, he learned that Andrew and McKibben were frequenters of a local pool hall with a questionable reputation. He called the boys into the library for a private talk. "I hear that you're interested in improving your billiard game," he began. "I suppose, though, that I'll need to resign. I don't believe that I could judge a case where my sons might be witnesses." The sons moved their interests elsewhere.

Mary, as oldest daughter, was already her father's adoring companion before much younger Margaret and Virginia appeared on the family scene. Mary happily absorbed the tastes and values of her parents, seldom questioning their opinions and offering even less resistance than did her brothers to family rules. Mutual parent-daughter satisfaction accompanied the blossoming of Mary, the child, into Mary, the popular young lady. What his children did and with whom they did it seldom escaped Major's notice and never his interest. When his watchful father's eye focused on Mary, he found it easy to like what he saw.

One outstandingly attractive girl was a part of the young social set Mary enjoyed when she was in Jackson. From one of the town's most prominent and prosperous families, this Helen personified the same charms as those of the Greek beauty with the same name. Helen exuded sex appeal before that term was commonly applied in Middle Georgia. And she became Mary's friend.

On one of Helen's Macon visits, talk reached Major that the girl seen with Mary on downtown Cherry Street had turned every male head. There were other eyebrow-raising comments. As soon as Mary's guest returned home, Major made a request of his daughter, "Better to consult with your mother and me before you invite Helen again. She seems to have more 'come hither' than we might be able to take responsibility for."

Major made no judgmental, negative commands, but Helen's visits were doubtless curtailed. Mary and Helen remained friends through many years—years that for Mary held conventional marriage and motherhood in Jackson and for Helen several marriages, divorces, and nothing conventional anywhere.

By 1914, the year of Virginia's birth, the Lane house had become a favorite gathering place for Macon's college crowd. "This generation gap that seems to disturb so many people now doesn't affect us," remarked the adult Virginia at a family party where she was nearer the age of several of her nieces and nephews than of Andrew, McKibben, and Mary. "I've always lived in a generation overlap." Then she added, "And loved it."

The Kappa Alpha fraternity brothers of Andrew and McKibben at Mercer made Mary their sponsor. The appeal of the Lane house for them was heightened when they found Mary's Wesleyan friends there, too.

More student presence resulted when the class taught by Major for Mercer's new law school occasionally met in the library of his home.

At the same time, Louis was meeting early adolescence with intense interest in pretty girls. Treating his current favorite at the sweet shop depleted his funds and found him complaining that "it sure is hard to flirt on a nickel." Meanwhile Margaret was walking to and from Vineville School where she was mastering new associations along with a first grade primer. In the months before Virginia's birth, only pre-school Harry remained at home.

Hattie, at the center of it all, stirred in her own interests. She became a charter member of the Saturday Morning Music Club that met in the homes of its members or in the Wesleyan parlors. Hattie reveled in the company of women who performed for each other and worked to promote music events and music education throughout the Macon community. Hattie cultivated friendships with other Macon women whose concerns and conversation extended beyond the confines of kitchen and nursery. The *Macon Telegraph* printed an account of the first meeting of a history club held in the home of Mrs. A.W. Lane, who was to serve as its president. Later Hattie joined the Macon Writers Club. With or without such stimulation and encouragement, she had long turned her experiences, musings, and strong opinions into verse.

After breakfast and the rush of departures for offices, college classes, and school, Hattie could sometimes claim an hour or so for herself while Ellen Green began morning housework and attended to the immediate needs of Harry and the new baby. On one of the very few days when faithful Ellen could not come, Major left without papers he had brought home. He sent the young man beginning his legal career in the Lane firm to get them. Finding the front door ajar, he called, "Mrs. Lane . . . " She answered from the kitchen where he found her perched on a stool. In the middle of unwashed breakfast dishes, she held a pencil and writing pad. "Our cook couldn't come today, Bill, and I'm writing a poem."

My uncle Louis, reminiscing about his boyhood, said that he knew then that his mother was different. "While other boys' mothers were insisting that they eat vegetables, brush their teeth, and wear clean underwear, my mother was advising me always to keep pencil and pad by my bed to be ready for any nocturnal original thought."

With mother's milk Hattie nourished her children on words and music. While she was rocking Virginia to sleep, Mary came in from a Wesleyan English class with news of a new assignment. She must write a poem. Hattie and Mary looked at the child just closing her eyes, smiled, and whispered agreement that the poem could be a lullaby. Mary's verses, in regular rhythm and rhyme, described early evening when the first stars are peeping out just as Earth's flowers, birds, and babies are ready for rest and sleep. Hattie helped Mary polish every syllable of the conventional poetic language—all the thees and thys and eventide and nigh—until they exactly fit. A lullaby should be sung, and Hattie gave herself the assignment of setting Mary's words to music. Mary sang them to her baby sister and then to five children of her own. We blue-eyed little Mallets knew our brown-eyed Aunt Gigi was the inspiration for our song's concluding lines:

O eyes of brown with lids cast down!
O gleaming golden head!
Sleep, too, and rest on mother's breast
While angels guard thy bed.

Although they had both excelled as students, Hattie and Major did not require perfect school work from each of their children. They did expect that good effort, which was required, would bring acceptable results. Academic achievement had come so happily and easily to Hattie that she simply did not understand why lovable, lively Harry was finding reading, the key to school success and a favorite Lane activity, so hard. Mary, or "Sister" as the three youngest Lanes called her, had more patience with her brother's struggles. With Sister's front porch tutelage, Harry learned the words that announced the destination of the street cars that clattered up and down Hardeman Hill. He began to see how the letters fit to form the sound of the words. He could put the whole reading puzzle together. When he was ten, he could proudly write "Sister," who was a student then in New York: "I told the story yesterday in school of King Arthur and my teacher said I told it better than the others. After we got our lessons Thursday night we played Rook. Mother and I were partners."

Harry could also read aloud to his mother while she worked at the family mending. For that job Hattie considered a reader almost a necessary as a thimble. What was read varied with the reader and the reader's interests as well as Hattie's. It could be columns from *The Macon Telegraph,* a school or college text, or a chapter or two of a novel. Dickens was a favorite for reading aloud. Sometimes it could be the Bible.

In those early years of the twentieth century, those years before World War I, Hattie and Major made their home and shaped the lives of their children in peace and prosperity. After the war began in Europe in 1914, they were too intelligent, too well informed not to see the distinct possibility that the United States would not remain neutral. They were personally involved; if war came, Andrew and McKibben would fight in it. In 1916, although one of the slogans of President Woodrow Wilson's re-election campaign was "He kept us out of the war," American involvement seemed inevitable.

On April 6, 1917, the United States declared war on Germany. On that day, the Lanes were celebrating Virginia's third birthday. Harry came home from school to repeat what his teacher had said: "We don't have to hate the Germans. We hate the things they do." As the Great War—so named before a second world war was to designate it World War I—changed the course of world history, it reached and wrenched the home Hattie and Major had made.

Their older sons were fired with patriotic fervor. Andrew had not made a professional or career choice at either Mercer or Georgia's Institute of Technology in Atlanta. Within weeks of the Declaration of War, he enlisted in a Savannah company of volunteers. McKibben, with two degrees from Mercer, had gone north for more law study. At the Yale University commencement in June of 1917, he received another law degree, but already he was scheduled for officer's training.

Major Lane, all his life called by the military rank attained by his father in the old Indian Wars of the nineteenth century, was a man of peace. His dreams for his twentieth century sons were those of peace. His ambitions for them had not included soldiering or any kind of military career. Yet by the summer of 1917, war had climbed out of trenches in France, crossed the Atlantic, and torn through headlines to stand in the Lane parlor. From recruitment posters all over the country, a stern Uncle

Sam saying "I want YOU" had pointed his finger directly at Andrew and McKibben. Handsome in new U.S. Army uniforms, they were ready and willing to go to war.

The popular song "You're in the Army Now" seemed to be addressed to their sons, but Hattie and Major had no heart for joining in its singing. Everywhere they were hearing, too, the bugle call rhythms of another song—the one George M. Cohan had written especially for the American Expeditionary Forces embarking for Europe to the war Americans were being told was "The War to End War":

> Over there, over there,
> Send the word, send the word
> Over there
> That the Yanks are coming,
> The Yanks are coming. . .

McKibben, Georgia born and bred, would be one of the "Yanks." Any hopes Major had of having his son join him after Yale in an expanded Lane law firm were tangled in the last lines of the song:

> And we won't come back
> 'til it's over
> OVER THERE

Besides Kib's from Yale Law School, there was another Lane graduation in 1917. Mary received the bachelor of arts degree from Wesleyan College that year. She and her classmates, swept up in patriotic excitement, mixed graduation parties and plans for their futures with tears and cheers as every day brought news of the enlistment of another brother, boyfriend, or fiancé. Their song would be "Keep the Home Fires Burning." Mary sang it, but she believed she could do more than hearth tending. She learned to drive when her father bought their first automobile just as she was entering her teens. Mary confidently volunteered for homefront ambulance driver training.

For Hattie, keeping the home fires burning cheerily became harder and harder. Anxiety for her soldier sons spread to concern for Major. He seemed to try to avoid talking about the war, never voicing his worries about Andrew and McKibben. Hattie could see pain behind his attempts at usual good humor, and there was no shame in confessing actual physical pain.

The doctors he consulted could find neither cause nor cure for his discomfort. Could he have a kind of rheumatism? Could neuritis be his problem? Rest and the curative effects of mineral water treatments were recommended.

In December of 1917, while Major was seeking to recover his health at an out-of-state spa, Hattie learned that McKibben's company was expected to leave Camp Gordon, near Atlanta, for France. When Major received a letter from Hattie telling him that she was leaving for Atlanta to see McKibben, Major wrote Mary, who had been left in charge of house and younger children.

> . . . your mother . . . states that she will leave for Atlanta at 7:30 in the morning. I'm so glad she has arranged to go. It will be so nice for her to see McKibben not to mention numerous Atlanta friends. I haven't a word of news to write . . . Think I'm about over my neuritis or rheumatism but will have to build up after I get home. My plans are not definite, but will probably leave Sunday night or Monday morning . . . I know you will take good care of the home & the children while your mother is away. Be careful in every way. I am always so afraid . . . the little ones will get hurt. Kiss the children for me.
>
> *Your loving father*

The letter seemed to refer to Hattie's journey as a mere pleasure jaunt to Atlanta where it would be "nice" to see McKibben and her friends. Major could write his oldest daughter of his being afraid that his "little ones" might be hurt. Perhaps her good care could keep them from harm. He could not express fears for McKibben and Andrew when there was no way to protect them.

McKibben was soon to sail for France. Andrew's company remained in Savannah. Major returned to "build up" at home. But by January he was in a Macon hospital in critical condition. Andrew was given emergency leave.

Packed away in the boxes of old Lane letters was a handwritten note postmarked Atlanta, January 10, 1918, and addressed to Mrs. Andrew Lane, Macon, Ga. On the stationery of his Atlanta firm, Little, Powell,

Smith & Goldstein, A. G. Powell had written, "I am so grieved to hear that Major Lane is seriously ill. I sincerely trust that he will be well again soon . . . " On January 12, 1918, on the back of the envelope containing that letter, Andrew scrawled the words of the request he telegraphed to his sergeant in the 121st Regiment, Field Artillery Headquarters in Savannah: FATHER DIED TODAY. AM DUE BACK MONDAY. CAN I HAVE A FEW MORE DAYS?

Andrew Washington Lane, Hattie's husband and the major theme of her life for twenty-five years, was dead at the age of forty nine. Love survived. It lived in the shattered heart somehow still beating beneath Hattie's black dress. It lived in seven young Lanes—from two soldiers in their country's khaki, down to a not-yet-four-year-old in a ruffled pinafore. Love had flourished in youth and health, in comfort and success; and surrounded by friends and laughter and song, love had grown. Love had been tested by illness, loss, grief, and war and proved itself strong and resilient. In the home that had held it all, a fragile-appearing widow would keep love alive.

Herself

"DON'T EVER FORGET WHO YOU ARE, Hattie McKibben," her father had said, giving proud courage to the little girl afraid of the dark. And the girl—good daughter, loyal friend, bright student, belle of winning ways—was happy to be who she was. She had chosen to marry Major, and she learned and loved the role she took as Mrs. Andrew Washington Lane—wife and mother. In the year just beginning, 1918, she put on the costume of a widow, a part she never chose to play. Still and always to be mother, she could no longer be wife. Yet "just a widow" was not who she was. For the rest of her life—thirty years more—she would be Hattie McKibben Lane—woman—as only she herself could define who that would be.

In the bleak winter weeks that followed Major's death, she could not allow herself to withdraw behind a curtain of tears. Claims for her attention invaded every hour of the day, and those of her children came first. Her fatherless sons and daughters must have the best start she could give them. She was spared many of the most common of widows' woes. She did not face poverty or even drastically reduced income. There was no pile of bills she could not pay. No child of hers would have to drop out of school to earn the meager wages needed for a family to eke out subsistence. The Lanes had never been extravagant, but they had lived well. After Major's death, there was no need for Hattie to shave off the little luxuries she and her family had taken for granted.

Hattie was, in fact, an heiress. She already owned the McKibben farms and other properties in Butts County. To them was added control of Major's considerable estate. Modest wealth did not mean pampered leisure for her. It came with the responsibilities and daily demands of single parenthood, absentee farm and real estate management, and investment decisions. Her mother's head for business, however, was not part of her legacy.

She could not expect help from her two oldest sons. Andrew could be sent from the Georgia coast to Europe at any time; McKibben was already there. Neither was there help she could give her soldier sons except writing them cheerful letters and praying for the early victory that would bring them and all mothers' sons home soon and safe. Children and unfamiliar business matters crowded her days, but they could not push the war from her nights. The notebook kept by her bed held her fears and prayers shaped into lines of verse.

> Through days of stress and hours of strain,
> The fiercest of the whole campaign,
> How anxious solders' mothers feel
> For their brave sons who face the steel.
> Help us, O Lord, to match our men . . .
> God, bring our heroes home again.

Hattie did find help in twenty-one-year-old Mary. "Sister," always an important presence in the lives of Margaret, Harry, and Virginia, gave more time and attention to them than ever. She helped Margaret and Harry with their lessons; she played with Virginia, read to her, and brushed her shining hair. She shared the games and jokes and knew the playmates of all three. She let them into her social life. Margaret and Virginia could watch and help when she got ready for dates. Harry could answer the door for her girlfriends and her beaux. He seldom missed a chance to talk sports with grown-up young men until Sister came downstairs. Hattie could depend on Mary's seeing to it that her papa's "little ones" never lacked for care or love.

Louis was another matter. Not yet seventeen, sorely needing a man's example and companionship, he had lost his father to death and his older brothers to the army. Hattie was advised that the Virginia Military Institute could supply the discipline she could not. Louis rather liked the idea of going away to school. A uniform, marching, and guns seemed appropriate in the education of a boy whose country was at war. If Louis could be persuaded or coerced to buckle down to the course work required for admittance, he could enter VMI in the fall.

In July, from the McKibben House in Jackson, where she had gone as in past years to spend the summer months, she wrote to McKibben, "somewhere in France."

> Dear Son,
>
> Three weeks ago to-day we came to Jackson . . . Your last letter was written June 19th and I'm expecting another one daily. Glad the war news is so very encouraging and trust your regiment will not have to get into the fray. Andrew came up here to see us Thursday, and he told us Good-bye Sunday eve, expecting to leave soon for service overseas. Of course, this was a shock to us as we were hoping he would be allowed to do duty in coast defense over here. But if he has to go, I'm trusting office work will keep him safely behind the lines. You are the one for whose safety I feel the most anxiety. Don't be rash and court danger. Take care of yourself and your men. I'm hoping it will be over before you have to go to the front . . .

Hattie wrote her son the news—Jackson, Macon, and family news. The farm crops were "looking good." Mary, with her own automobile, divided her time between Jackson and Macon, often bringing her Macon friends and Hardeman Avenue neighbors up to Jackson with her. Little Massie Lane, the youngest daughter of Major's brother Tom, had been with them since their arrival in Jackson. "She's a nice little girl. I'm glad she's here," Hattie wrote of her husband's niece and the visiting cousin playmate for her children. "Brother Tom and family" were expected to drive up the following week for a brief visit of a day or two before taking Massie back home to Americus in South Georgia. Tom, like Major, was a lawyer and was giving Hattie legal and financial advice.

Hattie was glad she could send McKibben positive news about Louis. He had become one of the growing group of Jackson boys responding to the leadership of the minister of the Baptist Church just up the street. Hattie had rented two of the upstairs rooms of the McKibben House to that popular bachelor divine, Dr. Robert Vandeventer. The location near his church was convenient for him, and Hattie liked having such a distinguished tenant in the house, now unoccupied except for the Lanes' brief visits and long summer stays. Dr. Vandeventer, believing in wholesome recreation for young people, had put in a swimming pool in the basement of the new church. That imposing edifice of yellow brick with massive dome and columns had replaced the simpler wooden building where Hattie and Major were married. Perhaps the learned Dr. Vandeventer saw a theological connection between his denomination's doctrine of Holy Baptism by total immersion and teaching young Baptist converts to swim. In any case, Louis and his Jackson friend, Joe Buchanan, who was also to enter VMI in the fall, were among the summer swimmers. More of Louis's plans concluded the letter.

> Louis is planning a trip to Savannah with Dr. Vandeventer starting Friday in Dr. Van's car . . . only a short visit . . . Louis will complete his course in Geometry under Prof. Martin here this week then Mary and I will coach him in history. Louis and Joe Buchanan will stop over on their way to Lexington in Charlottesville with Joe's Aunt Rosa Lane . . . They have to be at VMI Sept. 1 . . . We return to Macon about August 23rd to get Louis off in time.
>
> All send love to you & ask you to write often.
>
> Your devoted
> *Mother*

Hattie wrote the long letter on the stationery she removed from Major's downtown office desk. She was not brought up to waste usable goods. Besides, the letterhead—ANDREW W. LANE, ATTORNEY AT LAW—could hold significance for a son prepared to enter his father's profession.

Several weeks after the family returned to Macon, Hattie received a letter from McKibben, dated August 24, 1918.

> Dear Mother:
>
> For the first time in some two or three weeks, I can sit down and write you a real letter once more . . . We are somewhere along the front . . .
>
> Don't worry about me as I am feeling fine and getting plenty to eat. Everything is very quiet just at present also . . . lots of work . . . even had I written you sooner I would have had no opportunity to mail the letter.

My job . . . is Regimental Information Officer and I'm on the Colonel's staff . . . Just at present I am quartered in what before the war was a very beautiful chateau. After four years of fighting around it, however, there's not much beauty left.

For the last month I have ceased to wear my glasses as it is impossible to put on a gas mask over them. My eyes, so far, have not troubled me much . . .

This war game is just like any other business and you've got to know your job to get by with it. The spirit of the army is fine—they take whatever comes with far less complaint than we had in the States.

I have received no more mail since I wrote you last but am expecting a big batch any day . . . I know all of you have continued to write . . .

. . . hope you have passed a pleasant summer and that all of you have continued well and happy, even though this is war time and you have had to attend to many things which Andrew and I would have gladly relieved you had conditions been normal. I have felt all along that the contribution you have been called to make is far greater than any Andrew or I could offer but you have always been such a wonderful mother and woman that I have never felt the slightest fear either as to your courage or ability to meet whatever comes with the same spirit you have always possessed.

. . . just received word that there is a whole sackful of mail for us back in the echelon . . . looking forward to reading lots of letters from you within the next eighteen hours . . .

Affectionately, your son,
McKibben

Summer ended; Louis left for VMI; Margaret and Harry returned to school; Andrew's company was not sent to Europe after all. In November, Hattie's prayers with those of millions were answered when the Armistice was signed. She wrote in her notebook:

ELEVEN, 'LEVEN, EIGHTEEN! GLORIOUS DAY

When all the world is thrilled that War should cease.
That the appeal to force, intent to kill
Should substituted be with Justice, Peace. . .

Andrew was mustered out of service soon after the Armistice and returned home to explore the opportunities of civilian life. Neither Hattie nor anyone else knew exactly how long American troops would remain in France, but she looked forward to McKibben's homecoming in a matter of months—surely by spring. It was Mary's turn to try adult wings, and the time was right. In early January of 1919, she joined several of her friends for an expeditionary force of their own to New York. Frankly admitting that their purpose was to enjoy as much as they could of what the great city had to offer, the Macon misses enrolled for a variety of graduate studies at Columbia University. Mary would take courses in English and history and continue the voice training begun at Wesleyan.

Hattie remembered her own year in Boston at the New England Conservatory. While dreading the loss of Mary's help and companionship, she urged her daughter's going. Besides, she wanted to prove to herself that she was as strong and unselfish as her friends told her she was. Mrs. Baker and Mrs. Neel laughed when she told them that she wanted nothing to interfere with Mary's attaining her PD degree—Doctor of Pleasure.

There would be other adults with her at 316 Hardeman Avenue. Andrew, after a few weeks of looking into beckoning employment possibilities in New England, returned to Macon to be man of the house, at least for a while, and investigate further a future in his hometown. Also, the first recipient of the Mercer scholarship, which Hattie gave in memory of Major, was living with the Lanes. Ernest, student and enthusiastic member of the Kappa Alpha Fraternity to which Major and his sons belonged and of which Mary had been sponsor, seemed to fit easily into the family circle. More young male attention came from Bill Turpin, who had begun his legal career with Major as his mentor. Just opening his own practice, Bill chose to be another big brother to Margaret, Harry, and Virginia. Hattie could count on his company and the children on his candy, especially on Sunday afternoon—that time in former years when the Lane house had been the scene of informal, open-house entertaining.

From January to June of 1919, Hattie addressed letters or cards almost daily to Miss Mary Lane, Whittier Hall, 1230 Amsterdam Avenue, Columbia University, New York City. Writing on whatever was at hand—Major's office stationery, pages torn from the children's school tablets, backs of bank correspondence notifying Hattie of Mary's drafts on her account, backs and margins of concert programs—Hattie mixed business matters, family and neighborhood news, and motherly advice as her moods and inclinations directed.

> 9 o'clock Sunday eve
> Jan. 5th, '19
>
> Dear Mary,
>
> The children are but this minute in bed, teeth all brushed, prayers said "'nevry-thing." . . . Before Ernest went out, we all sang . . . "When the Boys Come Marching Home" and "The Long, Long Trail A-Winding." Harry and I recalled singing The Long Trail with his father just a year ago this aft. Trust Harry will always remember singing with his father.
>
> . . . When we came back from church, Ernest was playing the piano. He ate dinner with us & we had a good one—Butts County ham . . . Ellen is good as gold.
>
> . . . about 3:30 Bill Turpin came out bringing a box of peanut brittle . . . said he'd come out to help me nurse, and I can give him an unqualified recommendation . . . Va. felt muchly "set-up." . . . They are all trying to make up for your absence, even Bill. He said he hoped I'd be able to get along with you away. . . thought it rather "fool-hardy" in me to let you go . . . Forgot Marg's music lesson at noon yesterday.
>
> Don't you forget yours . . . How's your cold? Buy what warm things you need. Take no risks with cold. Va. kissed me for all the absent ones tonight . . . We're doing famously without you—trust you're doing equally well . . .

The "doing famously" first letter was followed in a matter of days with a postcard picturing a pretty girl whose brown hair, blue eyes, and pensive pose must have reminded Hattie of Mary. In the space for correspondence, she wrote,

> I feel bad. Feels like the flu.
> I feel bad. 'ndeed I do.
> I feel bad. I feel blue.
> Miss my blue-bird. Missing you.
>
> Love,
> *Mother*

Hattie did not strain her recurrent blue moods and worries from the outpourings to her absent daughter-confidante . . .

> Margaret doesn't seem very well . . . not getting over her cold . . . don't want her to get catarrh . . . By the way, does your head do alright? (I know your heart does.) If your voice teacher finds any obstruction, have an operation if necessary. Take care of yourself . . . I've been fighting the blues as well as fleeing the flu lately. Everybody hasn't got your patience with me. I've been indulged . . .

Indulged Hattie still managed to set her jaw and infuse every inch of her five foot frame with strength or a show of it to confront the major and minor situations of daily life. When she was served with a notice that a bootleg liquor still had been found on one of her Butts County farms, she paid bail bond for the farm hands arrested for making and selling "moonshine." Then she hired her Jackson lawyer-cousin to accompany them to Macon and defend them in federal court. When Margaret feigned illness and refused to go to school, Hattie let her stay home. "I don't believe she'll try that again. She didn't have much fun."

Louis's reports from VMI were not what she had hoped.

> "Fear I'm not working up a good state of mind to write Louis, and I try to write him nice newsy letters as free from lecturing as possible . . . Bill Turpin said he wrote Louis a good man-to-man letter a few days ago. Hurrah for Bill!"

She wrote about concern for Andrew as he looked for a job and participated in a social life of his own. He told her little of his comings and goings, but Hattie heard that he was "playing the devoted" to Adeline Small. "He's so secretive, I don't dare inquire about what he really does. Andrew needs a different sort of mother, maybe one he wouldn't hold at arm's length but could take into his confidence . . . He needs his father . . . He doesn't find a job easily. His chief occupation is running the Olds about."

Yet almost every letter told of Andrew's helpfulness with the children and in maintaining the big house. His "running the Olds about" was often to chauffeur Hattie and her friends to church, a meeting of the History Club, or some other event. He was available, too, to drive Hattie up to Jackson for business or pleasure. Either always included a visit with Hattie Buttrill. During his weeks of job search and even after he began work with an insurance firm, Andrew was a willing participant in family financial matters.

> . . . we sold our hardware stock yesterday . . . Andrew will . . . deliver the stock as soon as the cash is forthcoming . . . too good an offer to turn down, especially now while we're holding the cotton—a long time I fear before cotton will sell again for what it did just last year—but I'll wait. In the mean-time, we must make another crop, also meet those expenses . . . afraid we're going broke on farming but there are some investments bringing good returns . . . tomorrow bank certificate pays . . . don't think I'll loan any more for fear of running short of cash.

Hattie Buttrill was a surprising Jackson source of investment tips. Contemptuous of the gossips who disparaged old maids, Hattie B. let it be known that her own spinsterhood was by choice. "More married than doing well," she often observed. Prominent Miss Hattie Buttrill certainly was doing well financially while she cared unselfishly for her aging father and ailing sister, Mary Smith, just across the street. "Invest in Coca Cola, Hat," Hattie Buttrill advised her widowed friend. "Then you won't have to do a thing but just clip coupons." Hattie Lane's response was, "The only clipping I'll do may have to be my children's wings."

Unfortunately, she did not invest in Coca Cola. The wings of her progeny remained intact, and the cash continued to flow. Hattie might practice thrift by using expensive stationery only for formal correspondence or by re-using fine fabric in clothes no longer worn by her or Mary. "Had good luck," she wrote, "in a peg top skirt cut from your blue foulard." She did not intend, however, to cut corners or to scrimp on her priorities.

Several letters to Mary were written on the backs of correspondence from the Atlanta company from which she had ordered the monument for the Lane lot at Rose Hill Cemetery. She was disappointed that it could not be erected by Memorial Day, Confederate Memorial Day observed in Georgia on April 26. She was also having new altar furniture made for the First Baptist Church as a memorial to Major.

Mary was instructed to meet her New York expenses by writing drafts on Hattie's Macon bank account. The Citizens and Southern Bank then sent Hattie listings of each draft in letters signed by "A. Bird,

Cashier." Hattie sent them on to Mary with her own messages filling any blank space in margins or on the back of the letter. Hattie never questioned Mary's expenditures; theater and concerts were, after all, prime reasons for Mary's being in New York. At the bottom of one of Mr. A. Bird's letters, Hattie wrote a rhymed paraphrase:

> MY SONG BY A. BIRD
>
> We have today an order to pay
> Some cash to Miss Mary Lane
> We charge the amount to your account
> We'll be glad to do so again.

Hattie added, "I trust the bird can keep on caroling."

As winter wore on and began to wane, Hattie's spirits rose above worries and blue moods. The Great War was over, "Miss Genie," a favorite younger friend who shared Hattie's interest in music, was making plans for study and travel in Europe. Hattie invited her and two other music-loving friends, along with Andrew and Bill Turpin, for a bon voyage Saturday night supper party. A long letter to Mary described the first adult party Hattie had hosted in more than a year. Virginia had been allowed to greet the guests. Bill Turpin arrived first.

> . . . before I could get into the hall to welcome him, Va. told him that "Mama has on a new dwess." I look quite new in the dress you sent. . . The 3 Dears fully exemplified their name. Va. stayed strictly in the kitchen (while we were at the table) and Harry & Margaret helped cook serve . . .

More details of the evening followed—rose velvet and beaded georgette dresses, Valentine place cards, five-course dinner menu, piano playing and singing, and finally a late supper with the ladies presiding over chafing dishes and toasting forks and Hattie tying on the pretty little French apron McKibben had just sent. "Andrew was well pleased with it all & said he hoped I'd invite him again."

A March letter headed "Sat. Morn" let distant Mary see that day as Hattie painted a word picture of it:

> A little before 8 o'clock this a.m. the fire department responded to a call on Hardeman Ave. . . . Mr. Johnson's old home . . . only a roof

> blaze. We all went to the fire & then had breakfast . . . some mending done . . . Andrew read me some columns from the *Telegraph.*
>
> Andrew & Harry are to go again to the ball games between Mercer and Tech. . . Yesterday Mercer beat 12 to 1. Harry finances his way to both games by selling an old left-hand ball glove of Louis'. . . got 50 cts. Margaret has gone to a picnic & I fear cut her only music lesson for the week. But what's that compared to a wiener roast out at the pumping station?
>
> Harry has finished an ice cream cone and is buckling down to his Sunday School lesson for tomorrow. The children of Israel seem a long way off on a bright Spring morning. There goes Harry now with a racket and tennis ball out to the porch. It's as hard for him to do one thing at the time as 'tis for me. Thank goodness my History Club paper is all ready for next Mon. Va. is with Mary Baldwin . . . Va. and I keep up with the movies—saw "Woman" Thursday. Her birthday will be a week from tomorrow . . . I'm going to get her a new dress . . . 5 yr. size is almost too small. Andrew is enjoying the songs you sent, but I don't get to practice much. You must come home a good reader at sight so you can accompany A. or I'm afraid Adeline may cut us out of the job . . . A. expects to go into business Apr. 1st, but I'd better let him write you . . . You know he's very reticent about both bus. & pleasure.
>
> Enough for this time . . .

Another spring letter was written on the back and cover pages of the Fourth Annual Concert of the Wesleyan Glee Club, Tuesday Evening, April 8th, 1919. Mary had sung in the group's first and second concerts, but Hattie proclaimed the fourth "the best performance yet."

Hattie wrote that "bestowing" Harry and Virginia on willing neighbors had allowed her to attend with Margaret. Andrew had driven them to the old Wesleyan auditorium in their Merry Oldsmobile, filled to capacity with friends they had invited to join them: ". . . glad to state both our children were pleasantly placed. Va. had enjoyed a nap and was good—Harry is always so." The always–good Harry had been taken to the movies by the Hatchers while Virginia was entertained by Dr. Clark and his little daughter Verna. Mrs. Clark had left the good doctor in charge when she stepped into the Olds with the music lovers.

There was still space enough on the glee club program for Hattie to write reviews of recent family performances. "Marg. took me and Mrs. Malone to her expression recital at the Y.W.C.A. yesterday aft. She far excelled the rest. She looked nice in the blue silk with the organdy collar and cuffs Andrew selected for her. She recited 'The Runaway Doll' and 'The House that Jack Built.'"

Virginia's birthday party was the subject of the last paragraph. Three little girls had been invited to join the family for Sunday dinner to be followed by the birthday cake. Beneath the icing, the small fortune-telling favors had been inserted for whoever cut a slice with one of those extra rewards.

> . . . how much we missed you at the birthday party . . . roast —mighty good . . . as to the birthday cake—beautifully dressed for I dressed it—Marmee Hatcher cut the ring—a gold one, Harry the dime—Andrew the luck piece—a pretty horseshoe pin—and presented it to Mary Baldwin who together with Verna Clark failed to cut anything. Andrew presented Verna with a dime—Harry was sufficiently gallant to part with the one he cut. Marg. cut the bachelor button & Va. greatly to her chagrin also—cut the thimble. They consoled themselves with lots of candy and ice cream.
>
> Love,
> *Mother*

Macon was on the circuit in 1919 for the tours of a number of renowned classical musicians, including several opera stars. With Andrew to be her chauffeur and escort and Mercer student Ernest to be at home with the children, Hattie bought two tickets for a week-long Chautauqua series and several other concerts. For half the evenings, she gave both tickets to Andrew for "another date." She wrote Mary that she "wouldn't dare to inquire who will sit in my seat." Hattie was free with both praise and criticism for the performers she heard and saw, including the diva Rosa Ponselle.

> . . . attended the opening of Chautauqua last evening & heard Ponselle . . . Rosa was great. A remarkable voice—but oh, such a fright to behold; she should sing from behind the scenes. She has no more neck than a frog & a barrel for a chest—fat arms hunched up to her ears almost. But she can sing & play her own accompaniments with dash and brilliance. . . . seven encores, playing her own accom-

> paniments for all except the first two "Coming Thru the Rye" and "Goodbye to Summer". . . she would do well to sing for the victrola . . .

Several days later, Hattie continued writing Mary about Miss Ponselle, using the back of the program for *The Music Festival of the South* for her opinions:

> I wrote you of the wonderful voice of Rosa Ponselle. On dit she came to Atlanta a year or so ago to sing in vaudeville & took a room over a fish market. This year as the particular star in grand opera—put up at the Georgian Terrace.

Hattie declared soloist Sophie Breslau "charming both to hear and behold—a decided contrast to Rosa of fish market fame," and pronounced the Belgian prima donna Raymonde Delaunois the audience's favorite of the four Metropolitan Opera singers appearing in the festival program.

Hattie knew that Andrew "tired of so much chamber music" and was aware that he was finding the accompaniment of Adeline Small—not only at the piano—more pleasing than anything he was seeing or hearing on the concert stage. "I'm afraid Andrew will weaken before another week of Maconian Nights roll "round," she wrote. "But me—not me."

There was far more than concert–going to keep Hattie's spirits high. For months, ever since the November Armistice, she had hoped to hear that McKibben and all the soldiers still in France were headed home. He wrote about his duties, about his billeting in the town of Hortes. He wrote about his impressions as he traveled more freely in post-Armistice France. He wrote of motoring some distance over bad roads to the general's dance where he found no lady there very appealing. He wrote of that night ending with his military vehicle mired in the mud and himself and his compatriots spending the chilly night in the hay of a French farmer's barn. But he could not write what Hattie most longed to know—when he would be home again. Finally, in April, the rumors he had heard seemed to be changing to more positive information. The 321st Field Artillery in which he served would probably sail in a matter of weeks for New York, then continue by train for Atlanta.

He wrote Mary that he thought he would be in New York for several days and hoped to squire her and "the Georgia girls" around town before boarding the Atlanta bound train with his company. She could expect a wire from him. Mary relayed that news to her mother who replied immediately that she wanted to be in New York, too, when Kib arrived.

Hattie dreamed and schemed how she might manage to be on the dock when the troop carrier landed. Then she might enjoy a few days of New York sightseeing. If Kib did not come until late May, perhaps she would remain until early June and return with Mary and her friends on a ship that sailed regularly between New York and Savannah. Perhaps she could leave Virginia in Jackson with Hattie Buttrill and take Margaret with her. Inviting Hat to go to New York with her would be even better. Maybe she would ask her cousin Eva Compton to come down to stay in Macon while she was away. "She's such a perfect old Maid," Hattie wrote Mary, "she'd manage beautifully with Andrew. But what would become of the world if it wasn't for old maids?" All the while she was dreaming, Hattie really knew that she could not go to New York. The dates of Kib's landing and his stay in New York were too uncertain for her to plan either to take the children with her or leave them at home. Mary would have to welcome Kib for her.

McKibben would be twenty-four years old on May 8, 1919. Hattie wrote him a birthday letter and sent it to Mary to deliver to him. She composed a song, too, which she sent to Mary to sing to him for her. "Mind your mother," she wrote her substitute, "and meet Kib with 24 kisses for me." The birthday letter contained instructions for Kib, too.

> Remember Mary has a checkbook and draws on the exact amount I do. She is in my place—I sent her on to be there when you land—so get whatever you want . . .

Even if she could not be waiting on the pier in New York, Hattie let McKibben know that she was determined to be part of his welcome to Georgia. "Hattie B. & I have a solemn pact to see you if you come to Camp Gordon, so notify us in good time if you are to be there before coming on to Macon."

A later letter to Mary, written on Ansley Hotel stationery and postmarked May 27, 1919, Atlanta, described just how the pact was kept.

> . . . While Kib gets a shine, Hattie, Harry and I are dropping you a line—We reached Camp Gordon a few minutes after twelve to-day just as Kib's fellows were detraining. . . Harry saw him first & with a whoop, ran & jumped on his brother's shoulders just as the camera

> man snapped him. Hat said coming up here . . . that she wanted to be present at a demonstration for returning soldiers—Well, she came, she saw, she demonstrated . . . the camera caught her kissing Kib—the one she'd been saving her kisses for—all the son she'd had in France . . . We've had a great day . . . Kib had registered for us with lovely connecting rooms . . . We all dined together on the roof—all trellised with roses. Harry's having the time of his life . . . Kib says you're looking fine—Isn't he just splendid? Hurry on home.

Packed away with the letter was a clipping from the *Atlanta Journal,* dated May 29, 1919—a feature story headlined, "Isn't it Great to Have Them Back?" Among the cameraman's pictures that made it to the paper was one of the two Hatties and the ten-year-old Harry greeting a good-looking young officer whose smile matched theirs. "Lieutenant Van McKibben Lane of Macon," read the caption, "is all smiles, and who wouldn't be with both his mother and his brother right there when the trains pulled in."

Summer found Hattie with all seven of her children under one roof: Andrew and McKibben were home from the Great War; Mary was back from New York; Louis had returned from Virginia Military Institute with plans to swap that school's drill and discipline for Mercer University's gentler liberal arts; and Margaret, Harry, and Virginia were each making unique contributions to home life that only carefree, beloved children can give. It was the last of such seasons before the lure of marriage and adult independence would begin to separate her family. Hattie could not hold her children with her indefinitely, and she had the good sense not to try to do so.

Hattie had lived through the first year and a half without Major. She had done more than survive. She had wept, worried, prayed, and mothered. Sometimes she had fallen into pits of deep, dark blues. But she had not been too proud to take out-stretched arms and helping hands. She had found her own footholds in music and reading and writing. She had often felt frustrated with her children and with her own shortcomings. But she could laugh at and with the children and herself, too.

She had made mistakes, and she would make more. Some of her decisions must have been good and right. She was far from finished.

Variations on the Theme

ANDREW—FIRST BORN, FIRST LOVED—was first to marry. Hattie had written Mary in New York that Andrew was "playing the devoted" to Adeline Small. Andrew was not "playing"; he was. When he dutifully arrived to pick up his mother after church services or a musical event at Wesleyan, Hattie would expect to see Adeline ensconced beside him on the front seat of the Oldsmobile. At home, Andrew spent less time in the living or dining room talking with his family to spend more of it in the back hall, talking with Adeline over the telephone. Brothers, sisters, even his mother often had to wait to use that convenience until Andrew left the voice on the other end of the telephone line to seek reunion with the whole woman.

The reams of sheet music Andrew bought for the new songs he wanted to sing were destined for Adeline's piano, not Hattie's. Hattie knew what it was to be the center of a group gathered around the piano and to accompany a voice she would rather hear than any other. But she had never followed the close harmonies of "The World is Waiting for the Sunrise," then turned away from the keyboard, crossed long legs, and waited for her beloved to light her cigarette.

On June 10, 1920, Adeline Small and Andrew Wade Lane were married.

Two decades later at a family gathering hosted by Mary in the old Jackson house, Adeline was again at the piano, accompanying the Lane brothers' quartet. Virginia, still and always the lively, red-haired family pet, mused aloud that she could barely remember when Adeline had not been her sister. Beside Virginia, on the loveseat that had once belonged to Janie McKibben, Hattie sat smiling, nodding approval especially for Andrew's tenor notes.

"Drew's always been your favorite, hadn't he, Mother?" Virginia teased.

"I don't have favorites," the little gray-haired woman replied. "I've just known Andrew longest." In the year between McKibben's return from France and Andrew's marriage, Hattie reveled in the companionship of her adult children. Before matrimony claimed another of them, a train tour of the American West and the Canadian Rockies with McKibben, Mary, and Louis allowed her to enjoy their company and a new travel experience, too. Hattie liked travel and said she had a "go-foot in need of exercise."

During Macon's sultry summer, McKibben could manage to be away from his new law practice, Mary could let go of her volunteer duties, and Louis was on vacation from Mercer law classes. Janie McKibben was no longer in the Jackson homeplace to give a grandmother's care to Hattie's younger children, but Major's sister, Mrs. Wilmer Dozier, invited Margaret, Harry, and Virginia to visit her—their "Aunt Molly"—and be with Lane kin in Jasper County. The time was right for Hattie to give herself a grown-up get-away.

Mary, who was writing occasional pieces for The *Macon Telegraph,* intended to keep a journal of the trip and tucked a notebook into her handbag after inscribing on its first page, *My Diary—Western Tour,* July 15 through August 23rd. She made the first entry soon after the tour assembled in Birmingham.

> July 15, 1920
>
> Aboard train leaving Birmingham "Off again, on again, gone again . . . We're on our way at last now that we have joined the party, 200 strong . . . pretty tough to leave Macon at 4 a.m. . . . Birmingham in time for lunch . . . Kib made final arrangements with Mrs. Elliot . . . grand to have McKibben and Louis to look after Mother and me . . . First impressions of Mrs. Elliot are most encouraging . . . glad we are joining her and not Prof. Foster . . . Kib says he's too slow to fall fast asleep . . . Our party is mostly ladies . . . due to Kib and Louis we are most popular . . . may have school marms with us but no one has

admitted so far . . . Old Maids in the majority . . . a selfish bunch . . . school girls in plenty so I am preferring to class myself with this group . . .

July 16, 1920

Have been up since six o'clock seeing Indiana country with its fields of corn and wheat. . . leaving Terre Haute. We will arrive in Chicago in time for lunch and a rubber neck ride. Feeling fine. I love traveling.

July 17, 1920

Chicago is very much like New York, but it lacks the theater district that I loved. . . Great Northern Hotel was our headquarters. . . ate at the lake shore.

July 19, 1920

Today is the best day of the trip so far. Nothing can be more beautiful than Banff where we are spending this glorious day. This is the Canadian National Park . . . Lake Louise, fields, and glaciers are to be stops on our tour of Canada's playground . . . snow capped mountains stand out in bold relief on either side . . . lunched at the Banff Springs Hotel amid music and flowers and enjoyed excellent service . . . hotel affords every diversion . . . had a swim in the pool . . . hot and cold plunges . . . tea on the terrace as is the English custom . . .

July 29, 1920

Sunrise in the Rockies . . . dash for train for Lake Louise after breakfast in the magnificent hotel in an alcove overlooking the lake.

That was the last of Mary's travel diary entries although more than a month of Western travel still remained for the Lanes. In a box of old pictures there was photograph of McKibben and Louis astride donkeys with a narrow, steep waterfall behind them. There was also a Yellowstone Park folder addressed by Mary to Margaret, Harry, and Virginia "c/o Mrs. Wilmer Dozier, RFD, Monticello, Georgia." Inside the flap of the packet of twenty colored postcards showing streams, canyons, woods, bears, and geysers was printed "Reach by Union Pacific—Oregon Short Line R. R."

There was no letter or notebook jotting or line of verse written by Hattie. Whether she wrote about them or not, she preserved her memories.

She liked to repeat one tour member's comment at the Grand Canyon: "Ain't the gorge gorgeous!"

The following year, McKibben, next after Andrew, was married. As my Uncle Kib's dramatically told version of the courtship went, it began with Hattie's urging him to go with her to a recital at Wesleyan. When Linda Anderson—tall, fair, beautiful—walked with confident grace to the piano, he recognized the girl of his dreams. Undeterred by talk that she might be pledged to another, he determined to claim the lovely Linda as his prize.

The only daughter of the president of a leading Macon industry, the Bibb Cotton Mills, Linda had been brought up a staunch Methodist and instilled with ideals of self-discipline, responsibility for the use of her time and talent, and nothing short of excellence as her goals. Mastery of the social skills expected of southern charmers was taken for granted.

The Lanes could have nothing but approval of Kib's choice. Mary already knew, liked, and admired Linda as an outstanding fellow Wesleyanne of the class just following her own. So Mary could lead a family chorus of congratulations to Kib and welcome to Linda.

Linda, brought up with one younger brother in the well-ordered Anderson household, had accepted more than McKibben. His big, close-knit, free-spirited family came with him. With Andrew and his wife only blocks away, the Lane house was home to Hattie and six children whose ages spanned the years between Hattie's forty-nine and Virginia's seven.

A visitor calling at 316 Hardeman Avenue might see skates in the front walk and a doll left in a porch chair. On the library table, visible through the door leading from the reception area, arithmetic homework could lie beside an open legal tome. The young woman talking over the telephone in the back hall would be Mary, accepting a date to see Rudolph Valentino in *The Sheik.* The giggles coming from the direction of the kitchen meant that Margaret and a friend were eavesdropping while they made fudge. From her desk in the parlor where she might be revising the paper she would present at the next meeting of her history club, Hattie would rise to greet her guest.

This was the family Linda Anderson saw, knowing her McKibben was a part of it. She could not have realized the extent he was and would continue to be depended upon by his mother and every one of his sisters and brothers. But with her marriage, she made Kib's family hers.

Mary was the maid-of-honor at the wedding of Linda Katherine Anderson and Van McKibben Lane on November 2, 1921. Hattie, as mother-of-the-groom, was a model of composed pride as she became "Mother Lane" to another daughter-in-law. She was later to remark that she truly loved her in-laws because they took up where she left off with her children and the faults she had not yet corrected.

Mary's marrying was another matter altogether. Hattie vicariously enjoyed Mary's popularity. Loving romance, she took sides with first one, then another of Mary's young men as though the courtship of Mary were a spectator sport. She would have said that she wanted for her daughter a happy marriage to an exceptionally fine fellow. She expected that—in some distant, vague future.

The present was fine just as it was. Hattie had proved she could manage on her own during the months Mary had spent in New York. She saw no necessity for another long separation in the immediate future. When Mary was away from Macon even for a few days, Hattie's letters let her know she was missed and needed at home. One of them, addressed to the home of Mary's friend Ida Britain in Atlanta was headed "Friday night—if you were here, it would be an evening." When Mary was visiting in South Georgia, Hattie wrote a detailed account of trying to get ready for "a simple musical evening" without her. The date was set and guests already invited. First Louis was very late dragging himself out of bed to take her shopping for party necessities. Then she realized that the dresses she had chosen for Margaret and Virginia would have to be altered. The hair of both girls needed attention before they would be ready to make an appearance and help serve refreshments. "Another good thing about heaven," Hattie wrote, "is there'll be no bother about food or clothes there." Before she mailed the letter, she wrote across the top of the first page, "Let your conscience be your guide."

When Hugh Mallet, young widower from Jackson, called on Mary in Macon, Hattie welcomed him as a gentleman from her hometown and a member of the Mallet family of Covington Street. He was bit older than any of her children, and Hattie had seldom been in his company.

His younger brother Joel, however, had been one of Mary's Jackson favorites. Hattie remembered Joel's part in an episode that had caused her mother to telephone Major at his office—a long distance call from Jackson. Janie McKibben had refused permission for visiting Mary to be a part of an outing to the town of Oxford where Joel Mallet was a student at Emory College. No granddaughter of hers would be seen riding through the countryside four in a buggy. Joel had later been McKibben's 1917 classmate at Yale University Law School. From New Haven he had wired Mary congratulations on her graduation from Wesleyan. The Lanes knew that Joel's enviable Yale record had led to a prestigious wartime position with the rank of major. They had heard, too, of his peacetime launching of a promising career in Atlanta and marriage to an Atlanta socialite.

Of Hugh Mallet, Hattie knew much less. When his visits, letters, and calls to Mary became more and more frequent and her pleasure in them more and more evident, Hattie made it her business to learn more. To what she knew of his family and her own recent impressions, she added information supplied by Hattie Buttrill and other Jackson connections.

The Mallets were strong Methodists, and Hugh had preceded Joel in that denomination's Emory College—later to move from Oxford to Atlanta as Emory University. After graduating in 1911, he returned to Jackson. At the outbreak of the Great War, Hugh Mallet was superintendent of Butts County's rural school system and married to cultivated, pretty, and much admired Jane Stanfield. Hattie did know something of that young woman's many virtues because Hattie's own girlhood friend, Mame Ellis, who had attended New England Conservatory of Music with her, was Jane's aunt. As childless Mrs. John Moore of Atlanta, Mame had heaped attention and advantages on niece Jane, already receiving the best upbringing the Stanfields could offer an only daughter.

As a married man and school superintendent, Hugh Mallet did not join the wartime military forces in which his brothers George and Joel both served as army officers. The war years brought Hugh tragedy on the home front. Jackson did not escape the worst pandemic since the Black Death of the Middle Ages. Jane Stanfield Mallet, pregnant with her first child, died in the Influenza Epidemic of 1918.

After the war, Hugh left professional education for more responsibility in the management of his mother's farms and his own agriculture-related business. He was active in the community life of his hometown, joining the new Kiwanis civic club. He was serving on the building committee of the new red brick Methodist Church that would replace the old white wooden house of Methodist worship Hattie had seen all her life with its steeple directly confronting the home of the Presbyterian McKibbens just across the street.

Hattie could find no fault at all in Hugh Mallet. At thirty, he was somewhat older than the other men populating Mary's social life, but perhaps maturity was a part of his appeal. What Hattie did not like was the distinct possibility that he might persuade Mary to leave the Lane Macon home for one in Jackson with Hugh.

Jealousy and possessiveness were unworthy of Hattie. She would not own them as she posed the question that so disturbed her. "Mary, do you want to live in Jackson? That's where all this Hugh Mallet coming and going is sure to take you."

Hattie did not have long to nurse the dread of what she saw before her. When Hugh formally asked for Mary's hand, she knew he already had her heart.

Neither a long engagement nor a big church wedding was in the couple's plans. When they told Hattie about them, they had already set a date less than a week away—Wednesday, November 15. Hugh did not like elaborate social fuss. He could arrange to be away for the last two weeks of November and much preferred that time to be spent for a honeymoon trip to New York. Mary could foresee that more time would add just more tension to the cords pulling her two ways. The pain Hattie was feeling would not be lessened by putting the wedding off to make a show of it.

Had not Hattie declared that her heaven would be without the bothers of food and clothes? But those bothers, along with in-person and telephone invitations to family and a few close friends and arrangements for minister, music, and flowers, must be crowded into three days. Evidence that it all could be done was presented in headlines of the society page of Macon's evening newspaper on November 15, 1922: "The Wedding of Miss Mary Lane and Mr. Hugh Mallet Solemnized at High Noon Today." Somehow it all came together. "The home was beautifully decorated" according to the next morning's *Macon Telegraph*. Palms and flowers had created an altar in the living room.

> a pathway . . . from the library, across the reception hall and into the living room was formed by white satin ribbons borne by Miss Margaret Lane and Master Harry Lane, sister and brother of the bride . . . Miss Virginia Lane, youngest sister of the bride, was a dainty little figure in a French dress of blue chiffon, and carried a basket of pink rosebuds . . . The bride and groom entered from the library together and joined Mrs. Andrew Washington Lane, who gave her daughter in marriage." Dr. Rufus Weaver, President of Mercer University, performed the ceremony. Professor and Mrs. Joseph Maerz of the Wesleyan music faculty, whom Hattie and most of musical Macon had come to appreciate as piano and violin virtuosos, supplied the music.

Hattie could be pleased. Of the invited relatives and friends, only a very few had been kept away by the short notice. Linda, whose wedding had been the family event just a year before, was missed. But the reason for her absence was a happy one. The birth of Van McKibben Lane Jr. just a few days before Mary's wedding had made Hattie a grandmother!

Mary was a radiantly happy bride, and the children played their roles as well as they could. Virginia's tears and wails that "Sister's leaving us for Hugh" were cut short with the prospect of being a wedding flower girl and by Hugh's promise that a pony would be waiting for her to ride when she came to Jackson. So the wedding day ended with Mary and Hugh on the afternoon train for New York and Hattie and her three youngest in the strangely quiet house. Before going to bed, each of them would write a letter to go in the envelope Hattie addressed to "Mr. and Mrs. Hugh Mallet, Hotel Pennsylvania, New York City."

Several days later Hattie wrote another letter to the same place but addressed only to Mr. Hugh Mallet.

> Thursday Night
> November 23rd, 1922
>
> Dear Hugh,
>
> Your letter this morning was most timely and altogether welcome . . . Mary said you were the best addition to the family she could imagine—quite reassuring. I had thought my little grandson all that could be desired—had never quite seriously considered a son-in-law. (But you are not the first to make me a mother-in-law, or I might hold it against you.) However, I have come to rely so completely on Mary's

Hattie McKibben c. 1880–81, as a school girl in the second grade.

Hattie McKibben with her brother Van c.1886.

Hattie McKibben probably at the time of her graduation from Southern Female College in La Grange, 1890.

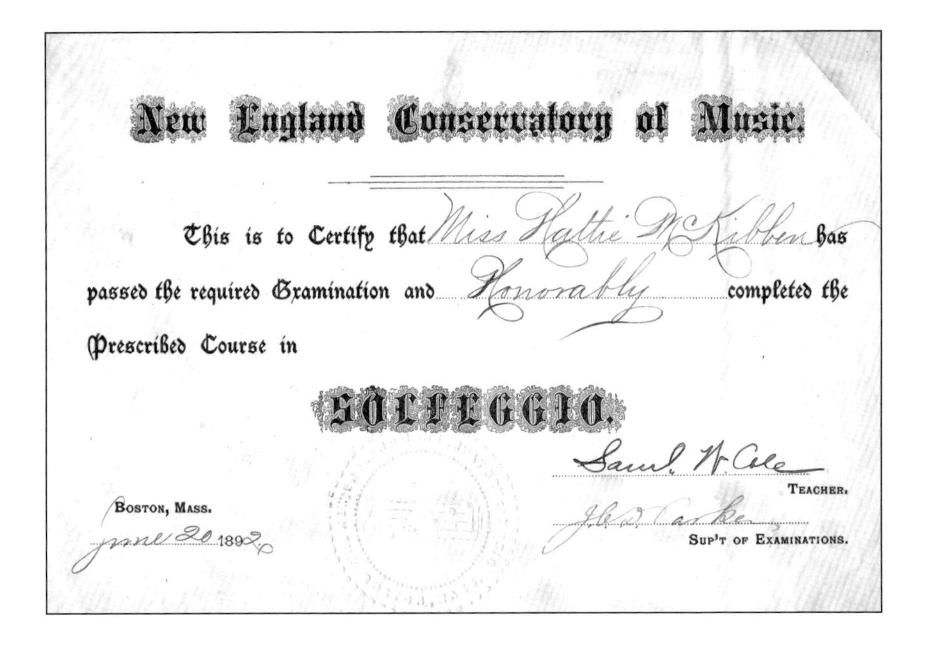

New England Conservatory of Music.

This is to Certify that Miss Hattie McKibben has passed the required Examination and Honorably completed the Prescribed Course in

SOLFEGGIO.

Saml. W. Cole
TEACHER.

Boston, Mass.
June 20 1892

SUP'T OF EXAMINATIONS.

Hattie McKibben's certificate from the New England Conservatory of Music in Boston, dated June 20, 1892.

Hattie McKibben at about the time of her marriage to Major Lane in 1892.

Major Lane, c. 1892.

Hattie McKibben Lane, c. 1895.

Hattie and Major Lane with their first three children, Andrew, Van, and Mary, in the late 1800s.

Major Lane in the early 1900s.

The first four children of Major and Hattie Lane, c. 1898. Standing left to right are Mary, Van McKibben, and Andrew. In 1900, Lucia (in the center) fell victim to Scarlett Fever.

Major Lane shortly before his death in 1918.

The Lanes are seen enjoying a Gulf beach holiday in Galveston, Texas, where they visited Major's sister Eugenia. Major stands beside daughter Mary. Hattie kneels in front to the left of Eugenia.

The Atlanta Journal *captured the scene when Hattie Lane, Hattie Buttrill, and 10-year-old Harry met Kib upon his 1919 return from service in World War I. The caption reads, "Isn't it Great to Have Them Back Again? . . . Lt. Van McKibben of Macon is all smiles and who wouldn't be with his mother and brother right there as the train pulled in."*

The last photograph of Hattie with her seven children was made on December 30, 1943, in the parlor of her home on Hardeman Avenue. Virginia was married the next day in an elegant noon wedding to George Beattie. Hattie is seated at center; gathered around her are (left to right): McKibben, Harry, Virginia, Mary, Margaret, Louis, and Andrew.

The seven Lane siblings gathered in Macon in the early 1950s for the presentation of a portrait of their father, Andrew Lane Sr., to Mercer Law School. He had been one of the first teachers in the law school, and had sometimes taught classes in the library of the Lane home. The portrait, painted by George Beattie from Major Lane's last photograph, hangs in Mercer University Law Library.

A detail of Hattie from her family portrait of 1943.

judgment, whomever she recommends I accept without question. And when I think of Mary's newfound joy and read with pleasure your letter of appreciation, I congratulate you two upon finding the sweetest thing in life—perfect love and its consummation. Your brief engagement was long enough for you fully to make up your minds. 'tho I was amazed at your hurried plans, I am persuaded that you were right. I am experiencing the ratio between unselfishness and happiness that Mary has always beautifully illustrated. Since I have given her into your keeping to love and to cherish, she is none the less my own dear daughter, and you my own loved son. I have gained. That you will perform your promise in making her happy and in caring for her, I do not feel the least doubt. My confidence in you is well founded.

But you must know how I miss her unfailing help and care, especially during the five years since her father's death. She has brought joy to me and three little children, for whom she has always thought and planned. Her life of unselfish devotion has, I trust, been impressed upon their young lives because they are showing it in their love and sympathy for me at this time.

I am wishing for you and Mary all the joy and sweetness of true companionship. May you be blessed with all the happiness you so richly deserve. We are eagerly awaiting news of your return. Your apartment is ready here whenever you can occupy it, and I have your gift almost done—a comforter for your bed, provided you keep it down here.

All send love and hope to see you soon.

Fondly,
Mother

Not for the first time, Hattie thrust her narrow shoulders back, lifted her chin, and got on with what she knew to be her job—preparing her children and herself for their leaving her wingfold for flights of their own.

Louis was nearing the end of her supervision. After six years at Mercer University, he had a bachelor's, a master's, and a law degree. He was comfortable at home in Macon with his family, his guitar and ukelele, harmonizing friends, and as many pretty girls as he could attract. His university advisor made clear that his years as perennial student were at an end: "Mr. Lane, unless you'd care to enter the Theology School, I'm afraid Mercer has nothing else to offer you."

Ready or not, Louis could postpone no longer the serious business of earning his own living. Following his father and brother in the actual practice of law was not for him, but he did not know what was. The textile industry was booming in Georgia where cotton was king, and Louis accepted a job with the expanding Bibb Cotton Mills as sales representative in the St. Louis area.

His outgoing personality seemed fitted for sales. With new samples from the looms of the Bibb Manufacturing Company and his own tall man's clothes, Louis took with him the jokes and songs he had contributed to the home on Hardeman Hill. He could not pack his older brothers to get him out of scrapes or Hattie to oversee the daily routine that got him up, ready, and out.

When business and home ties drew him back to Macon, his dress and manner proclaimed his new life a success. He was the star of reunion parties. Louis shone as his new jokes and songs twinkled through the old ones in the accepting heaven of family laughter and affection.

He did not consult Hattie when, in 1924, he married a midwestern divorcee with a small daughter. It was some time before he brought Lillian, Hattie's third daughter-in-law, home with him. That marriage, lasting more than a decade, was the only one of those of Hattie's seven children to end in divorce.

After Louis, Margaret was next to leave home. Margaret had inherited her mother's small frame. With her mother's fine bones came also the same strong will. Hattie saw Major in Margaret's brown eyes and would not describe her daughter as stubborn. She had decided enthusiasms and dislikes affected by frequent mood changes. Margaret excelled in "expression" classes. She preferred memorizing pieces for recitation or lines for a play over practicing scales and etudes for piano lessons. A studio photograph preserves young Margaret in a becoming costume for her role as an Indian maiden—beaded headband for long, braided hair, fringed dress of faux leather, and moccasins. High school French may have been a bore for her, but she liked sprinkling her letters to Sister in Jackson with "je ne sais quoi." After all, being "au courant" was part of "joi de vivre."

For college, Margaret wanted more change and challenge than swapping Macon's high school classrooms for others in the same little city at Wesleyan College. With Hattie's approval, she joined other Macon girls at Randolph-Macon College in Lynchburg, Virginia.

That choice seemed good until the end of one vacation at home. With all arrangements made for her return, Margaret announced that she was not going back. Hattie suspected that her most constant vacation beau (a young man Hattie did not much like) was the reason. Margaret would not admit that he was; neither would she explain why Randolph-Macon had become so onerous. But she was adamant.

Virginia witnessed and later described the dramatic mother-daughter confrontation staged at the foot of the stairs. Hattie's firm stance was a show of irresistible maternal force. Margaret, clutching the newel post, was immovable. Hattie's withdrawal to call for reinforcements ended the scene.

Virginia was not allowed in the audience when son-brother-negotiator McKibben appeared, but she soon knew the ending of the drama. Kib himself accompanied an agreeable Margaret back to Old Virginia. The welcome there became even warmer when Kib hosted a reunion dinner off campus for his sister and several of her favorite college friends.

Hattie continued to be thankful, so she said, that she and Major had given older brothers and a sister to their younger offspring. When Margaret, college behind her and unexplored choices ahead, visited Louis in St. Louis, she discovered her future. McKibben, now as son-brother-investigator, made a trip of his own to St. Louis. Before Hattie began preparations for another home wedding, she had his favorable assessment of the man Margaret declared she would marry.

Earl Moore was a practical midwesterner—born, bred, and educated in Indiana. Fourteen years Margaret's senior, he was an engineer already well begun in the corporate world. He knew what he wanted; it was the southern belle—lovely, volatile Margaret—as his wife in a well managed home appropriate for his well managed life.

More than fifty years after she posed for it, Margaret's wedding photograph, cut from the society pages of The *Macon Telegraph,* was found with other newspaper clippings between the pages of a ledger some family member intended for an organized scrapbook. Holding an enormous bouquet of roses, wider than she, Margaret gazes thoughtfully into the eye of the camera from beneath the narrow brim of a fashionable cloche. "Mrs. Earl Stanley Moore" is the identification under the picture, followed by these lines:

> Mrs. Moore was before her marriage, which was a beautiful event of July 11, Miss Margaret Lane, the lovely daughter of Mrs. Andrew Washington Lane, of this city. Mrs. Moore is now a resident of St. Louis.

Between Margaret's June wedding in 1929 and Harry's five years later in December of 1934, Hattie with all America, entered the decade tagged the Great Depression. Hattie saw her income shrink along with the family under her roof.

Hattie had turned over the management of her Butts County properties to Hugh Mallet after he and Mary were married and living in the McKibben house, which Hattie gave them as a wedding present. With an overseer, Hugh supervised the operation of her farms with those of the Mallet family. For years Hattie had counted on the fall sale of cotton, the main cash crop, to boost the bank account she and her children regularly depleted. September usually began with hundreds of Hattie's acres white with a good crop ready to be picked by hand and then hauled by mule wagon to the gin where the seeds were removed and the cotton graded and baled to be sold. But not all the plowing, planting, chopping, fertilizing, fighting the boll weevils, and praying for rain to fall or to cease could mean profit when the price plummeted. Hugh advised against selling until the market improved.

In the meantime, Hattie would have to pay taxes, pay farm hands, and buy seed and fertilizer to keep the farms going. Selling some of her property was out of the question. There were no buyers except those looking for give-away prices. Hattie, the heiress, had become one of the "land poor."

Financial matters had never been Hattie's forte. Her children were the investment she knew best, and they were costly. PERSEVERANDO was inscribed beneath the Lane family coat-of-arms. Kib wryly remarked that the actual family motto was "We Spend." But Hattie would persevere.

She had never tallied or compared exact dollar amounts expended on each her children. Their needs and desires were as different as were circumstances. Even if Hattie had believed in exact dollar equalization, it was impossible in 1930. Fair or not, her two youngest—Harry finishing college and Virginia beginning—would have to make do on less.

Lane cash could be in short supply for Harry and Virginia but never Lane family attention. Big, handsome, sports-and-people-loving Harry would never lack for companionship. Popularity at Mercer, where older brothers had paved a fraternity path, was assured. Andrew and McKibben were only blocks away to advise on male matters beyond Hattie's ken. Andrew understood clothes and helped his far-from-little brother select the right ones. McKibben was ready with all kinds of counsel. Harry walked—almost ran—all the way to Kib's house in Vineville to bring the result of serious career choice ponderings. Kib received the breathless announcement, "I've decided to be an engineer," with the calm query, "Passenger or freight?" Harry turned on his heels and strode back to Hardeman Avenue. Wounded pride would have to heal before that teasing brother could be forgiven.

Harry knew that Sister was only forty miles away in Jackson. She and Hugh and their growing family always made him and any accompanying friends feel at home with them. Their house became his headquarters when he and a fraternity brother took summer highway jobs. Not as the engineer he never became but as a laborer shoveling red dirt, Harry worked on a project to improve the state road between Macon and Jackson. Sister let him stretch out every inch and ounce of his big body and rest on her cool, polished parlor floor. Harry still had a vague memory, lodged perhaps in his aching muscles, of his grandmother Janie McKibben in that house, calling her youngest grandson from play to a cold supper and bed.

Hattie accepted and appreciated help with Harry's upbringing, but the voice of authority was hers. Even when Harry was twice her size, a formidable hulk on Mercer's athletic scene, and a popular fraternity man, Hattie required and expected him to be in by what she deemed a reasonable hour. Harry did not rebel. He could answer his mother's inevitable questions about late homecomings with, "I drove in between One and Two." Hattie was a long time finding out that he had given names to the gingko trees on either side on the driveway—"One" and "Two." On one memorable hour, however, Harry experienced the consequences of stretching credulity and tolerance too far. When Hattie heard him in the drive in after three, she was ready to meet him. As he stepped onto the lighted porch, he could see that the front door had been opened and the screen door behind it latched. Through the screen he could see the small, white-gowned figure of his mother with her hair in one long braid over her shoulder. "It's entirely too late to open the door to anybody," she said. When Harry heard the key turn in the firmly closed wooden door, he knew she meant what she said and that he had become "anybody." He walked down Hardeman Avenue to the firehouse and spent what was left of the night with the familiar firemen.

By the time he graduated, Harry could pass tests in adult resourcefulness and responsibility beyond those of college texts and lecture notes. And by the time he and pretty, petite Martha Mayo set their wedding date, he had something many college graduates in the mid 1930s did not have—a job. As a traveling salesman for Happ Brothers, a Macon menswear manufacturer, Harry could afford to take a bride to Nashville, Tennessee, the center of his territory.

Martha, from the South Georgia town of Waycross, was at Wesleyan while Harry was at Mercer. Since Mary Lane had walked to her Wesleyan classes, the liberal arts college of the old school had moved to new, classically styled brick and marble buildings on landscaped country acres at Rivoli, just beyond Macon's north limits. The Victorian towers dominating College Street were left for Wesleyan Conservatory and its students of music, art, and drama. Martha pursued the liberal arts at Rivoli, and Harry pursued Martha.

The wedding that was the happy culmination of their college romance called for celebration, and the Depression gripping America could not hold Lane spirits down. Louis came from Chicago with his ukelele on his knee to be best man at the ceremony and add music and merriment to the reception. Virginia was chosen as the bride's maid of honor since Martha had no sisters of her own. The Lanes were joined in Waycross by Mary and Hugh, who drove down from Jackson with their two oldest daughters. Mary had assembled appropriate wedding attire for herself and her little girls (borrowing little Mary's party dress from Bitsy Redman, daughter of the neighbors across McKibben Street) and arranged for care in Jackson of the three youngest children. Hugh had stretched expendable cash to finance the automobile trip and Waycross hotel accommodations. Again Hattie was mother of the groom and ushered to her front row place. There she saw and heard her youngest son pledge himself to another woman. She could tell that Harry meant every word of his vow.

The 1930s would play themselves out with only Virginia under Hattie's roof and eye. Like Margaret, Virginia did not choose Weslyan for college. Unlike Margaret, Virginia did not chose a husband soon after graduation. A strikingly attractive "brickyard blonde" (Kib's term for her coloring), Virginia was ready and set to find what her hometown might hold for a modern career woman.

"Career" was hardly the word for Virginia's first job. Possessing college honors and degree, speech and writing skills, and a seemingly natural ability to get along with people, she was still another inexperienced woman entering the work force. Promising openings were scarce for both sexes, and potential employers often assumed that "work" was something a young woman probably needed to do while she looked for a husband. Educated women often taught school while they looked, but Virginia was not interested in teaching. In the business world, women seldom rose from the ranks of secretaries and bookkeepers to top management positions, but Virginia accepted employment in the offices of the Bibb Cotton Mills. Kib's wife was daughter of the Bibb's president and sister of young Billy Anderson, who succeeded his father. For a while Virginia could postpone pounding Macon's hot pavement with her high heels to search for the dream job to match her qualifications and ambitions.

But family connections at the top of the textile industry were some distance removed from Virginia at the bottom of it. She felt trapped and stifled until she could find a way out. Means of escape appeared when she became secretary to the manager of Macon's motion picture chain. With offices in the Grand Theater, Lucas and Jenkins Enterprises supplied Virginia with a more congenial and certainly more dramatic environment.

Meanwhile, Hattie in her sixties and Virginia in her twenties were making their shared home a mixing bowl in which age and youth stirred together their common and separate interests and desires and tasted a new flavor of mother-daughter companionship.

The old opera house had become Macon's "grandest" movie house. Virginia's job there meant that Hattie, a motion picture devotee ever since the first nickelodeons and silent films came to Macon, had free admission. Besides, Hattie was a kind of unofficial critic and censor. If respected Mrs. A. W. Lane Sr. gave her approval to a film, it must be decent entertainment.

As the years piled up and her household and income dwindled, Hattie found in movies escape from situations she could not change and reward for tackling tasks she disliked.

I undertake the hardest things
  And credit to myself
A lot for undertaking what
  I wouldn't do for pelf.
I wonder if I ask too much . . .
  For what should such things go?
I take a chocolate soda
  And add a picture show.

On days Hattie did not go out to another picture show or to a meeting, she could fall victim to blue moods. In her nightgown and with her long hair still undone, she might spend the morning hours roaming through silent rooms darkened by closed blinds. In 1936, she wrote about reaching the age of sixty-four:

NO ONE NEEDS ME ANY MORE

No one needs me any more.
Now I'm three score years and four.
Somehow I don't make a hit;
For a job I'm not quite fit.

You don't think I'm feeling sore?
No one needs me any more.
In the Fount of Youth I dipped;
Since then maybe I have slipped.
I'll not act the coward's part
But will try to take new heart.
No one needs me any more?
To that thought I'll close the door.

For today I'll hope and pray
I shall have no cause to say
What a mother does deplore:
"No one needs me any more."

Fitting self-pity into a contrived, rhymed verse pattern pulled Hattie back into the determined optimism of the last stanza. By the time Virginia arrived for their mid-day dinner together, Hattie was ready to be good company. Hattie Buttrill had reached her sixty-fourth birthday three months earlier. When the two Hatties were together next, Hattie Lane locked arms with her best friend since childhood and pronounced them "two old Hats as good as new."

Through the highs and lows of moods and blood pressure, Hattie heard the echo of her mother's work ethic wisdom: "Idleness is the Devil's workshop." Hattie took up crocheting. As with her verse, she learned to copy any pattern and to devise new ones. She crocheted caps of all sizes and colors for her grandchildren; she made elegant placemats for her daughters and daughters-in-law; she made afghans. Hattie could sit, chat, and crochet without missing a stitch or a syllable. Her crochet bag became an ever-present accessory, and it was reported that she crocheted while watching movies.

Hattie seemed driven to pass along what she knew and to learn more if she could. She did not like to miss a meeting of the History Club, the Saturday Morning Music Club, or the Writer's Club. She was one of the teachers of the Major Lane Class of adult Bible study, named for its first teacher. When Virginia found her mother seated at the piano with the cook, Hattie explained that Salathia was learning to read music.

During her summer visits in Jackson, we Mallet grandchildren were her audience and her students. She kept her notebook in her crochet bag so that she could put away her needle and current project to read and write poems for us. One afternoon she introduced us to limericks and made new ones from our names. I remember the lines that began mine: "There was a sweet Miss called Jane Anne/Who was made from a marvelous plan . . ."

I liked playing with words and rhymes, but I managed to escape when Grandmother singled me out to be taught music theory and harmony. If Grandmother was headed my way with a little text and a writing pad, I fled to the concealing branches of the apple tree. That climbable, leafy hideaway and one nearby pear tree were all that remained from Janie McKibben's orchard that my grandmother and mother had known.

When we three oldest Mallet girls visited Grandmother in Macon, we were in her territory. Unless we were with our cousins, Grandmother Hattie entertained us with her activities. We might see two movies in one afternoon, stopping on our walk from the Grand to the Rialto for a drink or ice cream. If we were old enough to visit her without our mother, then we were old enough to go with her to club meetings: to the Washington Library where the history club program was about the years poet Sidney Lanier lived in Macon, to Wesleyan Conservatory where we heard an excellent pianist play for the Saturday Morning Music Club. When Grandmother introduced us as "Mary's daughters," we were on our best behavior.

My sister Mary and I went to church with her on one Communion Sunday. We young Methodists knelt at the altar for that sacrament in our Jackson church; but there we were, beside Grandmother in her pew at Macon's First Baptist where an usher was about to serve us the broken bread and tiny glasses of grape juice. We had heard that Baptists believed in something called "Closed Communion," which meant that only members of their denomination took it together. Yet Grandmother nodded for us to take it when it was passed to us, and we did. After church, she explained that she was indeed a Baptist but also "ecumenical." That big word meant, she said, that her religion was big enough for all Believers—including us out-of-town grandchildren.

When we were about nine and eleven, my younger sister Emily and I spent more than a week with Grandmother Hattie during a polio scare. In those years, before poliomyelitis vaccines, precaution meant no movies or swimming pools. We could not visit our Lane cousins or the neighborhood children we knew and they could not come over. Grandmother had Em and me to herself, and she planned and directed our schedule.

We were to piece a quilt with her. She had seen and admired a fan pattern, and fans we made—scores of them. She cut out the precisely shaped components from her vast accumulation of colorful scraps. Then we arranged some seven separate pieces to form each fan, which had to gain her approval before it was stitched together. It was a time-consuming process with instruction for us in needle threading, knot tying, sewing tiny, straight stitches, and coordinating colors according to her principles.

That's not all. Each of us took turns reading aloud to the other two quilt makers. Grandmother selected *David Copperfield* from her thirty volume set of the complete Charles Dickens because we had seen and loved the movie with Freddie Bartholomew as young David and W. C. Fields as Mr. Micawber.

For more frivolous entertainment we played cards. She taught us Fan Tan, a Chinese gambling game. Toothpicks were our money. On the piano with Grandmother's favorite songbook, "Heartsongs," was the new sheet music that our Aunt Gigi (Virginia) brought home. Fred Astaire and Ginger Rogers danced across covers of tunes from "Shall We Dance." Em and I were taking piano lessons, but we only managed the melody lines of those.

Grandmother was directing us granddaughters ably, but she knew she was no longer a director in the affairs of her own adult children. In fact, Virginia at home and Andrew, McKibben, and Mary nearby were assuming responsibility for directing hers, accepting her opinions and advice with respectful, amused tolerance. In her dark moods, Hattie voiced the real fear that she was becoming their burden. But not ever did any one of her seven use that word for the mother who was the proud, sometimes anxious, always caring observer of their triumphs and tragedies.

In 1939, Louis, no longer associated with the Bibb Manufacturing Company, was again in Macon and at Hattie's house. He had come alone and not just for a visit. With his job at an end and probably his marriage, too, he had come home to decide on new directions. Perhaps his two older Macon brothers could provide counsel and help. Old friends and young Virginia offered companionship and social life. Hattie gave him his old room back and again a place at her table with the space he had never vacated and could always lay claim to in her concern.

In March of that year, unexpected tragedy struck. Hugh Mallet, Mary's husband of seventeen years died of his first and only heart attack. Hattie and all her other children, except Margaret with two little boys in Saint Louis, rallied to Mary's support in Jackson and attended Hugh's funeral.

Hattie intended to remain in Jackson for as long as she could be of help to her daughter. But shocked, grieving Mary was surrounded by bewildered children, unwilling to accept their grandmother's attention for what comfort they could find in their mother's presence. Mary's kitchen was the domain of Onie, the cook, and Hattie was as much an interloper there as she was in the business conferences where Mary had Hugh's two brothers, Kib, and the overseer, Rupert Washington. Hattie was busy for a few days greeting the stream of sympathizing callers, inviting them into the house she had given Mary and Hugh. They had made it their home; it was no longer hers.

So, leaving Louis—willing but knowing little about either farming or Hugh's business—to work with Mary and Mr. Washington, Hattie returned to the Macon house she and Major had made home. She had held it together for more than twenty years without him, and it was still home for her and for Virginia. Hattie had done little to heal Mary's pain. No one could. But she had given her daughter, so suddenly a widow with five children to support and educate, living proof that the job before her could be done.

Hattie's job with Virginia and Virginia's with her was still unfinished. On her birthday, April 6, 1939, Virginia wrote a letter to Mary and Louis which was a kind of progress report:

> Dearest Sister and Louis,
>
> Here I am at the quarter-century mark . . . Sis, we appreciated your letter so much this morning. And Louis . . . the card really touched me—I think I'll frame it . . . I'm a fool about my family, and you two have always meant so much to me.
>
> We're enjoying Harry, Martha, and little Merritt being here. Merritt has made quite a hit with Mother. She said this morning, "Well, I'm going to the movie today." And Merritt quickly replied, "Me, too, but it's not open yet." We'll take him to see Popeye this aft.
>
> Linda is in Atlanta . . . be back the end of the week. Andrew and Adeline and little Adeline came over last night . . .
>
> We enjoyed the Writers' Club breakfast yesterday. Allan Tate and Caroline Gordon spoke. Also Evelyn Hanna and John Donald Wade . . . Mrs. Wade said she remembered you, Sister, so pleasantly, and

so did J. Donald. I wish you both could have been there. The whole theme of all the speeches seemed to be "don't be thinking about Zanzibar or some such place, but think about what is around you"—the idea being to develop a Southern literature.

My little Mother is doing fine—worrying about housekeeping a lot—which can't be helped I suppose. She went to the Music Club this morning and is off to the History Club this aft. So I don't see why she worries so much, except petty things and habit make it so.

Take care of yourselves and come down to see us.

Adding her enthusiasm for spoken and written words to Hattie's, Virginia had joined the Writer's Club, too. Her job with the movie theaters could have been merely secretarial, but she added a talent, continually cultivated, for apt, witty expression. From the secretarial beginning, she moved into public relations, advertising, and her own radio program on local WMAZ.

At home she encouraged Hattie's poetry writing and bought a book of blank pages, bound in a flexible blue cover for it. On the first page she wrote:

To Mother
Herein put the lines that express
your Hope, your Joy of Living—
in all, your wisdom—that I and
others might have inspiration.
Virginia

On the next page Hattie wrote:

This volume of verse is lovingly dedicated to one whose memory blesses—To Major

On the third blank page she wrote her title:

Hopes and Memories

Hattie selected for the first poem of her collection one she had written at the end of 1918, the year that began with Major's death.

ECHOES

I woke before the dawning
While all around was still.
The darkness sealed my eyelids;
The morning air was chill.
Before the new day's duties
My head and heart could fill
Some happy recollections
Their joy began to trill.
Now some glad phrase is sounded
As music from a rill,
And now the cadence echoes
As from a wooded hill.
These thoughts play on my memory
With an Aeolian skill
'Till I am lulled to slumber
With ne'er a thought of ill.
Ah, 'twas your happy phrasing
That time can never still
Had made the morning music
Through all my being thrill.

Hattie perhaps intended the new *Blue Book* for what she considered her best verse—polished, arranged, and carefully copied. But the *Blue Book* came to include much more. Prose of many kinds—notes on writing, quotations she liked, family history, memorial tributes to friends, and a biographical sketch of her quite alive best friend, Hattie Buttrill—found a place between the covers. Some of the entries were pencil drafts. Virginia sometimes collaborated with revisions and contributed of few lines of her own.

The *Blue Book* was the beginning of another poetry project instigated by Virginia, Hattie's volunteer editorial assistant. Hattie selected one of her poems for each of her seven children; then Virginia handled the details of a private printing of the collection to be distributed to Hattie's sons and daughters and several chosen friends. The end product was the little booklet *My Rainbow* by Hattie McKibben Lane. The first page announced its theme and purpose.

The arching Rainbow flings
Its colors overhead
In violet, indigo, blue, green,
Yellow, orange, red.

To My Rainbow of Children
Andrew
Margaret
Harry
McKibben
Louis
Mary
Virginia
From Mother—1942

Andrew's poem was the first of the seven poems and Virginia's the last, but the others were not arranged in birth order. They followed instead the sequence of colors Hattie saw in the rainbow. Virginia claimed the last rainbow hue, red, and the poem, "My Daughter," with the concluding lines:

She is fair; she is rare; she's the costliest pearl.
She's a sphinx; she's a minx—but always your girl.
Though she travel as far as that queer Zanzibar,
She'll never forget you wherever you are.
And once you have loved her and thoroughly taught her,
Your heart thrills in ecstasy over "My Daughter."

The last little page was printed on pale gold.

RAINBOW'S END *or*
THE POT OF GOLD

As the morning brighter grows
May your purples change to rose
'Til at last, when day is ended,
Violet with the rose is blended.

The United States had entered World War II when Hattie gave her children the rainbow collection. Hattie's memories of Andrew and McKibben in their soldier uniforms of "the war to end war" rubbed painfully against the reality of another conflict twenty-five years later. Her youngest son, Harry, married and a father, was wearing a naval officer's uniform while her two oldest grandsons, McKibben's boys, were swapping college clothes and books for government issue gear.

Macon, with both Camp Wheeler and Robins Air Base, was filled with servicemen; and Virginia's male companions—old friends or new acquaintances were usually in uniform. Hattie joined in the patriotic fervor of wartime and made her country's defenders welcome in her home. As Air Force Sergeant George Beattie edged out competition for Virginia's time and attention, Hattie recognized a winner.

A native of Cleveland, Ohio, he was educated in art, particularly painting, before he was called to military duty. Virginia came to know him through her involvement in the Macon Little Theater where he was using his off-duty hours designing and painting sets. She found him as multi-faceted as the gems in his parents' jewelry store in Cleveland. When I, a freshman at Wesleyan in the fall of 1943, came in from the Rivoli campus for Sunday dinner at my grandmother's house, I met him and could tell that he was a frequent guest there. My Uncle Kib thought the situation warranted a trip to Cleveland and returned with an excellent report of the background of the serviceman who was about to take as his the little sister he had cherished since her birth.

At noon on December 31, 1943, with family and a few close friends present, Virginia Harriet Lane and George Hamilton Beattie Jr. were married in the living room of McKibben's and Linda's house on Hines Terrace. (Virginia had added the "Harriet" to honor Hattie and surprise her when names were called with presentation of diplomas at Virginia's high school graduation.)

During the reception buffet that followed the traditional wedding ceremony, Hattie was seated on a sofa between Hattie Buttrill and Mrs. George Beattie Sr. Virginia was to call that esteemed gemologist "Queenie" because she was the queen bee of the Beattie family. She had come down to Macon for the hastily scheduled but carefully planned wedding of her son. Hattie B had been so deaf for years that she had no idea of how loud her own voice was or how well her every southern-accented word could be heard by the other nibbling, sipping guests—including Mrs. Beattie Sr. at the other end of the sofa.

"Well, Hat," they heard, "what do you think of Virginia marrying a damnyankee?" That designation was ever one word for Miss Hattie Buttrill, Daughter of the Confederacy.

Hattie could not know what lay beyond the immediate war years when Virginia would be following her new husband from one air base to another. She could not foresee the years ahead when Virginia would continue to follow George Beattie, artist. From his native Ohio back to Georgia, from their home in Atlanta to Florence or Venice—wherever opportunity and inspiration led, Virginia would be behind as support or sometimes a bit ahead as scout and promoter and as guarantor of family survival.

Hattie would have smiled, though, if many years later she could have heard her chat knowingly with patrons and connoisseurs at a Beattie exhibition.

> "Tell me, Mrs. Beattie, do you paint, too?"
> "No, no. I can scarcely draw my breath."

Hattie had written "The Fine Arts of Living" long before Virginia met George Beattie. In the *Rainbow* collection that she gave her children in 1942, it is the poem selected for Margaret, but some of its lines seem now especially for Virginia, too.

> We are all of us painters—the pictures we paint
> Are our lives with their twilight and dawn,
> Their hills and their valleys, their sunlight and shade
> Make character as they are drawn.

Coda

IN THE WINTER OF 1945, only divorced Louis was living with Hattie in the Lane house on Macon's Hardeman Avenue. When attempts to mend his marriage and live and work again in the Chicago area failed, he had returned to Macon and found wartime employment there. After a January evening spent with friends, he came home to find his mother lying unconscious on the floor. At the hospital, he and his Macon brothers learned that she had suffered a massive cerebral hemorrhage—the stroke her children had feared as the result of her often soaring blood pressure. Mary came from Jackson to join Andrew, McKibben, and Louis in a hospital vigil. Distant Margaret, Harry, and Virginia were notified of a grim prognosis: Death could occur at any moment.

Days went by. Hattie did not speak; she moved hardly at all; extensive paralysis and brain damage had probably occurred. But she did not die. Vital signs stabilized. When she appeared to be stronger, her doctors recommended that she be moved from the hospital. The care and attention she would continue to require could be provided at home or in a commercial nursing facility.

"Mama can go home, home with me to Jackson," Mary declared. The old house there had been Mary's, not Hattie's, for the more than twenty years since Hattie had given it to her after her marriage to Jackson native Hugh Mallet.

But it was Hattie's home when Van and Janie McKibben had hosted her wedding reception in its parlor, dining room, and wide halls. It was Hattie's home when Major had followed her, his bride, up its staircase on their wedding night. It was their home when a year later their son Andrew Wade Lane was delivered in the downstairs front room, the room Mary and Hugh had made their library-sitting room. Whether Hattie could still cherish those memories or not, her children must decide as soon as possible where and how Hattie could be cared for. Mary's proposal could not be dismissed.

Mary had no special training in nursing and no interest in the tasks and paraphernalia that accompanied it, but she was a caregiver. From girlhood she had cared about and for almost everything and everybody in her life. She cared intensely about her family, and her family began with her mother. The care Hattie needed most, according to Mary, lay beyond obvious physical and medical attention. She—oldest daughter—could best supply that "beyond" care, and somehow see to it that the rest was provided, too.

Hattie's other offspring, while protesting that Mary had her hands full already, were relieved. Every one of them pledged support and help.

Arrangements were begun. McKibben handled the financial and legal matters that were immediately necessary. All seven Lane brothers and sisters agreed with his realistic decision to sell the Macon house that had been their home from their earliest memories. Virginia, who had come from her husband's air force assignment in Florida, volunteered to remain long enough in Macon to take charge of emptying and closing the house that held fifty years of Lane living.

Mary went to work in Jackson. She had all the furniture moved from the back bedroom adjoining hers. She could remember when that room was filled with hat boxes and stands for her grandmother Janie McKibben's collection of fine millinery. She and Hugh had made the room a nursery and filled it with their children and what accompanied them: cribs, cots, a play pen, and a rocking chair for lullaby times. When the girls were all old enough for upstairs bedrooms, new wallpaper printed with sailing ships prepared the room for a male occupant, young Hugh Jr. The wallpaper ships would remain moored for a while longer, but Mary and her son moved his books and boy stuff of ball games and scouting to the upstairs room just above it. The room was ready for Hattie's bedroom furniture to be moved from Macon along with another small bed for the practical nurse already employed to accompany her patient to Jackson.

With its own connecting bathroom and two closets, the space was converted into a suite for Hattie that could hold anything necessary for her care and recuperation.

When the frail old woman arrived, three of Mary's five children were still at home. Young Mary was working in Atlanta; I was at Wesleyan College. Still at home with their mother were Emily and Hugh, both in high school, and Marcia, in sixth grade. There was also the third grade teacher, Mrs. Smith, who had occupied an upstairs front bedroom since before Hugh Sr.'s death.

Mary was convinced that her mother could and would improve. She did. Hattie, with persistent encouragement, began to take a few steps. She began responding to questions with "yes" and "no." Occasionally she made brief, simple requests or comments. With Mary beside her, she walked on the porch and in the yard. Mary took her for automobile rides that usually combined errands with opportunities for Hattie to be outside and see more people, some of whom knew who she was and spoke to her. Those outings often ended on the square, where Mary parked in front of Carmichael Drug Store where young Hugh worked after school. A familiar toot brought him out with their afternoon treat—cups of vanilla ice cream served on a tray he attached to the window frame of his mother's old red Buick.

Hattie Buttrill, whose own health was failing, visited often. The two "old Hats" seemed to need no conversation to feel companionship. Hattie Lane's Macon sons, with the wives of Andrew and McKibben usually accompanying them, came frequently. In August of 1945, Virginia came for an entire week so that "Sister" and her children could go to St. Simon's Island. Those late summer days in a family-style beach hotel were to be the only real vacation that closely bound group of six—nobody else included—ever had together.

One of my memories of my Grandmother Hattie in those years is a scene of her sitting on the front porch with Uncle Andrew. He had pulled his big, heavy rocking chair close enough to hers for him to hold her hand. She was smiling. I remember another time when I saw her standing in the parlor and then tottering toward the piano, her college graduation gift from her father. After all the years in Macon, it had been brought back to the Jackson parlor where it had been first placed in the early 1890s. I watched an old lady reach out her hand toward the keyboard, but she did not touch it.

Shrunken in mind and body, that old lady usually ate in the dining room with her daughter, her grandchildren, and any guests. Sometimes she sat with them on the porch or in the library-sitting room.

Hattie's final sojourn in the town of her birth spanned the years that included—along with the world-changing end of World War II—major Mallet events: three graduations, two weddings, and the birth of her daughter Mary's first grandchild. In January of 1947, the baby and her mother, Mary Lane Mallet Carr, were occupying the bedroom adjoining Hattie's. Hattie was told, when the little girl was carefully placed in her arms for a moment or so, that she was another Mary Lane—the third generation of first daughters to have the name. To simplify family roll calls, this one would answer to just "Lane."

By January of the next year, Hattie's health had so deteriorated that she was confined almost completely to bed. Hattie Jane McKibben Lane, born December 8, 1872, in Jackson, a little town in the heart of Georgia, died there on April 16, 1948. Outside the window of her room, big leaf buds were ready to open on the "raintree" that had sheltered her childhood doll tea parties.

Two days later, she lay in a casket placed beneath the parlor mantel where she had received the guests at her wedding reception fifty-five years before. Again the room was crowded and scented with flowers. Hattie's seven children and several of her grandchildren received and greeted these guests.

Miss Hattie Buttrill said that her friend should have had a funeral in Macon's First Baptist Church where both she and Major had been prominent members. Hattie's children, however, decided on a simple home service. The scripture readings, prayers, and minister's remarks it included were soon over, and an automobile cortege followed the hearse down Georgia Highway 42 to Macon and Rosehill Cemetery. More Macon friends were waiting there for a graveside ceremony. Beneath the LANE monument, Hattie was buried beside Major and near the cradle-size graves of their toddlers Lucia and Eugenia.

As the twenty-first century begins, seven of Hattie's and Major's children, one granddaughter, and their deceased husbands and wives are with them in the family plot. When George Beattie was buried there in 1997, beside Virginia, their youngest, a member of the Atlanta art community remarked that he had never before seen so many family members buried together. One of Hattie's granddaughters explained, "Lanes, living and dead, would rather be with each other than with anybody else."

The Macon house that had been home to them all was demolished when Interstate Highway 75 required a Hardeman Avenue Exit. But Heritage, as Mary Mallet was calling the Jackson house, was home to Hattie, too. On a bedroom mantel there, two of her poems are framed together and propped against the chimney wall. In Hattie's handwriting and initialed by her, they are "Hearth Song" and "Wingfold."

HEARTH SONG

Home and the firelight gleaming
Cheery and blessed and bright
Faces of loved ones beaming
Radiate joy and light.
After our toil is ended
Sweeter the draught we sip,
Foretaste of heaven blended,
Rest and companionship.
H. McK. L.

WINGFOLD

When evening shadows deeper grow
And vesperings are sweet and low,
The dove her gentle mate has found
And happily they're homeward bound.
The world is wide, a-far we roam,
Then wearying, we turn to home,
That haven fair, than all more blest,
Serenely folding wings, we rest.
H. McK. L.

Mary

A Proper Courtship

THE WOMAN WHO OWNED OUR MIDDLE GEORGIA HOMEPLACE longest and left the most of herself in it was Mary Lane Mallet. Her life as a Woman of the House began when she came to Jackson in 1922, not as the visiting granddaughter of respected, formidable Janie McKibben or as a popular addition to the town's social scene but as the new bride of Hugh Mallet. Her death in 1985 in a nearby nursing home did not erase her imprint. Telling her story—telling it right—is the hardest assignment I ever gave myself. The third Woman of the House was my mother.

She left more than enough material. We children, grandchildren, maybe great-grandchildren may never sort it all. From attic to basement, sometimes jumbled with those of her mother, grandmother, husband, and children, Mother's documents, pictures, newspaper clippings, souvenir programs, and hundreds of letters postmarked from four continents stuffed three desks, innumerable shelves and drawers, trunks, boxes, baskets, even sacks. What they told me augmented what she and many who knew her told me. My own memories are in the glue that holds her story together.

The first correspondence between Mary Lane and Hugh Mallet may have been the sympathy note she wrote him in late 1918 after the death from influenza of his first wife Jane. Mary knew Hugh as the likeable older brother of Joel, a favorite companion for Jackson good times. Her letter to him was found bundled with other condolences addressed to the young widower.

Another was from Fannie Henderson, a local black educator. As Butts County school superintendent, Hugh was her professional associate and supervisor. Since the time she wrote that letter, five generations—black and white—have revered Fannie Henderson for her pioneer battle against black illiteracy in a segregated school system, in buildings that offered little more than primitive shelter, and with books and learning tools often the hand-me-downs from white schools. Her memorial is the twenty-first century Henderson Middle School—planned, built, and equipped for the public education of the county's children of all racial and ethnic backgrounds.

As Mary's husband and a father of five, Hugh kept the letters packed away with other mementos of pretty Jane Ellis Stanfield and his youthful love and marriage. Long after their deaths, I found pictures of Jane, albums and scrapbooks from her school years at Atlanta's exclusive Washington Seminary and at Gunston Hall School in Washington, D.C., and letters she wrote to Hugh before their marriage in 1915. One of those was written from a Washington hotel room where she was watching a suffragette demonstration from a window. "I might join it . . ." she wrote. With the correspondence there was a copy of a poem written and read at Jane's funeral by the Mallet's Methodist minister. There was also an unfinished batiste baby dress with a threaded needle still in it.

Four years elapsed between Mary's sympathy note and the date on the next correspondence with Hugh found in her memorabilia. A letter postmarked Jackson, Ga., July 10, 1922, and addressed to "Miss Mary Lane, Camp Dixie for Girls, Clayton, Ga." suggests that casual acquaintance had become something warmer.

> . . . Your celebration of the Fourth was the nicest I know of, and I was mighty glad to know you are so pleasantly situated . . . Jackson spent a very orderly Fourth . . . Kiwanis barbecue at noon . . . our star ball team entertained by trying to beat Conyers but failed nobly . . . Drove down to Indian Springs this morning and saw more people there than on any Sunday this summer . . . The pavilion had been opened . . .
>
> Add Nutt and Lucile were spending the day at the Elder Hotel and asked me to join them, but a whole day there would be too much so I came home and read the paper and *Saturday*

> *Evening Post* . . . must be strenuous being the leader for seven girls and I should think one of the first duties ought to be training an assistant as quickly as possible . . . After a month you will have yours so well trained you can get the day off you mentioned I hope. I already have a road map showing all crossroads all the way to Clayton and am counting on the trip . . . these days I keep cool thinking about the mountain breeze that's probably blowing through Rabun Gap . . . put your charges to sleep again and write me . . .

When Hugh sent Mary a book—whose title neither he nor she referred to—he wrote that he chose it as "the light, not to say frivolous, kind that's recommended for summer reading." Mary was to pass down to her daughters what she had been taught about suitable gifts from boyfriends: candy, flowers, books, perfume were acceptable; expensive jewelry and personal wearing apparel were not.

When Mary wrote to thank him for the book, she enclosed a snapshot of herself. Standing before a rough camp cabin and wearing pants and boots, she seems ready for hiking or riding the mountain trails. Hugh responded immediately:

> . . . The picture is a darling . . . The campers must be getting along with their training of ten mile hikes before supper. Think you did the right thing in getting appointed riding instructor and life-saver, but you should be careful not to be appointed hiking instructor unless the lecture method is in vogue there . . .

Back in Macon by September, Mary found further opportunities to be instructor of girls. She was a substitute lecturer at Wesleyan that fall while a history professor was away. She also became the teacher of her adolescent sister Margaret's Sunday school class. According to my Aunt Margaret, "Sister" became a favorite teacher by combining Bible study with humor and fun.

Her social calendar was crowded with parties accompanying the autumn weddings of several of her friends. She knew there was speculation that she and her usual Macon escort—referred to only as "B.L."—might eventually become engaged and similarly honored with lavish entertainment.

Mary was of a different, although still undecided, turn of mind. Hugh—receiving and answering his letters, being available when business or she herself drew him to Macon, or attending shows and football games with him in Atlanta as well as Macon—began to occupy a lion's share of her leisure. In early October, he wrote:

> I think I will have a lot of business in Macon Wednesday with Watkins convention . . . not to mention the most important reason of all. I would like to see you after you finish instructing the youth . . .

When Mary's reply brought the news that a sore throat was keeping her housebound, Hugh wrote that "illness was most unkind to pick on you just at the beginning of your career as Professor."

Hugh confessed that he had accepted Joel's invitation to join him in attending the Macon convention primarily because it could give him a chance to be with Mary.

> . . . I called off my part of the program . . . really didn't care for it . . . I didn't want to run the risk of not seeing you. If you have recovered and have no plans for Sunday, I would like to drive down . . . I'm afraid to wait on the excursion you mentioned to Indian Springs . . .

The next week Mary accepted an invitation for the two of them to attend the Mercer vs. Georgia Tech game in Atlanta with the Witheringtons, an older couple of her acquaintance who had four choice tickets and planned to drive up from Macon. The route they would take did not pass through Jackson, but Mary suggested that Hugh join them in Forsyth. She had been invited to spend the night in Atlanta with her friend Ida Britain, whose father had recently become Georgia Tech's president. Hugh seemed agreeable to any plans Mary made:

> . . . You are an excellent planner. I will meet you in Forsyth at any time you say . . . Tonight I went out to hear Mr. McKay preach at the Presbyterian Church and found him very interesting as he talked about Adam and Eve, primarily about Eve. And so home to write to you that your letter has made it a happy day for me.

Mary's plans came together to further Hugh's suit. What happened is unclear, but some time during the weekend Mr. Witherington suffered a mishap or became ill while Mary was visiting with the Britains. To get the Witheringtons and Mary home, Hugh was called and gladly came to the rescue. He drove them to Macon, where they arrived so late that Hugh spent the rest of the night with the Lanes. His next letter to Mary declared his feelings and intentions:

> . . . the trip home was uneventful. I had passed Forsyth before the sun came up and reached home at seven just in time for breakfast. It was sweet of you to get up so soon, but I didn't like for you to do it . . . hope Mr. Witherington is beginning to recover and that he will soon be up again. I was glad we could go help bring the couple home. It was such a wonderful rideback I shall always be indebted to them . . . I can't begin to tell you how glad I was to be with you again.
>
> You are always in my heart and in my thoughts because you see, Mary Dear, my heart and my head tell me that I want you always and I love you.

Mary had encouraged and basked in Hugh's attention. Yet torn between what held her to Macon and what pulled her to him, she could not immediately accept his proposal. He did not take seriously her suggestion that he consider moving to Macon. Neither did he agree with her that "the wiser course" would be to leave things as they were for a while.

Indecision was the tone of her letter describing pre-wedding festivities for a friend:

> Macon has been unusually gay this week with wedding parties. I cut the thimble predicting spinsterhood in the cake at the Thorpe's buffet supper after the rehearsal . . . received much sympathy until I then cut the ring. Can't guess what cutting them both may portend. . . . The Witheringtons have invited us to take supper with them Sunday night and I took the liberty of accepting for both of us.

Hugh continued to plead his case and extol the advantages of Jackson's small town life:

> Your letter came this morning before I left for Atlanta and all the way up and all the way back and all the time there, underneath everything else I was thinking of all the advantages that a small town might have to offer, and if I could convince you that what you called "the wiser course" was not the wiser at all . . . if you would hurry and vote yes, you would make one person supremely happy. Would the consciousness that you had done that be any reward? . . . you would have all your old friends and many new ones—not new ones either because they already know you and love you. A house with no trol-

> ley cars to disturb you, a small garden with flowers and a rose or so, not many because I hate to dig. And Mary, a home with you, to love you and be loved by you would be Paradise . . . if loving you would make up to you for any of the things you left behind in Macon, you know I would make it up. It's hard to write everything that's in my heart. It's full of love for you, and if I were with you tonight, I believe you would decide with me.
>
> I love you and want you always.

Mary's answer revealed a young woman wrestling with the most important choice of her life while conscientiously fulfilling even trivial scheduled commitments:

> . . . giving my Sunday School class a "kid party." They're fifteen and think they can masquerade as kids . . . more parties and other engagements every night have kept me occupied . . . little wonder I made the low score when I had to play bridge so soon after reading your letter. My mind certainly was not on cards and my heart far from being present. I read some excerpts from the *Love Letters* of Whittier in Sunday's *Times* . . . they didn't compare with mine of this afternoon. If only I could convince myself that you're right! I know I'm making four people happy as 'tis but you say you could make up for all that. Now I wonder how it would be to have my happiness dependent on only one . . . You're trying to undertake a man size job . . . this note hurried to be given to the postman with thanks to you for all you are and with hopes of seeing you soon.

When Hugh arrived in Macon the following Sunday, Mary was waiting to tell him what he wanted to hear. She had also attended to a matter not mentioned in her letters to Hugh. Mary's conscience and sense of fair play must have demanded that she herself tell B. L., of her intention to marry "that fellow from Jackson" before the news was spread more generally. Mary kept B. L.'s reply to whatever she had written or told him. His letter was dated "Sunday," doubtless the same Sunday Mary and Hugh were making their wedding plans. The rejected suitor began his note with a rhymed quotation:

> "It's easy enough to be happy
> when life flows along like a song
> But the man worth while
> Is the man who will smile
> When everything goes dead wrong.

> . . . Mary, smiling is what I am trying to do, but it is hard . . . wishing you and yours all the happiness in the world."

On the same day she accepted Hugh's proposal, Mary agreed with him that their marriage would take place as soon as possible in a home ceremony not preceded by weeks of exhausting preparations and parties. With their decisions already firm, Hugh—in traditional and diplomatic style—asked Mrs. Andrew W. Lane for the hand of her oldest daughter. When he left Macon late Sunday evening, the time and date was set for the wedding to take place at twelve o'clock noon on the next Wednesday, November 15, 1922.

While Hugh was on the road to Jackson, Mary was writing him a letter begun within the hour following his departure.

> Little Later
>
> My Dearest,
>
> The only thing I can possibly think of which might be a disadvantage to our quick wedding is my failure to have written any love letters . . . How I will ever be persuaded to let you leave home in order that I may have some future opportunity I simply can not see. Telling you everything I feel will have to compensate. The only thing superior to being loved, Sweetheart, is for me to love you and I do love you with all my heart.
>
> Mother refuses to let me stay up a minute longer and you've only been gone a few minutes so I'm off to dream the night away. To me love means the placing of my happiness in the happiness of him I love. Love casteth out all fear so there's nothing to make me scared.
>
> Devotedly,
> *Mary*
> *Yours—truly heart and soul, My Love*

Seventeen Years Begin

JUST AFTER THANKSGIVING, 1922, THEIR WEDDING TRIP to New York City and Washington, D.C., declared "perfect," Mary and Hugh reached journey's end in Jackson. There, welcome awaited the new Mrs. Hugh Mallet in the big, porch-wrapped family home on Covington Street.

Emma Nutt Mallet was the widow of William Maurice Mallet, the father of whom Hugh had only childhood memories. Son of a French immigrant, W. M. Mallet had risen to success in Butts County as landowner, planter, businessman, and community leader before his death in 1900 at the age of fifty-five. Since then, Emma had been the unquestioned, quietly effective center of family life.

Hugh's family must have known since early autumn that his courtship of Mary Lane was serious. Emma may well have anticipated an announcement of his engagement when, on Monday, November 13, Hugh told her he had happy news. More than an announcement, it was an invitation to be in Macon at the Lane house at noon on Wednesday for his wedding.

As soon as Hugh rushed from her presence to deliver more oral invitations, Emma wrote the letter Mary held in her hands the next day. The bride-to-be read that her future mother-in-law intended to be present at her son's wedding. The note ended with "I have always loved you, Mary, and I welcome you to my family and to my home."

She was in the midst of both—Mallet family and Mallet home. The house she was entering had been Hugh's home all his life, and the family he was part of was held together with ties as strong as those that bound the Lanes.

Hugh and Mary intended having their own house. Hugh had described the rose garden he would plant for it when he was persuading Mary to join him for an idyllic life in his small town. Their extremely brief engagement had allowed no time to move his dream house to a real address. For the time being, Hugh's bride would share his upstairs bedroom in his mother's house.

"Mama" to her children, "Miss Emma" to servants and field hands, or "Mama Mallet," as she would be to Mary, was in charge there. With little evident fuss, she supervised whatever was needed for the nourishment and comfort of whoever lived or visited there.

That number varied as did the life situations of Emma's family and the hospitality any member of it might need. When Mary's luggage, filled with trousseau and honeymoon souvenirs and gifts, was carried up to Hugh's room, she became the sixth of the current residents. First was Mama Mallet. She was known merely to smile when she was teasingly charged with encouraging her children to bring their spouses into the family home rather than leave it for one they might make. Annie, the oldest, did have her own house—right next door.

After Annie married Mote Watts, she received Mallet property on which her house was built. Mote, an affable fellow, worked at several of the big spa hotels—including the legendary Wigwam at nearby Indian Springs. When the prosperous resort era waned there, he became a manager for a Macon hotel. He spent little time at home, and Annie and her children were in and out of Mama Mallet's. There Martha, Elizabeth, and Jimmy found a second home.

When Hugh added Mary to the household, his older brother George and his wife Minnie were also living on the second floor. Tall, massive George seemed to be designed for military life, and good soldier he was. After serving as an officer during World War I, he continued and advanced his military career through leadership in the National Guard. His peacetime civilian work was ownership of a dairy where his prize, purebred herds grazed Mallet acres less than a mile away. Hugh had primary responsibility for other Mallet agricultural enterprises, but the brothers worked closely together.

Short, plump, good natured Minnie centered her life in George. When possible she accompanied him on military assignments to be by his side, hardly as tall as his chest. When he was away, she found company at bridge and dining tables or in front porch rocking chairs. Minnie had been the first at the breakfast table on the morning Hugh had been so eager to spread the news of his marriage. Minnie was the first to congratulate him and tell him how glad she was to have a new sister so soon.

Hugh's unmarried sister Pauline, little more than a year older than he, was a family force Mary was soon to recognize and accept. Pauline, of short bobbed hair and brusk manner, implemented Emma's plans for the smooth operation of the homeplace. Little interested in such domestic skills as cooking and needlework, Pauline could be proud of her driving ability in the 1920s when few Jackson women had either opportunity or desire to be behind the wheel of an automobile. Pauline was Emma's designated chauffeur, driving her to Methodist services and to meetings of the Women's Missionary Society, the Women's Christian Temperance Union, and the Daughters of the Confederacy. For membership in the latter, Emma could claim that her husband had served as a Confederate soldier and that her father, whom she never knew, had been killed in the fighting around Richmond. Pauline had her own interests and friends who accepted her loyal dependability and generosity along with outspoken, strongly held opinions. They looked elsewhere for tact and feminine charms.

Those were the Mallets Mary joined on Covington Steet. There was also Jane Ham Mallet, who lived across town with her homebound sister. As widow of Hugh's oldest brother Harold, who had died the previous year, Jane continued to be "family."

Joel was the only one of Hugh's siblings not living in town when Mary came there as a bride. Youngest of them and closest to Hugh in more than age, Joel had been Mary's favorite male companion for the Jackson good times of her girlhood. In 1922, he was living in Atlanta with his wife Helen and their little daughter Barbara, who became a family favorite on their frequent visits to Jackson.

Mary was still unpacking and settling into their room when Hugh received a late night telephone call from Helen. Joel had been drinking; he had not come home. Could Hugh come up and help locate him? Hugh left his new wife to find his brother.

It was not the first such mission for Hugh, and it was far from the last. This was the Joel who had enlivened Mary's Jackson social life. This was the Joel who, just before his own Yale graduation had wired Mary congratulations on her graduation from Wesleyan: PLEASE DEAL GENTLY WITH THE COLD WORLD. Before Mary became his sister-in-law, Joel had added inability to handle alcohol to his reputation for charm and brilliance.

Mary was called in a different direction. A picture postcard addressed to "Mrs. Hugh Mallet, Covington Street, Jackson, Ga., Box A" was waiting for her when she and Hugh arrived at the Mallet house. On the back of the picture of a pretty girl reading a letter was familiar handwriting. "We are hoping you and Hugh will drive down as early tomorrow as possible. Come on. Can't you stay with us a while? Till tomorrow—Goodbye. Mother." Letters between Mary and Hugh during the first years of their marriage tell why, how, and how often Mary stayed "a while" in Macon.

The less than fifty miles could be traveled either by car or by train. Jackson, half-way between Atlanta to the north and Macon to the south, was connected to both by Georgia Highway 42 and the Southern Railroad. Mary had learned to drive when she was twelve and liked the convenience and freedom of "going through the country," as automobile travel was described. But Mary had the use of their one car only when Hugh did not need it for Mallet farm or his own business. He also did not like for her to drive alone for more than a very few miles on unpaved Highway 42. Hugh himself often took the train for business trips to Atlanta and Macon. Jackson travelers going to either could expect to find their neighbors at the depot about to take the same train. On board they would not be surprised to find acquaintances from all over the state.

On December 8, 1922, after Mary's arrival for her first visit to Macon without her new husband, she wrote him that her travel companion had been his cousin and business associate, Add Nutt.

> Dearest—
>
> Traveling without you isn't a bit of fun even if Add Nutt did his best to keep me from missing you. Macon must have realized how sad I'd be to arrive without you because they had the band to meet me. Sho

> nuff! They did . . . Minstrels will be here tonight and the troop must have gotten off their train a little ahead of ours . . . We have just finished eating a company dinner. Evidently Cook thought you were coming home with me . . . You are in Atlanta by now, I guess, and too busy to miss me much. I'm dashing off to a movie where I know I can't forget you . . . I love you just as much as I did yesterday and the day before with an equal proportion added for today. Therefore I love you twenty-three times as much as I did when we were married—and then some . . .

On the same day, on Hugh's train trip to Atlanta, he had seen Mercer University's President Weaver, who had married them.

> Dear Mary—
>
> It isn't like the same room without you and all day I've been dreading coming home with you away . . . Dr. Weaver was on the train going up this afternoon. He didn't recognize me until I told him who I was, and then he told me again what a lucky man I was and how fine you were and as I thoroughly agreed with him there wasn't a chance for an argument . . .

Hugh drove to Macon the next day, spent the night with his new in-laws, and brought Mary back with him to Jackson. If Hugh and his family expected Mary immediately to absorb herself in their Jackson life, they underestimated Macon's magnetic pull. A week before Christmas she was in Macon, again without Hugh. She wrote him how the family celebrated her visit by pouring out their "Christmas schemes for giving presents . . . none of them have any money and Louis and Harry are desperate over means of providing gifts for numerous girls . . . I've laughed till I hurt."

The letter continued with an account of Mary, in the midst of her adorers, again slipping into her well-practiced daughter and sister roles. She had driven her mother out to Kib's and Linda's house, especially to see Kib, who had been ill, and little Sonny. Then she picked up Virginia from school and got her home and out of the rain before high school classes dismissed and she could do the same thing for Margaret and Harry. The letter concluded with "it's mighty bad for me to leave you . . . They need me to straighten out affairs here and I'll be home the first minute possible . . . I can picture you in your big chair, without me, enjoying your self-made fire. Goodnight, Dearest."

The new year began with a practice Mary was to continue for years to come—being alert for news of "passing," as she dubbed rides to and from Macon. In minutes she could be ready to ride with almost any driver she knew who would drop her off at 316 Hardeman Avenue. On January 2, 1923, she wrote Hugh of her arrival there as a passenger in the automobile of one of the Mallets' cousins from Florida who was paying his Jackson relatives an extended visit.

> . . . our ride was beautiful in spite of terrible roads. "Cousin John" is a fine driver and that Buick motor pulled thru deep muddy ruts without any trouble . . . ate some of Mother Mallet's crystalized fruit and enjoyed the luxury of lolling in a sedan. Such an opulent feeling!
>
> Just brought the children home from school and they are excited over getting their cards with their monthly reports. All three covered themselfs with glory . . . as a reward Mother is taking us all to see "Daddy Longlegs."

Macon beckoned Mary not only through her family but also with invitations from her friends to join them for social, cultural, and sporting events. Familiar shops were another attraction. "Passing" transportation merely supplemented the train trips to and from Macon, so frequent that Hugh bought an extended use ticket that the conductor could punch for each one-way journey. Add Nutt told Hugh that the ticket was the cheapest divorce he could buy. However, if Mary's Macon visits were longer than two days, she mailed Hugh the ticket so that he could join her for a mid-week overnight or for the weekend. They also made a pact that neither of them would allow more than twenty-four hours of separation without communication by letter or telephone.

Mary was in Macon for more than a week of parties preceding the wedding of her friend Emilee. Hugh had joined her for some of the weekend festivities and she had driven him to the train for a very early Monday morning return trip to Jackson. Writing him later in the day, she began with "How are you after nine hours of separation?" Before describing a day spent as she often had before their marriage, she let Hugh know that she was aware that his joining her had meant giving up the hunting he had planned with his Jackson friends.

> . . . I came home from taking you to the train and slept until nine . . . downtown with Helen Barnes and met Emilee at the beauty parlor

> . . . met Mother and purchased two beautiful all linen table cloths and two dozen napkins. I did find real bargains but they did seem terribly high.
>
> Then I bought a hat before I knew it! Here's hoping you'll be pleased with my selection. We would have saved a whole lot if you had let me go on home with you this morning . . . Now I'm going to the History Club and then tonight . . . to the buffet . . . Emilee confided in me this morning that she and Grady were both sick and tired of all the parties . . . Mother and the children said that they certainly did enjoy your visit. You know I did!
>
> Love,
> *Mary Mallet*

Underlining the surname she shared with her husband was perhaps intended to let him know that despite so much time away from him, she was proud to be Mrs. Hugh Mallet.

If Jackson was his home, then it would be hers, too. Friends, cousins, and Hugh's family had spread the description of Mary Lane of Macon as an accomplished young woman with a trained mezzo soprano voice. When she was asked to be in a local show, an ambitious production to be directed by an imported professional, she agreed. But before the rehearsals began for what could have been a kind of announcement of her intention to become a full participant in the town's civic, social, and cultural activities, she was again called to Macon. Hattie had been struck by an automobile, the extent of her injuries yet to be determined.

> Dearest—
>
> Kib and Linda met me to reassure me of Mother's condition but I find her feeling awfully nervous and sore all over. She is the bravest person in the world and has been trying to tell me how much worse it might have been and how badly she needed the rest anyway.
>
> She was knocked down right here on the hill in front of our house . . . to the hospital for an X-ray and they found a bone shattered . . . tomorrow will know just how badly she is hurt . . . I don't know how long I'll have to be away . . . She is depressed in addition to her injuries . . . I know I can make her feel better . . . You were all mighty good to get me off on that train and I'm so glad I'm able to he here when I'm needed . . .

> I don't know how I'll get along without you . . . Be sure to play tennis and not to work too hard, and most of all, to miss me as much as you please.
>
> . . . Mother will be all right soon . . . I'm going to help her get well as quickly as possible. Thank goodness it was a little car . . . only the front wheel passed over her leg . . .

Mary was convinced that she was needed throughout April and well into May while Hattie progressed from quiet bedrest to crutches and gradually to near normal activity. Hugh came down for weekends, and as her mother improved Mary managed to leave her for a day or two to join Hugh in Jackson. The train, dusty or muddy roads, telephone calls, and daily letters kept the couple united. After Hugh had just left Mary in Macon on a Sunday afternoon, she wrote:

> . . . to think that this is one of "our Sundays" and I could only claim six hours with you . . . can't help but feel lonesome and miserable . . . I've had my cry out . . .
>
> And I'm glad you came to see me and I'm glad I love you so . . . If it's not permissible for wives to write love letters to their husbands, I'll have to resign the exalted position of being Mrs. Hugh Mallet.
>
> . . . I've continued reading "Babbitt" to Mother, greeted numerous callers, & served supper to the family. That strawberry short-cake should have been sufficient inducement to prolong your visit. . . . try to love me as much as I do you. I already know you do but I want assurance . . .

Mary's letter was in Hugh's Jackson post office box A on Monday afternoon, and on Monday evening he was writing the reply:

> Today started off a regular "Blue Monday," beginning with no cook. Then I found one of the farm hands in the hands of the police and then had to preside an inning at police court myself. But most of all I was missing you and wishing I could see you and then the mail brought your letter . . . I hope you won't ever stop writing the love letters . . . You are the center of all my life, and hopes and dreams, and everything to me . . .

For several more weeks, while Hattie recuperated but still required attention, their letters declared devotion and gave descriptions of their separated daily doings. Mary seemed to have slipped again into her former role of accommodating, available "Sister," but with awareness of the "noise and confusion these Lanes insist on creating." As Hattie improved, Mary planned for them to "have some music" while the children were at school. "I've simply got to turn over a new leaf and practice . . . or lose most of the voice I did have instead of making you musical . . . "

Hugh wrote of getting out to the farms in the early morning to supervise spring planting before getting to his office in town where he ran his feed, seed, and fertilizer business. His days might end with a few sets of tennis. He wrote how his being able to get to Macon to see her was affected by George's being called away by National Guard matters and by his office assistant Jim Newton being ill. Her absence, he said, was felt throughout the family. Minnie was handling a bumper crop of Mallet farm strawberries. His niece Elizabeth Watts was sorry her Aunt Mary could not hear her play in the recital of Miss Viola Slaughter's piano pupils. Joel had been in Jackson for the recent Butts County Court session. He had been accompanied by his wife and daughter, and they all were disappointed Mary was not at home for their visit.

When rain and muddy roads prevented Pauline's driving down to Macon to bring Mary home for a day or two, Hugh mailed her the train ticket. "I hope Mrs. Lane will be well enough for you to leave her. I want to see you and have you with me if you can get away for a few days . . . not for a few days only either . . ."

Before Mary returned to Jackson, her mother implemented a decision she may have been considering since Mary and Hugh were married. Hattie deeded the house she had inherited from her mother Janie to her daughter Mary. It would be her wedding gift to Mary and Hugh, who was successfully proving himself.

Hattie and her children had but seldom used her Jackson house for several years. Accepting it with gratitude and joy, Mary and Hugh began planning renovation and painting to be begun just as soon as possible even though part of the house had been and still was occupied by a renter.

Dr. Robert Van Deventer, longtime and popular pastor of the big yellow brick Baptist Church just a block west of the McKibben house, lived in two upstairs rooms. Knowing that "Dr. Van" was soon to retire and return to Savannah, the new Mallet owners assured him that the coming invasion of carpenters, plumbers, painters, and paper hangers would leave his suite undisturbed. By early summer Mary and Hugh were ready to begin the work that would make the house built by her grandparents distinctly theirs.

Mary wanted it light and airy and decided that the dark woodwork would all be painted oyster white and the wide, dark pine floor boards would be replaced by narrow, lighter, oak hardwood. Another window would be cut in the parlor to balance the one already on the other side of the handsome fireplace and mantel. "Den" was not a word often used in 1920s house plans. Hugh and Mary planned that their informal sitting room would be their "library" with built-in bookcases. In that room, the Victorian mantelpiece would be replaced by sturdy red brick topped by a simple wooden mantel. Serving on the building committee of the new Methodist Church going up across the street had broadened Hugh's knowledge of masonry and carpentry and introduced him to the area building contractors and artisans. A brick mason working on the church building was hired to build their library fireplace.

They chose the large room behind the sitting room–library to be their bedroom and built a new, small but complete bathroom in one corner of it. Their room would be private but central and connected. One door opened into the front hall near the foot of the stairs; another led into the sitting room.

A third door connected what would soon be their bedroom with another downstairs bedroom that could also be reached through the back hall. That room already had an adjoining bathroom where an enormous bathtub stood on its claw feet. Janie McKibben had added that first bathroom to her house some twenty years after she and her husband Van had built it. The City of Jackson completed its first public water system in 1907, and that significant civic project had made indoor plumbing attainable for older town houses as well as standard for new ones. In 1923, Janie's granddaughter Mary and her husband envisioned the back bedroom and its bath the ideal nursery for their little Mallets.

In July, Mary was called from the renovation just begun on the house. She was needed in Macon again. Hattie Lane, her injured leg almost completely healed, had decided that a vacation stay on St. Simon's Island was exactly what she and the children needed. She had asked Hattie Buttrill and motherless little niece Vera to accompany them. Harry, however, needed to be in Macon for summer school if he was to be up with his class in September. Who, but Mary, could oversee Harry's getting to school every morning—prepared, breakfasted, and encouraged? Mary wrote Hugh from Macon on July 12:

> The family got off in a cloud of dust . . . Miss Hattie and Vera were almost an hour late in arriving but the Brunswick train waited . . . I'm feeling powerful lonesome without you! It will be nice and quiet down here for the week-end but if you think you had "oughta" be at home, let me know and Harry and I will hie away Jacksonward . . .

Hugh's reply to the special delivery letter began with "George left for camp last night and I can't get off for the week-end." A progress report on their house renovations followed. The carpenter had completed his part of the new bathroom and was ready to begin lining one of the closets with cedar. The new window had been cut, and Hugh wrote that it "adds lots to the appearance of the parlor."

Mary and Harry drove up to Jackson in the Lane family Buick, and during the weekend there Mary inspected the work herself. They returned to Macon early Monday morning in time for Harry's class, and Mary wrote Hugh that she had let Harry drive because "he was so crazy to be able to say he drove from Jackson to Macon when he was only thirteen. The ride was beautiful." After a plea for Hugh to come down to see her on Wednesday, Mary concluded that letter with "B.L. just passed and waved most cordially just like he knew you were not here. Please be J!"

Hugh was a delegate to an all-day church conference in Thomaston that week and could not come to Macon. He had hoped that Mary would be with him. Of the two Jackson matrons who also represented the Jackson church at the meeting, Hugh wrote his wife that she need not "be J—whatever that is."

Throughout July daily letters connected Mary and Hugh between weekend reunions in Jackson. Mary described the Macon she had always loved as "absolutely dead with everybody I know away." McKibben had joined Linda and their little Sonny in Marietta where they were visiting her relatives.

After driving her brother to catch the northbound train, Mary wrote Hugh why she and McKibben would no longer be company and consolation for each other while both were separated from their mates. "The doctor told Kib he has malaria and ought to go right back up to Marietta and rest up for at least a week. I'm convinced that Jackson is healthier than Macon, especially in the summer. Harry is pecking on the typewriter trying to compose a letter to Mother. He is the most lovable little boy I know and is doing his best to take care of me."

In what may have been the final letter Mary wrote Hugh that summer, she asked her husband if she should look for a less expensive wallpaper. She had learned from the decorator that her first choice "would make the job cost $400 . . . I'm wanting to see how the house looks again and waiting to be with you!"

Hugh answered that he did not want them to choose a cheaper paper and then be dissatisfied."I miss you all the time . . . What is the surprise?"

Mary returned to Jackson with the announcement that the Hugh Mallets could begin getting ready for an anticipated March arrival of the first occupant of their newly painted and wallpapered nursery.

Family Expansions

Tuesday afternoon

Dearest Daddy,

Mama and I are feeling fine and looking forward to seeing you tomorrow.

Your loving daughter,
Mary Lane Mallet

Written in pencil on stationery headed OGLETHORPE PRIVATE INFIRMARY, that letter was addressed to Hugh Mallet in Jackson and postmarked Macon, April 8, 1924. It was his wife's first attempt to get thoughts into words and onto paper since their baby's birth more than a week before on March 30. On Wednesday morning, as soon as he received the letter, the new father responded.

Dearest Mama—

I am overjoyed this morning on account of your note and that you and Mary Lane are feeling fine and well enough to write a note. So I know you will be well enough to read this . . . just found that I have to go to Atlanta today at noon and probably won't get home until the late train and will have to postpone my trip until tomorrow night . . . with a heart full of love to you and the baby

Mary's next letter was written on Friday afternoon:

> My dear Hugh
>
> After your visit last night I dropped off to sleep thinking what a lucky girl I was to have such a husband and such a baby. Life has always held so much happiness for me and now it seems I have everything in the world to make me glad. Mary Lane has gained one ounce—probably from the joy of seeing you—and now weighs 8 lbs. 14 ozs.
>
> . . . Elizabeth Felton brought me some tulips and jonquils and went into ecstasies over our darling daughter . . . also I sat up an hour to add to the morning's activities. (Please excuse writing as I'm flat on my back.) Less than 30 hrs. and I'll be still happier 'cause you'll be here . . .

Mary's pregnancy had not been easy. She and Hugh were still selecting and arranging furniture and had just begun entertaining their friends in their own house when bleeding indicated a threatened miscarriage. Hattie insisted that she could best supply what the doctor ordered—almost complete bed rest—as well as proximity to doctor and hospital.

Mary had been moved to her mother's house in Macon. Hugh, back in his mother's house in Jackson, again became a visiting, letter-writing husband.

> . . . I know you are in the best possible place but wish I could be with you . . . I go by the house two or three times a day to feed the dog and look in to see if Dr. Van [the renter] is behaving. If he pulls a party I want to be in on it . . .

In that letter Hugh enclosed receipts for taxes he had paid on Lane holdings in Butts County, which he asked Mary to give to McKibben, the lawyer son who had become his mother's financial advisor and manager. Hugh wrote that he had also paid the taxes "due on your house."

Mary replied immediately that her mother had written a reimbursement check and asked her to "send it on to you with many thanks for your valued and esteemed services et cetera . . . You made a mistake in writing that you paid the taxes on 'your house' when you should have said 'our.' I accept your apologies."

Two days before the birth of their daughter, Mary wrote her husband that she was feeling "pretty good" and hoped he was not worried about her.

> . . . of course husbands have to work to support growing families and you've been fine to come down as often as you have. How glad we'll be to start keeping house together again soon! Our baby will make it better than ever and even tho he will be a third party, he won't make it a crowd . . .

It would be more than a month, however, before the new parents and their baby girl would be together in their own house. After Mary and the baby had spent eighteen days in the hospital, Hugh arrived—not to take them home with him but to drive them to the Lane house in Macon and return to Jackson alone. Mary wrote him that night.

> Dearest—
>
> This is the life!. . . as there are no rules against spoiling the mother I'm accepting petting from everybody in the house. . . our baby has been as sweet as possible . . . slept all afternoon. . . had dinner in my room after which I went to bed and to sleep while Mother read to me. I just got up to eat supper and while up to send this line to you . . . not much company today . . . Mrs. Neel came by . . . Frances Mathews brought her son by for a few minutes and gave Mary Lane a pair of white shoes, the smallest yet. Mrs. Clark and Mrs. Baldwin came in for a little visit . . .
>
> . . . rest assured that I'm going to be cautious and take the best possible care of the baby and myself. Look out for your own dear self until I can get back on the job. . .

"Love, Mary" filled the page to the very bottom edge, but before sealing the letter, Mary returned to the first page and wrote on the top margin, "I have you here in miniature 'cause really she does look just like her daddy tonight."

Hugh was far from idle during Mary's long stay in Macon. To running his own feed, seed, and fertilizer business, managing Mallet and Lane farms, and being caretaker of their home during his wife's absence, he had added active involvement in the completion of the new Methodist Church and parsonage. He had been appointed to the building committee before his marriage to Mary. Throughout the year and a half since, planning and watching over construction had been major concerns for Hugh and, therefore, Mary.

Without any pressure at all from him, Mary had decided to join the church where Hugh and his family were devoted, active members. She could leave the denomination into which she had been baptized without much alteration in the practice of her faith. The big, stained glass window in the new church would be before her every time she opened her front door, every time she sat on her front porch. Her closest neighbors would be the progression of Methodist ministers and their families inhabiting the parsonage. She could anticipate the probability that Mallet children and theirs would be playmates and friends.

On Monday afternoon, May 4, 1924, she wrote the father of their first child, who at five weeks old had yet to sleep in her parent's house across the street from the church.

> Just read in the *Telegraph* that our new church will hold its first service Sunday and you know we want to be there. So for that and one other reason, I've decided we can come back home Saturday . . . Mother doesn't like for us to leave her at all. However, guess she will go up and stay until Sunday with us. Now this is my plan . . .

The rest of the letter detailed it. Hugh was to arrive in his car on Thursday night or early Friday morning and drive back to Jackson on Saturday with the car loaded with his wife, baby, mother-in-law, and Frances—Mary's Jackson household "help," who had been taken to Macon when Mary and the baby left the hospital for the Lane house.

> . . . I'll have my trunk all packed so you can check it thru Friday afternoon and we'll celebrate by attending vaudeville or a Macon ball game in the aft and go with Mother and Linda and Kib to the open meeting of the Music Club Friday night. It's an annual affair . . . I've already accepted Mother's invitation for us both.
>
> Then early Sat. morning you and the Baby and I on the front seat and Mama and Frances and the grips and bandboxes in the back, will leave here and arrive in Jackson in time for Frances to cook dinner before the heat of the day sits in. I believe it will be better for us to go thru the country instead of on the train (and incidentally I have no traveling costume.) The baby can lie on a big pillow. I'll have time to stock up the pantry for the week-end and get things running smoothly while you do your regular Saturday finish-up work.
>
> Does this plan suit you? If so, Georgia Anne can go right ahead and clean up our house under "Sister's" supervision and I hope you'll be

> able to finish up the work on the "grounds." Now that you've gone and I've already started missing you, I'm getting really pepped up over the prospect of returning. I wish we could have Allegra or Gussie or somebody come in every morning and clean up and wash and iron while Frances helps me bathe the baby and cook. I gave the bath this morning and managed better than I expected. Hope you'll O.K. my plan, especially the holiday celebration.
>
> Excuse scribble. I'm nursing the baby while Frances does the washing.
>
> Love & kisses from your wife & daughter.
>
> *M.L.M.*

These many years later the pencil "scribble" is still legible. Her planned return probably went as she proposed. Our memories of "M.L.M." include ample evidence of the reality of what she called her "executive ability."

In Jackson, homecoming welcomes from the Mallet family were waiting for both Marys and much admiration for the newest member, who tiny as she was, clearly resembled her father. Family lore has it that Hugh proudly placed his daughter in his mother's outstretched arms with the instruction, "Be careful, Mama; don't drop her." Emma's response was, "I didn't drop you."

That homecoming was followed by months stretching into the years Mary was to describe as near perfection. As wife and mother, Mary set her will and imposed her ways to bring a new reality to Hugh's courtship word painting of an idealized picture of small town life. Their early married time and space of content withstood its first invasion when little Mary contracted pneumonia. While their baby struggled for breath without the pediatric wonder drugs still years in the future, Mary was able to exhibit a practical strength that neither she nor anybody else had seen before. With her first child's full recovery, she showed, too, an awareness of everything that made her ordinary Jackson days good—from pouring Hugh's first cup of coffee in the morning to rocking and singing their baby to sleep in the evening.

Hugh did say, though, as Mary managed to squeeze frequent trips to Macon into their schedules, that every time they reached that city's north boundary area of Vineville he saw his wife on the outskirts of paradise.

In October of 1925, citizens of Butts County marked the hundred years since its founding with two days of centennial celebration. The entire Mallet family were supporters or participants along with most of the population of little Butts, whose farthest reaches were little more than ten miles from the courthouse in Jackson, the centrally located county seat. George was one of the masters of ceremonies. Joel crowned Miss Virginia White, daughter of a Flovilla doctor, the Queen of the Centennial. Hugh and Mary contributed far less visible committee service with Mary lending her energies and background to the music and pageant groups.

They also were hosts to a number of out-of-town visitors, including Mary's mother. That Butts County native, Hattie McKibben Lane, began her poem about the occasion with "Oh, 'twas splendid to have been there. . ."

The front porch of the McKibben-Lane-Mallet house provided excellent Third Street viewing for the opening parade. Among the floats admired by the group there was a reproduction of a log cabin, the kind of dwelling built by some of the earliest White settlers in the area that became Butts County. Hugh saw the little cabin as playhouse for his daughter. After the parade ended, he bought it and had it moved to the side yard beneath the shading branches of a big pecan tree. Little Mary was soon stepping through its door. Over the next decade, she was followed by three more Mallet sisters who prepared and served mock tea parties to dolls and playmates before their playhouse was moved into the backyard. There it became the entrance to a "secret" underground cave that had required days of determined digging of Hugh Mallet Jr. and his fellow adventurer, the preacher's son from across the street.

On September 11, 1926, again in Macon at Oglethorpe Infirmary, Mary gave birth to a second daughter. Black-haired, blue-eyed, even-tempered Mary Lane had a sturdy, reddish-blond, curly-haired, tantrum-prone sister; and Mary and Hugh had two very different little girls. They had given the first her mother's given and family names, and in the Southern way she was often called by both of them. This second daughter is the author of this memoir. I was named for my father's first wife, Jane Ellis Stanfield, and for her mother, Anne Ellis Stanfield, and christened Jane Anne. Young Jane, who died before she could become a mother, was the last direct descendant of the Ellis-Stanfield line. Hugh, his second wife

Mary, and their children were considered family by Robert and Anne Stanfield and by her childless brother and sister for as long as they lived.

There were no complications before or after my birth, and Mary returned home without a lengthy Macon stay. It was in Jackson that she was finding growing satisfaction in marriage, motherhood, and house-keeping as she combined them her way.

A cook took what could have been drudgery out of meal preparation. Throughout the 1920s and 1930s, the cook, Mary, and her household depended on a black, wood-burning iron stove for cooking and more. Hot water for kitchen and basement sinks and four bathrooms was supplied from the water tank connected to the kitchen stove. So its fire, demanding constant tending and feeding from innumerable arm loads of wood carried up the high back steps to the wood box, was seldom allowed to go out. In winter the kitchen and adjoining breakfast room meant warmth and com-fort; in summer, heat and sweat. There was no electric refrigerator for Mary's kitchen until the mid 1930s, but the Jackson Ice Corporation, for seventy cents a block, delivered ice regularly for the wooden refrigerator on the back porch. Except for electricity and running water, supplied and sold to its citizens by the City of Jackson, and her grandmother's pantry converted into a breakfast nook, Mary managed a kitchen little changed from what it had been under Janie McKibben's supervision in the last decade of the nineteenth century.

Mary and Hugh had made the rest of the house, with very few struc-tural alterations, lighter and brighter. A housemaid who also helped with the children relieved Mary of some of the most monotonously tiring aspects of housekeeping. Mary had absorbed much of her philosophy of that female occupation from her mother. Its entire purpose was to make a mere dwelling the place a woman, her husband, and their children want-ed to be or to come back to when necessity or desire led them elsewhere. They must find comfort and what they most enjoyed and loved there, and their friends must find welcome. Wesleyan's "domestic science," as Mary called her college home economics course, and her family position as old-est daughter and sister had provided training and internship.

Miss Hattie Buttrill dropped by almost daily to "look in" on Mary, the daughter of her lifelong friend. Years later, Mary was to tell and retell us about one of her visits. On a spring afternoon, after Hat had found the front porch and hall empty, she responded to Mary's called out invitation to "come on back." In the bathroom behind the nursery, the impeccably groomed maiden lady found the obviously pregnant Mary on her knees beside the big claw-footed tub where Mary Lane and Jane Anne were splashing through their bath. "It looks like to me," the caller observed to our damp mother, "you need a bigger apron instead of a college diploma for what you're doing now." Mary seemed proud to recall and to pass on her response: "This job calls for everything I know and has me trying to learn more."

In her own house, on June 20, 1928, Mary's third daughter was delivered by a Jackson doctor assisted by a "trained nurse" driven up from Macon. Mary had not wanted to leave Hugh and their two children for days in a hospital more than forty miles away. "After all," she said, "having babies is the most natural thing in the world."

The name for the new baby—Harriet Emily—was chosen to honor both grandmothers: Hattie and Emma. She would be called Emily or "Em." Hattie Buttrill's complete given name was Harriet Emily. Unmarried, childless Hat now had a namesake whom she singled out for special attention and gifts. She was more than half serious when she asked Mary to just let her have Emily since she and Hugh already had two other girl children.

Mary loved children, welcoming each of her own with abundant mother's milk, rocking, smiles, and singing. She never admitted having favorites, but the most recent baby naturally received the most constant care. Baby Emily seemed to have been born with a happy goodness and appealing charm that turned baby tending into pleasure.

Husband, children, and housekeeping did not prevent Mary's fitting into town and county civic and social life. She accepted an invitation to join the newly organized Jackson Garden Club. Limiting its membership to twelve so that meetings could be held in the members' homes, the club was as much social as horticultural. Its official purpose was learning about the cultivation of trees, shrubs, and flowers and beautifying their community and their private homes and garden with them, but the monthly afternoon meetings meant more than programs about plants and flower arranging and voting on the next civic project. Designated hostesses performed major housekeeping and sometimes persuaded husbands to agree to a bit of redecorating. Member guests had an occasion to wear their best clothes, which could lead to a survey of new merchandise at the two main emporiums on the town square—The New York Store and The Star Store—or even to a shopping expedition in Macon or Atlanta. Evening supper parties to which husbands were invited were annual events. The garden club "girls" and their families were our mother Mary's friends for as long as they and she lived.

With Hugh, who served on Jackson's Board of Education, Mary was intensely interested in school issues. Little Mary Lane had been allowed to join the children who walked daily by their house and down one block of McKibben Avenue to reach the red brick, two story building just across College Street from their barn lot. That edifice was school to Jackson students from first grade through high school graduation. Miss Annie Lou McCord, the already legendary first grade teacher, persuaded Hugh and Mary that their five-year-old oldest daughter was ready for her instruction. Besides, her early enrollment would bring Miss Annie Lou's class roll up to the desirable number of twelve. My sister Mary remembered that she was given a desk by the window so that she could see home from her first seat in academia.

In January of 1930, our Mother spoke to the county branch of the Georgia Education Association at its meeting in nearby Jenkinsburg on a subject dear to her. The *Jackson Progress Argus* reported that "Mrs. Hugh Mallet delivered an interesting talk on the background and value of public school singing. This discussion was pitched on a high plane and stressed the esthetic value of music in the life of the student. The community is fortunate to have a so highly cultured personality as Mrs. Mallet and one who so generously serves in all forward movements."

A few months later, the "forward movement" most important to Mary was happening in her own home. On Sunday morning, September 7, 1930, while their fellow Methodists were gathering for worship in the church across the street, Mary and Hugh had reason for grateful praise at home. Their son had just been born, and Mary was resting from labor. Their Jackson doctor, again assisted by a nurse imported from Macon, had safely delivered a perfect baby, healthy Hugh Mallet Jr.

With the crash of New York's Wall Street stock market the year before, the whole nation had been shaken into the first year of the

Depression. As part of Georgia's agricultural economy, the Mallets and their farming neighbors were faced with plummeting prices for their crops and a bleak financial outlook. But troubling money matters could not cloud the joy of the arrival of a male child for Hugh and Mary as the extended Mallet family rejoiced with them. Although we daughters never heard from our parents or anybody else any expression of disappointment that we had not been boys, we somehow knew that our brother, although not loved or valued more, was special.

Emma Mallet already had seven grandchildren: Annie had three—two girls and a boy; Joel, whose marriage to Helen had ended in divorce, had daughter Barbara, but the son he was to have from his marriage to Maria was still a year into the future; and Hugh was father to the three little girls who spent the morning of their brother's birth playing in her backyard. When that grandmother held baby Hugh in her arms, she could give thanks for her first grandchild with the possibility of passing on the Mallet surname.

Three years later on another September morning (September 28, 1933), distinctive heraldry announced the birth of a fourth daughter. For this lying-in, our experienced mother chose an upstairs bedroom where she and the new baby could be somewhat separated from the often noisy activity below. So our father led us four older children in a little procession up the backstairs to see our baby sister for the first time. In the middle of the room across the hall from the one where our mother was resting, there she was—a little doll-person with black (soon to be blond) hair and blue Mallet eyes, open and peering up from a white wooden cradle that had been borrowed from garden club friend Ruth Settle. In quiet repose, she seemed to be awaiting admiration and awe. At age seven, without knowing those words, this memoir writer possessed both.

On the sidewalk below, school children and teachers were walking past our house to school. Hearing and seeing them through the open window, three-year-old Hugh ran out onto the upstairs balcony where he shouted an invitation down to the passers by: "Come see Teenie! Come see our Teenie Weenie!" Several of them, including first grade teacher Miss Annie Lou, did.

We learned later that the baby's name was Marcia. Mother had chosen that name because it combined syllables of the names of all four of her sisters, including the two who had died as toddlers but whom she remembered—Lucia and Eugenia. Marcia was the namesake of all her Lane aunts—Margaret, Lucia, Eugenia, and Virginia.

THE MALLET BROOD COMES TO TOWN headed a "Lotta Slips" column in the *Macon Telegraph* after Mary's first visit to her hometown accompanied by her husband and their complete set of five little Mallets:

> . . . a peep of Mary Lane Mallet, the wife of Hugh and Hugh himself and their gorgeous brood. They had motored down from Jackson for the day to show Mrs. Andrew W. Lane how well the six-week-old baby is getting along.
>
> When I saw them, the back seat of the car was filled with children and Mary had the baby in her arms. With a broad, proud smile, Mary nodded her head to the back seat and said: "They are all ours. The next time we come we are going to bring a trailer." There are just five children all together, so, of course, you see, Mary was joking. There are four girls and one boy. And all of them grand looking.

In a Decade of Depression

"SISTER," VIRGINIA TOLD MARY, "YOUR ETERNAL OPTIMISM is just too much. If somebody's got double pneumonia or any other awful thing, you're apt to say it's the best kind to cure." That youngest sister, herself a red-haired seeker of a bright side, could sometimes find Mary's outlook exasperating. So could the rest of her family.

Mary's justification and her explanation for rose-tinting reality was a quotation from the Old Testament Psalms with which she identified: "My lines have fallen in pleasant places. I have a goodly heritage." She also might remind nay-sayers of a motto her mother Hattie had penned and recommended: "Blend the Ideal with the Real."

During the early years of her marriage, the ideal that Mary had envisioned for herself—happiness as wife and mother and enthusiastic participant in the life around her—seemed to be fulfilled. In the 1930s, economic hard times were "the real" for the nation, the South, and the Mallet family. As Mary Lane of Macon and young Mrs. Hugh Mallet of Jackson, she had seldom, if ever, actually worried about money. She had simply taken for granted that there would be enough of it. In the 1930s when there was not, she managed to make do and do without. Life went on. Mary's own words in a letter to her sister Margaret describe the ideal part of it preserved in a blend with Mallet daily doings.

Margaret, eleven years younger than Mary, was living in St. Louis, with her Midwestern corporate engineer husband and their two little boys. Remembering that Margaret would be celebrating her twenty-fifth birthday on June 25, Mary wrote her a long letter.

June 21, 1932 Jackson, Georgia

Dear Margaret:

Emily celebrated her birthday yesterday and reminded me that "your day" comes next. Blackman Settle and Howell Heflin, the new Methodist preacher's son, have the same birthday so the Settles, Heflins, and Mallets with Miss Hattie had picnic supper at the Springs after an afternoon swim in the pool. You won't recognize Indian Springs on your next visit. The state is spending $5000 there, building a huge spring house and piping the water a short distance. We'll miss dipping it up the old-fashion way. This afternoon the children will go to Frances Harper's birthday party. Tomorrow we return to the Springs for the Methodist picnic and Thursday Miss Hattie is taking Emily and me to Atlanta. She has talked for a year about having Emily's picture taken so she is giving her her own photograph for a present. Emily is such a darling, decidedly the most winsome of any of my children but I guess the tender age of four found all the girls just as sweet. Jane Anne will enter school in the fall and Mary will be in the Fourth Grade. She made an average of 95 for this year's work.

We had a long siege of measles followed by swollen glands and Jane Anne had a terrible time with boils on her arms and face. The scars are still there and I worry about them continually but think they are gradually growing dimmer. Hugh Jr. is a regular boy, pushes Emily on her velocipede, rides a billy-goat, holds cats and dogs, and climbs everywhere. He weighs 34 lbs. and is rosy-cheeked and lovely—well proportioned now that he has grown taller.

Mary and Jane Anne are waiting to take this to the P.O. Mary says to hurry and bring Stanley and Malcolm "up here." It's a long way down here and we sure do want to see all of the Moores. Please send a kodak of the baby. I can appreciate the many reasons why you don't write but am anxious to hear how you manage. Be sure to get enough rest yourself and save your strength because a growing child demands more and more thought and care. Our big yard is a constant joy. With the acting bar and rings, two rope swings, a long comfortable swing, several new benches and lawn chairs, the out-doors holds us all day. The play-house has a new load of sand and Sonny plays by himself long hours at a time while I mend or read. The long summer days are fine in Jackson when we take a nap after dinner and get a fresh start. We need a new car along with many other necessities but see no prospect of getting anything soon. The trouble is to hold on to what we have with taxes so high. Hugh manages to get along and keep us going the same old usual cheerful way and all I hear of the depression is what I hear from others. I know he has last year's cotton on hand yet and refuses to sell at this low price. He is proud of a five acre carrot patch that is bringing in more cash than cotton has in several years. I manage the local sales and Hugh sells by car and truck loads. Of course we eat them every day. Carrots make a pretty dish when boiled whole and un-peeled like squash, then scooped out and seasoned and toasted bread crumbs added and served like croquettes. My black-berry acid turned out fine and I wish you had some. Give Stanley plenty of lemonade.

Can you believe that I weigh nearly 135? I look much better and feel fine. I haven't done a thing to reduce, simply convinced that when I wasn't nursing a baby I would return to my normal size. We have been home almost once a week lately.

Virginia and Mother are coming up when they choose but both seem lothe to leave Macon. Virginia grows prettier all the time but I continue to hear that Margaret is the prettiest one of the Lanes. Your picture with your babies was very good. Now, I've been talking about me and mine exclusively and what I must hear is about you and yours. May you have a happy birthday and the whole new year be overflowing with God's richest blessings.

Love from all the little Mallets and Hugh and I send best wishes to you and Earl.

Sister

We found the letter in Mother's keepsakes. Aunt Margaret had returned it to her with the following lines written at the bottom of it:

May 17-'57—"Long, long ago—long ago"—I have been reading and discarding some long-possessed letters—brings yesterday into today. Thought this reminiscing would be enjoyed by you and your family—No new news here. A wet, wet Spring but delightfully green—

Love,
Margaret

Years after Aunt Margaret returned Mother's letter, I sometimes mix my own reminiscences with its contents. In sleepless hours between midnight and dawn, I restore Third Street as it was in the 1930s of my childhood. First, I get rid of the traffic lights at the Covington Street corner. We Mallet children crossed Third Street there to trudge or skip along Covington to our destination—Mama Mallet's house. We were not intimidated by this century's timber trucks and fume belching eighteen wheelers. In those days, traffic was light and mostly local. Automobiles were most apt to be Ford or Chevrolet, seldom new. There was an occasional roadster with a sporty rumble seat and even a luxurious chauffeur-driven Buick belonging to one of the town's well-to-do dowagers. Drivers had no need for red and green lights to prioritize right-of-way. Drivers were patient, too, when they shared town streets with mule wagons loaded with cotton and headed for the gin. After the traffic lights, next to go were every one of the filling stations, fast food restaurants, and other late-coming intruders. Sparing only our old house and the Methodist Church across the street, I bulldoze them all with the concrete in which they are imbedded, the signs which advertise them, and the billboards that tower above them.

Next come the challenge and the fun—rebuilding the neighborhood. The trees come first. Again I have oaks and elms lining the unpaved sidewalks and arching over the street. Then meticulously, careful with bannister railings and gingerbread trims, I put the houses back. I plant front lawns and shrubbery, remembering the Slaton's oleander at the Indian Springs Street corner. On all the porches I replace the rocking chairs and hang swings on several of them. At Miss Liza and Miss Maggie Curry's house and at "Miss" Gertrude's, I step inside and arrange the furniture. There is little of that at Miss Viola Slaughter's where Mary and I had piano lessons. Her Steinway grand is recital ready again as is the upright that suffered my assault on Schubert. Miss Viola told me that my rendition of "Hark, Hark the Lark" would make Schubert turn over in his grave. I intend to work my way as far east on Third Street as the Depot Street corner before returning to McKibben Street and rebuilding in the opposite direction all the way to the Courthouse Square.

The following more-than-memory miracle came to me, though, in the sunlight of a late September afternoon shortly after I became the legal owner of our old house. Attending to routine chores, I had checked on work of the hired lawn maintenance man, cleared the walks of tossed drink cans and hamburger boxes from Burger King and McDonald's, and swept the porches. All was well. I walked down the drive to the backyard, remembering how the pecan and cottonwood trees had shaded our swings and log playhouse. Then through a magic golden haze, I saw—really saw, not just remembered—our backyard as it was only once for the greatest September celebration ever, the Mallet circus party.

September was a grand month when we were children. It was a money month. Cotton picking had begun, and cash, a little or a lot, circulated through planters, gin and warehouse owners, the merchants on the square, tenant farmers, and field hands. Children often picked cotton, too. Working after school or staying out for days or weeks, they might have a few coins of their own to jingle. One-ring circuses and cheap carnivals with wheezing merry-go-rounds and sleazy sideshows came to town. In our family, September meant even more. Four of us had birthdays: Hugh Jr.'s, the seventh; mine, the eleventh; Daddy's, the sixteenth; and baby Marcia's, the twenty-eighth.

But the year was 1935—smack in the middle of the Great Depression. Cash flow in Jackson that year was hardly a trickle. Cotton was so cheap that again Daddy didn't want to sell. Still, September called for celebration.

I seem to hear again the lilting enthusiasm in Mother's voice as I overheard her enlisting Daddy's participation in her plan. "This is the ideal year to celebrate all the birthdays together. September usually has wonderful weather for an outdoor party—a circus party. Peanuts and popcorn and lemonade won't cost much."

This is what they planned together and what they brought off. That I saw it all again so clearly so many years later on another golden September afternoon was only a minor miracle. Right in our backyard, there it all was once more—tents, balloons, a circus ring with a performing horse and rider, wonders behind the flaps of the side show tents, and children of all ages. It was glorious!

I know a little of how it came to be. Uncle George, a colonel in the Georgia National Guard, arranged for Daddy to get the tents. Our oldest boy cousin, Jimmy Watts, was the fearless bareback rider on Julia, the Mallet pony that was kept at the dairy farm. The Wild Man from Borneo, loose in our midst, was big Sam Compton, a teenaged neighbor with somebody's hearth rug slung over one bare shoulder. The Dionne

Quintuplets, stars of every newsreel since their birth the year before, had been transported from Canada. I recognized their nurse who told us so. Miss Hattie Buttrill had abandoned her everyday role of wealthy spinster of the Daughters of the Confederacy to don a white dress and her maid's starched cap and stand at the tent opening with a finger to her lips, demanding a quiet nap time for her five little dolls. In the next tent, an exotic gypsy with piercing eyes, wearing dangling earrings and the fringed scarf off the piano, read the palms of anyone daring to face what the future might hold. "Miss Ruby" Compton, Sam's mother, was the fortune teller. Who could have been better qualified? Hadn't she, just a few years earlier, been the first woman to cast a ballot in Butts County? And did she not continue to spread humor and zest after years of marriage to Cousin Clarence, who appeared to me to have the glummest face on Third Street?

Mother had invited all the children we knew. But there was plenty of pink lemonade dipped from big tubs on tables set under the trees, plenty of roasted peanuts from the farmer's market, plenty of popcorn.

1935 was a grave, critical year. In Germany and Italy, Hitler and Mussolini had wrested their dictatorships from economic chaos and were forcing national pride with uniforms and goose-stepped parades of military might. In the United States of America, President Roosevelt was bringing his New Deal to Depression woes and using radio broadcast "fireside chats" to restore confidence and hope. And in Jackson (population 2,000), we Mallets celebrated our September birthdays—Hugh Jr.'s fifth, my ninth, Daddy's forty-third, and Marcia's second—with a circus party. It didn't cost much.

Dealing With Death

On Monday evening, March 6, 1939, Hugh Mallet died of a heart attack. On Tuesday morning, March 7, in the bedroom she had shared with him, my suddenly widowed mother gathered her five children around her. "Little" Mary was almost fifteen; I was twelve; Emily, ten; Hugh Jr., eight; and Marcia, five. Mother said, "All night I've prayed over and over 'Thy will be done.' This morning I want you to know we'll be all right. If we just stick together, we'll be all right."

As our house filled up with people and flowers and the most food I had ever seen in it, I could not believe that anything could ever be all right again—not unless I could wake up from an awful nightmare. I could not. But Mary Lane Mallet, surrounded by Macon Lanes and shocked, grief-stricken Mallets, was able to bring and perhaps find for herself a kind of order in arranging and participating in the rituals of death. This is how I remember those for my father.

All Tuesday afternoon and evening, wearing his best suit and his favorite blue tie, he lay beneath the parlor mantel in an open casket. Mother's friends, one or two at a time, stood in the hall by the front door and directed the stream of callers who poured into our house. Everybody we knew must have come, I thought, and many I did not recognize. They stood before the coffin and then proceeded to our mother, who scarcely left the parlor throughout the afternoon and evening. Sometimes we children joined her as she accepted the sympathy expressed by the callers. Together and separately we stood with her by the casket or sat with her on the damask loveseat near the closed piano. We heard words about God and faith and "a better place." We heard talk from men and women about the man they knew and would miss. We heard declarations of willingness to help in any way at all. We saw tears in the eyes of women and men, too, who did not say anything—just took our mother's hand or put their arms around her. Later in the evening, after most of the visitors left, several other men came who would sit up all night with the body of their friend.

The next morning as the courthouse clock struck eleven, we family members were lined up behind the pallbearers for the procession that crossed Third Street where traffic (never heavy in 1939) had been stopped. We marched across the paved court and up the high, wide church steps (changed in later remodeling) and continued down the aisle to the front pews reserved for us in the crowded sanctuary. Between us and the altar was the casket, blanketed with red roses, Daddy's favorite flowers. Those he cultivated himself as a backyard hobby would not be blooming for two months.

There was music. The pipe organ planned for the church was still years into the future, but Mother had asked her classical musician sister-in-law to play the piano. Hymns were sung; passages of scripture were read. I do not remember which ones. Neither do I remember the words of the prayers or the eulogies delivered by three ministers—our present pastor and two former ones. They doubtless said what we already knew: that Hugh Mallet was good—good at living. Then, as Aunt Linda Lane played the recessional, we were directed to follow the casket and pall bearers up the aisle and down the steps. Mr. Harkness Thornton's hearse was waiting for the casket, and cars behind it waited for us. Loaded in them, we followed the hearse to Jackson's City Cemetery.

There, at the age of forty-seven, Hugh Mallet would be buried, but not in the plot we passed where a granite shaft lettered MALLET rose above the graves of William Maurice and Emma Nutt. Less than a year before, we had stood there when our grandmother had been laid beside the grandfather that we never knew. William Maurice had died unexpectedly in mid-life, as had our father; his son Hugh had lost his father when he was eight years old—only months older than his own son would be. Below my grandparents' tombstones was the granite cradle of their little boy, dead before his second birthday. Below that was the tombstone of their young adult son Harold. In that family plot, separated from those on either side by low marble partitions, space had to be left for Harold's widow and for Pauline. Other family branches would need other plots.

Uncle George already had a plot, bought in 1915 when the only child he and Aunt Minnie were to have died at birth. While his wife was still struggling for her own life, George had asked Hugh to go with him and the undertaker for the burial there of his infant son. Twenty-four years later, George asked Mary to bury Hugh in this plot, which had plenty of space for the two brothers and their wives.

Mary agreed. For the first year of her marriage, while she and Hugh had lived in the Mallet home, George and Minnie, along with Emma and Pauline, had welcomed her. Mother Earth's final reception of those two Mallet brothers and their wives would follow the hospitable accommodations of Mama Mallet.

On the day of Hugh's funeral, Mary's absent sister Margaret wrote from St. Louis:

> Dearest Sister,
>
> I have been thinking today of the happy years you and Hugh have known since that fall day you were married at home—your face was so radiant . . . the hurry and bustle to get to the train and on to New York City . . . Year after year since have added joy . . . You knew the man you were marrying and Hugh never deviated . . . so sweet, so calm, so helpful, so hospitable. I enjoyed being with him especially on my last two visits . . . you and Hugh and the children arriving at Linda's last summer, each of you looking so happy and gay and dressed up . . . Of course Hugh will always be with you in five pairs of blue eyes, ten hurrying feet, happy gleeful voices—always and always.
>
> . . . Your mem'ry world will be such a contented one to live in—and that is one of life's greatest blessings . . . "all loved women, greatly loved women, derive their beauty from their inner fire" and you are one of those!
>
> . . . I wish I could be one third as good a sister to you as you have always been to me. Please write me any problems you have that I might possibly help with and write me often of the children's accom-

> plishments . . . It is hard not to be with you . . . I feel so far away from you—yet mighty close 'cause I love—love—love you.
>
> *Margaret*

Mary kept Margaret's letter as intact as the memories it described, but she could not afford to live in a memory world of content. The five pairs of Mallet blue eyes and ten feet made demands. So did money and business matters. Decisions harder than those she had made for Hugh's funeral and burial were waiting. Looking back, I see us children determining almost every decision, every action. Without Daddy, how could she decide what was best for us collectively and separately? Without him, how could she make it happen?

During the next week, with her four oldest back in school and care arranged for preschool Marcia, Mary was sitting behind Hugh's desk, which for the coldest of the winter months had been moved into the library-sitting room of our house. There, surrounded by files, correspondence, documents, ledgers, and innumerable miscellaneous papers she assumed managerial responsibility for the financial affairs of herself and her children. It was an exhausting undertaking, but throughout the process she had the assistance and often the presence, too, of Hugh's brothers and hers. She respected and listened to their opinions before making her own decisions. She rejected outright the suggestion that she consider moving back to Macon and into her mother's house. Besides family support and advice, she had that of the Butts County farmer Rupert Washington, who was working for Hugh as farm overseer and general assistant.

Hugh had left a complicated farm and farm business juggling act without its central performer. Throughout the Depression, which was finally coming to an end, he had managed and kept in operation hundreds of acres of Mallet and Lane farms while he himself owned separately only a small tract of rich creek bottom land. There, often experimenting with cultivation techniques, he grew vegetables that were trucked to the Atlanta Farmers Market. Most of his personal income came from other sources. From a little office—the walled off front section of his warehouse—located just off the town square, he dealt in feed, seed, and fertilizers. When his oldest daughter asked what her teacher should write on her student card in the space marked for "Occupation of Parent or Guardian," he said, "tell her I'm an agriculturist, and that's spelled f-a-r-m-e-r."

In early 1939, Hugh was concentrating on selling commercial grade molasses to dairy farmers to be mixed with other cattle food for increased milk production. He had the heavy, black, sweet stuff shipped in rail tank cars from Savannah to Mallet-owned property at the end of Covington Street. There it was stored in a concrete pit until delivered in fifty-five gallon drums to dairy customers throughout Middle Georgia. Hugh had located them, come to know them, and called on them personally. When weather and their separate responsibilities permitted, Mary, often with preschool Marcia, liked to make the rounds with him. He said they helped him "peddle molasses."

On the evening of his death, however, he had just returned alone after a day of collection calls. Another tank car was waiting to be unloaded. A delay in paying for its contents and returning it empty to Savannah would be costly.

Responsibility for the Mallet and Lane farms, so recently Hugh's, must be delegated immediately because spring planting was at hand. George, whose dairy occupied many Mallet acres, assumed management of the farms and other properties, too, which since matriarch Emma's death the year before, were part of the yet unsettled Mallet estate.

With overseer Rupert Washington staying on, Lane farms could be worked primarily by tenants, each of whom had a separate share-cropping arrangement. Mary announced that she herself would continue Hugh's thriving molasses business. She was familiar with some aspects of it, and Mr. Washington, with experience gained from working with Hugh, agreed to assist her.

Louis, Mary's younger brother, now separated from his wife in Chicago and living with Hattie in Macon, volunteered to move in with Mary temporarily to help in any way he could while both of them represented their mother's interests in her considerable Butts County holdings.

At thirty-eight, Louis possessed three degrees from Mercer University; a pleasant voice he could accompany on guitar, mandolin, or ukulele or blend harmoniously with any assortment of singers; and an enormous, ever swelling stock of stories and jokes. His affable, easy-going disposition and outgoing personality had been social and selling career assets. But he had next to no knowledge of cotton farming besides the facts that it produced the raw material of the textiles he had sold and that it was the source of much of his mother's now dwindling income lavished on the upbringing and education of her children. Of Hugh's business he knew even less. What he offered was availability and willingness to learn.

Mary, leaning on Mr. Washington and Hugh's brothers while she and Louis were propping each other, returned the empty tank car to Savannah, its contents paid for and likely to be promptly sold. She had prepared and mailed bills, made collections, and assured customers that the Mallet molasses business would continue. One of those customers included the following note with her payment:

> My dear Mrs. Mallet:
>
> You are so sensible to take up the work just as Mr. Mallet left it. That, to me, is the only way we can stand up under such grief. I forget from time to time but if this check is not correct please notify me.You certainly have my understanding sympathy during these trying days.
>
> Sincerely,
> *Lucie R. Martin*

Under Mary's management, Hugh's molasses peddling continued to show a profit—enough to meet current personal expenses without drawing on the life insurance principal she intended to keep as a reserve.

After months of separation, Louis's wife Lillian joined him in Jackson. Mary, usually a model of hospitality, did little to welcome her; but Louis, of course, was free to share with his wife the upstairs room and bath assigned to him, and a place was set for her when the family gathered at the table. Rising without Hugh to busier days than she had ever known, Mary did not stretch her time or tolerance to pave entry for her sister-in-law into family or Jackson social scenes. What Lillian did with her time was up to her. After getting up later than the rest of the household, Lillian chose to walk to the town square for breakfast at the café there. Back at the house, she played solitaire and smoked the cigarettes Mary disapproved. Lillian was different from all the other women—Lane or Mallet—we Mallet children had known. Her presence was one more of the changes since Daddy's death that required acceptance, not approval.

All through that hot Georgia summer, Louis worked and learned with and from Mary as they tackled their mother's farm and business affairs in Butts County. At summer's end, he had done what he could. He and Lillian left Jackson to return to urban life in the Midwest. Perhaps in that setting, familiar and more congenial to Lillian, the couple could mend their unraveling marriage. Perhaps a career opportunity, suited to his interest and abilities, waited there for Louis. Neither was to be the case.

The time had come for Mary to prove—first to herself—that she could stand on her own two feet. She knew her situation as widow and single parent was far from unique. Her grandmother, Janie, her mother Hattie, and her mother-in-law, Emma, had all been widowed in their forties. Within Mary's own special circle of friends, the twelve young matrons of the Jackson Garden Club, Hugh was the fourth husband to die during the span of one short year.

Two of the deaths had been by suicide. The Great Depression, even as it receded to make room for World War II, had continued to heap tragedy on little Jackson with the rest of the nation. Sylvia Carmichael would soon put her attractiveness and social skills to work as a hostess in military clubs crowded with World War II servicemen. Pretty, petite Gertrude Wright had been hired as a secretary by the Settle and Robison partnership formed by two other "Garden Club husbands." Mary would continue Hugh's business.

Her participation in male dominated business affairs came, too, with lessons she took no pleasure in learning. Even longtime associates could not always be trusted when there was advantage to be gained from an inexperienced woman's ignorance or neediness. Some debts owed Hugh would never be acknowledged or were claimed to be bookkeeping errors. Even worse was the assumption of a married man, considered Hugh's friend, that a lonely widow, approaching middle age, would be flattered by his invitations to "discreet" out-of-town lunches and dinners.

The self-confidence Mary had seemed to posses may have been threatened; it was never lost. She began developing tougher new strength to go with it. Mary Lane Mallet, wife of Hugh and mother of his five children, had become a widow, a single parent, and a business woman. Change would inevitably continue, but her adaptation to it would not be passive.

Beginning College Years for Five

WHILE MARY WAS STILL FINDING HER WAY THROUGH THE DEMANDS OF HER MOLASSES business and fitting them together with those of her family and home, World War II eliminated the business. When needed for manufacture of explosives, molasses would no longer be available for feeding contented cows. It had, however, already supplied her with two years of experience in providing independent financial support for herself and her children.

Marcia had started school and joined her older brother and sisters in their morning parade down one block of McKibben Street to College Street and the two-story brick building from which local academic learning was dispersed. Young Mary, the oldest, graduated from Jackson High School (in the same building as Marcia's first grade) and entered LaGrange College in the fall of 1940.

Mary had long assumed that her namesake daughter would follow her footsteps to Wesleyan. However, Hubert Quillian, Hugh's best friend since their Emory College days, had become president of another old Methodist college for women—LaGrange—in the little West Georgia city of the same name. Having started school at five, "Little" Mary was only sixteen when she was ready for college. Her mother and Dr. Quillian agreed that her father would want his first daughter's education entrusted to the friend who had remained through the years as close as a brother.

According to frequent letters and occasional calls, Mary was thriving at LaGrange. She had been there for more than a month when Mother learned the dates of her first weekend visit home. This memoir writer and second daughter remembers and confesses jealousy as preparations for a gala homecoming got underway. When I overheard a telephone order to the town café for two lemon chiffon pies to be ready for pick-up on the day of my sister's arrival, the stains of green envy had not yet faded from my recollection of preparation for her departure.

It seemed to me that the assembling of an entire wardrobe for the one of us widely recognized as family beauty had already dominated too much of the past summer. The Marys had made countless shopping expeditions to Atlanta followed by just as many sessions with the seamstress reputed to be Jackson's best. Throughout the Depression, clothes and fashion had been near the bottom of any list of Mother's priorities. But the former Mary Lane of Macon had known about and been known for them. The Wesleyan College yearbook described her with a quotation from Shakespeare himself: "The glass of fashion and the mold of form."

In September of 1940, before packing for LaGrange College, another young, slim Mary modeled results of weeks of mother-daughter shopping before an admiring extended family audience that included the older advisor and envious me.

No one of us Mallet girls had ever before owned so many clothes all at one time without a single garment of them having been worn by an aunt, a cousin, or a sister. From head to toe this Mallet collegiate Mary would be as well clad as the former Mary Lane could make her. A creamy beige, wide brimmed hat was the crowning accessory for a tailored wool suit worn with classic pumps. For classes and casual campus activities there were skirts and coordinated sweaters and blouses. Toes could wriggle comfortably in saddle oxfords or loafers right for them, but only flirtatious high heels would do for the special occasion outfit of wine-red velvet.

Freshman Mary arrived for her first home weekend in one of the new skirts and matching sweaters. What we wore made no difference, but we were ready. While mother Mary was occupied with house and kitchen management designed to ensure two days of comfort and pleasure, she had been unaware that I, as self-appointed director, was rehearsing Em, Hugh, and Marcia in a mock ceremony of sibling welcome. Before Mary reached the front steps, she could see us lined up on the porch. With our arms outstretched and our bodies respectfully bent, we burst into a loud rendition of the grandest hymn we knew. Its melody is the theme of the chorus climaxing Beethoven's Ninth Symphony— "Joyful, Joyful, We Adore Thee."

In May of 1944, Mary was wearing cap and gown as she measured her steps to a solemn processional rhythm. She flashed a smile as she passed a beaming single parent and me. Was it mere or marvelous coincidence that "Joyful, Joyful, We Adore Thee" was the graduation hymn for the LaGrange College class of 1944 of which she was president?

From the beginning of her college years, Mary gave Mother assurance that LaGrange was a good choice for her. She had long seemed to possess a natural skill for selecting and making friends, and it was no surprise that she was soon surrounded by attractive, congenial peers, including her roommate. Dorothy Allen—petite, blond, high-strung and promising pianist—had chosen LaGrange for its music program. College authorities had chosen her to share with Mary the best freshman accommodations, a big room on the first floor of a vintage Victorian dormitory. With high ceiling for pre-airconditioned seasons of Southern heat and a not-taken-for-granted luxury of a private bath, it had formerly been reserved for visiting dignitaries. As different as were black-haired, even-tempered Mary and blond, volatile Dorothy in appearance and personality, they chose to remain together. They met for the first time with bags and boxes of new clothes to be unpacked as soon as they could agree on division of closet and drawer space. They hugged goodbyes four years later with new diplomas.

Student Mary found college classes interesting but not overwhelming; that is, except for French. For problems and mediocre grades encountered there, she placed blame on the shoulders of her professor, proud native of La Belle, France, who was, Mary said, prejudiced against her from the first rollcall. Madame B. had declared then that our French immigrant great-grandfather had made a serious mistake in Anglicizing our surname Mallet. It should have continued to rhyme with "croquet" and not become an ordinary American wooden-headed hammer.

French classes were endured and passed. Other courses, especially in her history major, offered stimulation and enlightenment. As for benefits that came her way from being protegee of the college president, Mary admitted that she simply accepted, appreciated, and enjoyed them.

War, Weddings and More

On Sunday afternoon, December 7, 1941, sophomore Mary was being driven back to LaGrange by a Jackson soldier boyfriend, Ralph Carr. Drawing on her allowed class cuts and time off campus, she had arranged to spend the same weekend at home that Ralph had leave from Fort Jackson in Columbia, South Carolina. Immediately after his graduation from high school, he had joined the local National Guard unit. Then, as European war clouds began to darken America, too, the Guard had been called to active duty.

Weekend conversation for Mary both with her family and with Ralph had been weighted with war threats coming from Japan as well as Nazi Germany. Mary had seized opportunities to exhibit and pass on her newly acquired knowledge of world affairs and to quote her favorite professor's opinion that Japanese envoys already in Washington would doubtless reach agreement with our diplomats and avert a Pacific crisis—at least for the time being.

As their weekend was ending, Mary and Ralph were headed west on the narrow Georgia highway that connected their hometown with her college. Suddenly the music on the car radio was interrupted by a news bulletin: Japan, in sneak attack, had attacked the U.S. Pacific fleet anchored at Pearl Harbor in Hawaii.

At the homeplace Mary had just left, our family had scattered to their individual Sunday afternoon pastimes. Only Hugh Jr. was at home in the library–sitting room where the radio was playing. Before running to find and inform his mother and sisters of what he had just heard, he penciled the note he left on the front hall table— "WE'RE AT WAR!"

For the next four years, news of war was delivered to our house daily by the *Atlanta Journal* and nightly by radio reporters and commentators. George Mallet, a colonel in the National Guard, had been called to active duty the year before. The Hugh Mallet family, with preteen Hugh, Jr., its only male member, did not send a son to fight World War II, but, like civilian families throughout the nation, adapted its plans and the minutiae of daily living to it.

First, with her molasses business a war casualty, head-of-the-household Mary needed to find other ways of supporting her family. She had learned lessons in stretching cash during the Depression. War assigned more. Many goods, whether money was available to buy them or not, were in short supply. Government issued coupons allotted gasoline, tires, sugar, meat, canned goods, leather shoes, and more. There were "black market" deals, of course; but if rules and ration books were required for victory, Mary could live with them and sing "God Bless America" while she did so. Representing her absentee landlord mother in matters relating to her Butts County properties, drawing on her own limited assets and resources, and getting by on less and less of almost everything, she met expenses without making any great to-do about it.

The greatest expense was the one she never considered eliminating—the college educations she and Hugh had intended their children to have. Financing five of them through years of peace or war required planning, doing, and doing without; but by 1954 mother Mary saw every one of her children receive a baccalaureate degree. Before her death every one had managed further graduate study and added an additional diploma.

Mary rightly assumed that they would be as determined as she was about education. The "Baby" did occasionally threaten to make the choices her mother designated as the worst a modern woman could. When feeling pushed too hard by her mother's high expectations, Marcia declared her intention to drop out of high school and find employment at the mill or behind the counter at the five and ten cent store. By then she would be secretly married. That last defiant act would be total rejection of her mother's values. Mary Lane Mallet, wife and mother, had ever extolled marriage as what it was intended, she said, to be: a blessed, lasting union deserving public proclamation. She merely smiled at Marcia's rebellion as what it was—a joke.

Wartime employment opportunities abounded when twenty-year-old Mary graduated. Within weeks, she was working in Atlanta at one of the multitude of federal agencies whose defining names were reduced to initials. The first was usually "W" for war. She lived in the city with a college friend and her family during the six-day work week and took a Greyhound bus on Saturday evening to spend that night and Sunday in Jackson with her own family. Manufacture of private automobiles had been suspended; even used cars would require rationed gasoline and tires. Career girl Mary did not consider buying one when public transportation was available and cheap—even if inconvenient and always crowded.

I had begun my freshman year at Wesleyan the same year that Mary began her senior one at LaGrange. For Mother that meant doubled tuition fees, text book costs, and small allowances for our personal expenses. It was an experience she was to repeat more than once. Help came from relatively small scholarships and the college jobs each of us held. We two oldest had tacked high school typing lessons onto full college preparatory class tracks. At LaGrange, Mary worked in the office of the college president, our family friend. I had no such clout with Wesleyan's president, but I was assigned a job in his office. There, under the supervision of his administrative secretary, I typed "personal" letters to prospective students. I was paid approximately forty cents an hour and worked ten hours each week with the amount of my earnings subtracted from my tuition.

The summer job I found at the end of my first college year paid more. An enormous U.S. Army supply depot had been built just south of Atlanta and only about forty miles from Jackson. Its function was receiving, storing, and sending supplies wherever American troops needed them. I became one of the thousands who were its civilian work force.

World War II was the beginning of Jackson's becoming a bedroom community of commuters. Every morning, Monday through Saturday, I was waiting at the curb by six-thirty for the car driven by its owner and fellow depot worker to transport himself and four paying passengers to our jobs. In less than an hour—weather and traffic permitting—we arrived at the entrance to the depot grounds where armed guards checked our faces against the pictures on our identification badges.

My mother and I had intended only a summer job for me in 1944. However, when a promotion raised my civil service rank and pay, we saw the opportunity for me to earn enough to pay for my entire sophomore year by skipping only the fall semester. By attending one summer school session and adding one extra class for several semesters, I could catch up and graduate with my class. That plan worked.

Before Mother could implement other financial plans—including updating her own educational qualifications for public school teaching certification—her mother's massive stroke brought other changes for herself and her entire household.

When Hattie McKibben Lane became a part of it in early 1945, it teemed with activity far different from that of the care of an elderly invalid. The three youngest children Emily, Hugh, and Marcia were still at home—each contributing separate aspects of adolescence. There was also the third grade teacher, Mrs. Eva Mae Smith. Since before Hugh Sr.'s death, she had occupied the front upstairs bedroom during the school week and was whisked away on Friday afternoons by one of her two married daughters. Both lived in nearby Griffin where Mrs. Smith divided her weekends and vacations between their houses.

Hugh Sr. had not been enthusiastic about swapping the family privacy that he, Mary, and their children were enjoying for the small amount Mrs. Smith's payment for room and board would add to their monthly income. However, he listened sympathetically to her plight. The room she had been renting from Mrs. Lester, whose house also fronted Third Street, would no longer be available. Its location, two blocks from the school, had made it possible for her, far from young or agile, to walk there every day. She must find another such place as soon as possible.

Like other old Jackson families, the Mallets knew the challenges Mrs. Smith had already met besides walking to her work—rain or shine. An orphan, brought up by an aunt and other relatives, she had married one of the up-and-coming Smith brothers. When her husband died young, she was left with two little girls and little else besides connections and courage. Taking her children with her to Macon and old Wesleyan, she fulfilled the requirements for one of the few reputable professions open to women—teaching. While her two very well-to-do brothers-in-law indulged their progeny with almost anything money could buy in those early decades of the twentieth century, widow Eva Mae was seeing to it that her daughters were adequately fed, clothed, and sheltered and surrounded by unlimited, unfailing loving care. By the mid 1930s, they were educated, married, and beginning productive lives of their own, and she was an independent though low-salaried teacher.

A room and bath in their house, Mrs. Smith told Hugh and Mary, would more than satisfy her housing requirements. She would be even nearer the school and the home of cousins on College Street, and she could easily manage just one more block to reach the square for shopping or a bit of business. From the front window of the room she hoped to occupy, she had a view of the stained glass windows of the Methodist Church where she was a fellow parishioner.

Hugh's interest in her welfare was civic and personal, too. As a member of the Jackson City School Board, he had assumed a responsibility for the teachers it employed. He knew Mrs. Smith had earned her reputation for excellence with young learners and their parents. His two oldest discovered American history when they made miniature Indian villages in her third grade classroom. They also brought home legible evidence that tedious Palmer Method handwriting exercises could be put to good use with copies they had made of little essays about paintings with children as the subjects. She had distributed tiny reproductions of *Blue Boy* and *The Age of Innocence* to be glued at the top of their pages of copy work. He remembered his own childhood when Mrs. Smith's aunt, long since a resident of her Promised Land, had added drama and excitement to Sunday school lessons of Daniel in the lion's den and Jonah's survival in the belly of a whale. Hugh, with Mary, was persuaded to add Mrs. Smith to their household.

By the time of Hugh's death, she had become more like a part-time family member than boarder. For widowed Mary she was worth her weight—considerable for her short stature—in gold as older adviser, morale booster, and real friend.

For more than three years, Mary's mother and her care had priority placement in the Mallet menage. After only a few days in Jackson, the practical nurse returned to Macon. Mary told her brothers and sisters that she seemed to require more service than she provided. Young Hugh helped with the lifting of his slight grandmother, and local women with caregiving experience were hired when needed. Teens Hugh and Marcia were the most affected by the presence of a mentally and physically incapacitated elderly woman in their young lives. Yet they could not consider their situation unusual. Several of their friends lived in homes shared with older relatives in various stages of senility.

The end of World War II and the return home of America's young servicemen started wedding bells ringing throughout the nation. They rang for Lt. Ralph Carr and Mary Lane Mallet on December 8, 1945.

Mary could not be enthusiastic about this early marriage of her first-born and namesake. She advised, urged her daughter, only twenty-one, to experience a little more of what life could offer before making a choice whose results would dominate the rest of her life.

However, she had come to like and appreciate Ralph as he rose in the ranks of her popular daughter's boyfriends as well as those from private in the National Guard through officer candidate school to lieutenant in the tank corps that invaded southern Italy, suffering heavy losses in the fierce fighting that was part of the turning of the tide for Allied Forces in Europe.

On the Christmas Eve before the young soldier was sent overseas, he had returned his date Mary to her mother's house at midnight, the decreed curfew hour, to find a frustrated woman surrounded by the parts of her twelve-year-old son's Christmas bicycle. She knew young Hugh had been long embarrassed by having to ride the family bike—a girl's—bought originally for his oldest sister. That year, when she could at last buy one just for him, wartime metal shortage had removed new bicycles from the stores. Her persistent shopping had finally located one created from renovated, painted, shined up parts that looked to her like new. Hours after it had been delivered only partially assembled, Mary was near tears. She knew she could not put it together before her children dashed into the library where their stockings had been hung with care and filled the same way.

The next half-hour could be titled "Ralph to the Rescue." Before he left, he and both Marys had wished each other "Merry Christmas," and the bike, leaning on its kickstand, stood in the middle of the holiday bedecked room. With wheels, pedals, seat, and handlebars satisfactorily aligned, it was ready for its new owner.

Three years later, Mary could plunge almost whole-heartedly into preparations that resulted in a Sunday afternoon church ceremony followed by a home reception. In later years she was to say of herself, "I can be a good executive." She must have been as she supervised wedding details while seeing to it that her mother's care was never neglected.

Grandmother Hattie's presence was the source of family stories to be retold for years. When Mary and Ralph assembled us siblings to announce that their engagement was so official that they had set a wedding date, Mother wanted to make the occasion festive. Almost a teetotaler herself, she proposed that we toast the bride-and-groom-to-be with the rarely touched wine she was sometimes given. We toasted, but one sip of what she poured into the tiny sherry glasses she had set out was enough. Somehow, what we got was Grandmother's medicine. Probably there was little difference, and we were none the worse.

A few days later, in the semi-invalid's bedroom, proud Mary slipped off her new engagement ring to show it to her grandmother and accidently dropped it into the fireplace. Within seconds, the older Mary, aghast and open-mouthed, watched the younger one thrust her hand into the glowing coals and retrieve the ring with no perceptible damage to white hand or bright diamond.

Mother could be satisfied that her black-haired, blue-eyed oldest daughter was as lovely as any bride could be as she walked down the aisle on the arm of fifteen-year-old Hugh Jr. to join Ralph at the altar where he waited in full dress uniform.

The entire production was affordable. The perfectly stitched and fitted traditional white satin wedding gown had been designed and made by the professional seamstress mother of Mary's college friend Paula Copeland with whom she lived in Atlanta. It had been worn just months before by Paula's older sister, and the entire Copeland family wanted our Mary to give it a second wearing. I, as maid-of-honor, wore a long, silvery dress and carried a red bouquet of roses and carnations appropriate for the Christmas season. The dress had been our Aunt Virginia's for one of her frequent Macon bridesmaid roles.

The newlyweds, after what they reported as a fabulous New Orleans honeymoon, took up residence almost immediately in Athens where Ralph entered the University of Georgia. He was taking advantage of the

G.I. Bill of Rights that rewarded returning veterans of the war with financing for their higher education.

In January of 1947, young Mary, leaving Ralph to his studies in Athens, was back in Jackson at Heritage House. Mother had insisted that she recuperate for several weeks from the birth of her daughter, a third Mary Lane. The oldest of them could welcome her first grandchild with the rocking chair and lullabies her five Mallet babies had experienced there.

Late in the same year, again in December, there was another Mallet daughter wedding. John ("Chuck") Settle and I announced in November that we intended to be married during our Christmas holidays. Chuck, a Jackson boy I had known all my life, was a student at Emory University. I, having received a fellowship for graduate study there, was at Emory, too.

With his first year of college completed, Chuck had been drafted in 1943, as soon as he reached his eighteenth birthday. After basic training, he was sent to Europe as one more infantryman replacement needed to push the German army back to final defeat in their own country. John Settle was among those wounded in fighting near the ancient city of Aachen. After a field operation to remove shrapnel, he was taken to a hospital in England. Healing did not begin until doctors discovered that bits of overcoat had been left in the sewed up wound. Finally he was returned to the United States to spend the rest of World War II as a sergeant assigned to office duty at Fort Jackson in Columbia, where his father was executive officer. When the war ended, he entered Emory. Like Ralph, he was using college benefits offered to war veterans by the G.I. Bill of Rights.

Chuck and I told our marriage plans to my mother and his parents with our assessment of the situation: instead of continuing to occupy separate dormitory rooms, it would be not only more to our liking but also more practical and no more expensive for us to find living quarters together. We did not intend an elaborate wedding—just a simple marriage ceremony attended by immediate family members.

Mary did not object to the husband chosen by her second daughter; Mallets and Settles had long been friends. But, as was the case when she was told marriage plans of each of her children, she recommended postponement; and, as was the case with every one, her advice went unheeded.

This couple was persuaded, however, that the "simple" ceremony must be held in the sanctuary of the church across the street and that "immediate family" attending must include grandmothers, uncles, aunts, and cousins as well as parents and siblings. Then, of course, a few special college friends of the bride and groom and the other ten members of the Jackson Garden Club (to which mothers of the bride and groom both belonged) must be invited. After the church ceremony, all guests would follow bride and groom across the street for a reception—nothing elaborate.

Mother, in insisting on this simple celebration, had not taken into consideration the deteriorating condition of her own mother. While making preparations and arrangements for my wedding, she was giving nearly constant attention to her mother. Help came from other family members. Daughter Mary knew of a bakery in Athens that could produce a nice wedding cake, which she could order and deliver. Margaret, in distant St. Louis, took care of shopping—including some trousseau items—neither she nor the bride had time to do. Studying and taking end-of-quarter examinations, I contributed almost nothing to the necessary pre-wedding busyness. With the ceremony set for Sunday afternoon, December 21, 1947, I would not arrive at home in Jackson until after I had taken my last examination on the preceding Thursday.

McKibben came up from Macon several hours before the wedding to offer his sister the support she had known and counted on since their childhood. Bursting into tears, she collapsed in his arms. The bride, wrapped in a cloud of self-centered insulation, had been oblivious of her mother's exhaustion. (In fact, I was not told of the incident until weeks later.)

At the wedding, Mother, composed and without a tear, watched as Hugh Jr., then a freshman at Emory, escorted a second sister down the aisle. She later confirmed to me the wisdom of the choice we had made of the white wool suit and white cloche-style hat studded with pearls as "perfect for a winter bride." Right, too, was the rose-colored outfit worn by my sister Emily, the maid-of-honor. We were both clad in the postwar "New Look," introduced by designer Christian Dior. With need no longer for wartime skimping on fabric, skirts were longer and fuller. The three of us—Mother, Em, and I—in one afternoon had selected and assembled our ensembles. We had the undivided attention of the two person staff of the women's ready-to-wear section of Jackson's department store, Etheridge-Smith—The New York Store.

Mary was gracious hostess, the role to be played by the mother-of-the-bride, at the reception. The grandmother of the groom, matriarch of the Settle family, was seated regally near the parlor fireplace where she had an unobstructed view of the cutting of the first slice of wedding cake. The grandmother of the bride—whose own wedding reception had been the first in that house, lay in the bedroom across the back hall. Onie—cook, nurse, and faithful friend of the Mallets—tended her and the fire burning in the iron grate on the hearth. Its flickering flames gave out little heat or light on that damp December afternoon.

Years of Change: The Land

"WE CAN ALWAYS COUNT ON CHANGE TO BE CONSTANT" was more handed-down wisdom Mary quoted. The death of her mother in early 1948 meant that she was released from three years of round-the-clock care of an invalid who was no longer the quick-witted, generous, demanding, stimulating, exasperating woman who had been her lifelong companion. Mary was set free to mix final grief with new duties added to ever present concern for her own children.

First, an equitable distribution must be accomplished of what was left of the worldly goods of Hattie McKibben Lane. Mary and her lawyer brother McKibben became co-executors of Hattie's estate to be divided among her seven children. Years of financing a comfortable home and wide-ranging educational choices for each of them had been followed by more years of the Great Depression and World War II. Bank balances were near nothing. There was only land—acres and acres of it.

Butts County property values had not yet escalated in the first years after World War II. Farmers were abandoning such labor intensive crops as cotton—the money-maker on which the entire area had depended for generations. Many returning veterans were choosing to leave altogether the daily sun-up to sun-down country lives their parents had modeled for them. McKibben knew that neither he nor any one of his brothers and sisters—except for Mary—possessed great love for the soil or knowledge of farming and land management. Cash was the material legacy suiting their needs and desires.

Mary had to agree with Kib, but her outlook had changed since she came to Jackson as a bride. She clung to memories of going with Hugh for early morning inspections of the vegetable crops he grew on his "bottom land." She had accompanied him, too, when he checked on the cotton planted on her mother's home farm, located less than half a mile from their house. There she saw the back-breaking labor required for the chief money crop of the 1920s and 1930s. Mary may never, with her own hands, have planted and harvested a crop or milked one of the cows she saw grazing Mallet and Lane pastures, but the land—Middle Georgia's gentle slopes of rich, dark dirt and hard, red clay—had become part of who she was.

She could find no joy in getting rid of it. Yet turning it into divisible, spendable money was the responsibility she shared with McKibben. Since their combined time for that task and their experience in the business of real estate were inadequate for handling sales of more than a thousand acres located throughout the county in plots of varying size and value, co-executors Mary and McKibben contracted with an Atlanta firm to advise and work with them.

Mary despised the event by which the Dozier Land Company began the enterprise. The *Jackson Progress-Argus* of September 23, 1948, blazoned a half page advertisement that asked in big, bold print: "Where can you buy a farm at a reasonable price?" The answer was in slightly smaller print except for the last two words: "Land being sold for division among heirs of an estate is generally the BEST BUY." The rest of the advertisement urged attendance at the public auction of the lands of the estate of Mrs. Hattie J. Lane, which would be held Thursday in front of the Buchanan Hotel at two o'clock "rain or shine." Money prizes were promised for the nearest estimates of the average price per acre. The first twenty ladies to arrive would each be given "a 1 lb. box of Nunnallys fine candy."

The auction was only the beginning. The final sale of the Hattie McKibben Lane estate was not made until almost six years later. Proceeds dribbled in and were subdivided among the heirs. Separate checks were seldom more than a few hundred dollars.

In November of 1953, McKibben and Mary had completed their job when McKibben wrote to his brothers and sisters: "I have collected final payments due Mother's estate on the sale of the farms and I have on hand $1990.52 so I am enclosing a check to each of you for $284.36." McKibben could inform his brothers and sisters that all debts owed by their mother's estate had been paid in full and that the estate had also "rendered some assistance" to Virginia at the time of her emergency operation and to Louis at the time of his remarriage. He further reported that assets of approximately $45,000 had been liquidated "with a minimum of expense."

The last sentences were more personal: "I wish the amount to each of you had been ten times as great but under the circumstances Mary and I have done the best we could . . . It is rather saddening to me to write this final report as somehow over the last six years it has given me one more warm tie and concern for each of you . . . the legacy Mother and Father left us of strong hearts, firm faith and fine intelligence and character represents far more than dollars . . ."

The Lane heirs may have hoped for and expected a greater monetary legacy, but "under the circumstances" they thanked McKibben and Mary for their work and a job well done. Louis, happy with his new wife Sara in a marriage that was to remain so for the rest of his life wrote them ". . . my appreciation of your fine performance. You have done an excellent job, without pay . . . each of us, I am sure, regards this income as being completely unearned but rather a memorial of . . . parents who gave us the best and finest things of life . . . as Kib says a legacy of faith, courage, intelligence, and character . . . I have applied the estate checks on our home which Sara and I so love and enjoy." Each of the other Lane heirs expressed in different words the same idea about Louis and his new life and wife: "Mother must be seeing Louis and smiling."

As for the money finally received from the sales of the McKibben-Lane lands, it was only a fraction, even in those times, of the value of the property. Within a very few years, the entire home farm was a residential extension of the town. Northwest of town, a part of one enormous cotton-growing tract became the site of a multi-million dollar business that manufactured soil-enriching products, some of them probably applied to earth depleted by cotton cultivation. In the twentieth century, the land holdings amassed by Van McKibben in the nineteenth made his daughter Hattie an heiress before she become one of the "land poor" of the Great Depression. As the twenty-first century begins, those acres in "little Butts County" are source and symbol of progress and prosperity.

Full House for the Fifties

THE 1950S BEGAN WITH MARY ALREADY IN HER OWN FIFTIES. The comings and goings of her children—all five of them—were winding in and out of her daily life and her house. Young Mary and Ralph had returned from Athens after his graduation from the university and were living only blocks away in the Mallet House. Pauline Mallet, now its mistress, had converted it into apartments with the best and biggest kept for herself. The Carrs were there long enough for Mother to be nearby doting grandmother to little Lane and Lucia before Ralph decided to return to the army as a career officer. On January 1, 1950, Mary became a grandmother to a third girl child. On New Year's Eve, Chuck and I, who had also returned to Jackson—the hometown of Settles as well as the Mallets—had become parents of another Jane Anne—Jane Anne Settle, to be called "Janie" as was her great-great grandmother

Heading a family of three generations, Mother was showing that she had the makings of a matriarch, with her Heritage House the setting for playing that role. Before the arrival of our baby, Chuck and I had moved into upstairs rooms of an apartment house recently imposed on the Victoriana of Indian Springs Street. Adequate and new, it had little insulation and neither air conditioning nor shade. We expected to move into our own house just as soon as Chuck's Uncle David ("Pac") and Aunt Thelma moved out of it and into the bigger, finer house they were building. It was expected to be ready for the family moves by the fall; but even before June, the Indian Springs Street apartment was hot. Mother decreed that five-month-old Janie could not wait out a long summer of above ninety degree temperatures while "Thelma insists on perfection in every single construction detail." The baby and her parents must move into her Heritage just as soon as the school year ended. Then the long-time roomer, Mrs. Smith, would leave the breezy upstairs bedroom and bath she occupied from September to June to spend the summer in Griffin. In early June, she was out and we were in for pleasanter, cooler living quarters—at least for three months.

September meant the start of school and Mrs. Smith's return, but the new David Settle house was far from completion. Mary managed that situation by moving the Settles downstairs and into the back bedroom and bath her invalid mother had occupied for the three years preceding her death.

That household shuffle was just the beginning of the 1950s further proof that Mary possessed the executive skills she claimed as well as a house that could stretch to hold her children.Young Hugh would be returning to Emory University and the ATO Fraternity House where his serving as business manager for his "brothers" helped with college expenses. Marcia was entering Wesleyan where she would be Mother's third daughter to graduate from her alma mater. After graduation, Emily entered Emory for a master's degree in library science. In the fall of 1950, she had finished all her class work and begun work on her thesis and planned to finish it at home in Jackson where she had taken a high school teaching job for the year while she made regular trips to the Emory campus for consultation with her faculty adviser. Em would be sharing the two upstairs east bedrooms and bath with two other beginning teachers whose room and board payments were part of that year's complicated, co-operative family financing. Somehow Mother saw to it that a welcome home and a place to lay their heads awaited Hugh and Marcia whenever their schedules at Emory and Wesleyan allowed them to come—sometimes with college friends.

When the back-to-school bustle began, Mary's Heritage House sheltered still another teacher. In late summer, the county school superintendent, coping with an unexpected vacancy in the English faculty, made a call. He had heard that a Mallet daughter with two degrees in English and a year of teaching experience in an Atlanta private school was home again with her native Jackson husband and their baby. Mary declared the time just right for her second daughter to take the job. Since babies were her forte, she could care for Janie while I re-entered a great profession. So it was that throughout the school year of 1950–51, Monday through Friday, five teachers sallied forth from the Mallet house to join local forces defending the community from long entrenched and ever threatening ignorance.

During after-school hours, Mary's house filled with sounds of young people. Doffing the dignity and decorum they put on in their classrooms, the new teachers ran up and down the stairs and laughed and called to each other as they played with little Janie or the puppy one of them had adopted. They giggled and whispered in the kitchen and dining room as they prepared and ate snack meals. They gathered around the parlor piano to combine musical talents and tastes. Emily and I could participate in that entertainment only briefly because work awaited us just as soon as Janie was tucked into bed. In the upstairs hall, on an ancient machine placed on their father's old office desk, I was typing Em's thesis. Careful that every word and line met Emory's guidelines, the soon-to-be master of arts required nothing less than perfection from her technical assistant. We sometimes worked long after midnight. Mother was proud and encouraging of Em's research into the differences in reading tastes of adolescent boys and girls. Neither the author nor her typist was sure, however, that their mother ever actually read the thesis. They did see her hold the finished product in her hands before it finally left her house and heard her say admiringly, "beautiful typing."

If Mary, control center of it all, was near exhaustion from care of a toddler and supervision of seeming chaos, she seldom admitted or showed signs of stress or bone-weariness.

An Only Son for Another War

"NO ONE OF THE CHILDREN IS MY FAVORITE," our mother claimed. "Every one of them is different and special." The very maleness of Hugh Mallet Jr., fourth child and only son, meant difference in his upbringing, but no girl born to Hugh and Mary Mallet would ever be less valued or less loved because she was female. As for young Hugh's being special, those who knew him—inside and outside the family—agreed with his mother that he was.

When she attended his graduation from Emory University in 1951, she could look back with justifiable maternal pride at his not yet twenty-one years. Hugh Jr. had been an eight-year-old third-grader when his father died. Already he was earning spending money by selling the magazine that was Hugh Sr.'s favorite—the *Saturday Evening Post*. His shoulder bag filled with copies of the latest issue, he regularly circled the town square in search of potential customers. He began reading before he entered school. His sister Emily, entering the first grade two years ahead of him, taught him while she learned. Their mother had their father laughing, too, when she told him what she had overheard during a pretend school session held on the front porch. "Hugh," teacher Em accused, "you're not giving me your undivided attention."

For widowed Mary, bringing up a son in an all-female household was a challenge. Her own husband and her youngest brother Harry had also been children without fathers, but they had older brothers. Young Hugh would have to depend on uncles, community role models, and family friends. One of these was next-door neighbor Morris Redman—also

Jackson's longtime mayor. He came to the rescue when Hugh could not descend from a precarious perch high in a backyard pecan tree. "I sure am glad you came," Hugh greeted him. "I'm the only little boy my mother's got."

Mary's worries, however, never had to include her son's school work. All her children were assured that their mother was interested and would give assistance when it was needed and asked for, but Hugh, like his sisters, took full responsibility for his own assignments. An avid reader since sister Emily's first instruction, he gave minimum time and attention to school textbooks. All "A" report cards seemed to come easy for him.

Hugh Sr. had enjoyed hunting. After his death, Mary locked his gun away until she engaged a trusted black tenant who had often hunted with her husband to show adolescent Hugh Jr. how to use and care for it. After one lesson and hunting experience, the boy returned the valuable gun to his mother with the admission, "I can't be a hunter; I don't like killing things."

As player and fan, he enjoyed most other sports available to him. He played on his high school's baseball and basketball teams and was the president of its letter club. Participation in football began, however, with disaster. When football was reintroduced into Jackson High School's athletic program after abandonment during the years of Depression and World War II, he was on the first team. Mother, flanked by daughters—including me—was in the stands to see her son and the rest of the completely inexperienced team run onto the field. Few of them had ever even attended a "real" game. Only minutes after the kickoff, she had a close view when a tackler's cleated shoe came down on Hugh's face.

On the Saturday morning after the Friday night that Mary had watched him finally struggle to his feet and be helped off the field, mother and son were together in her kitchen. His jaw was bruised, not broken, and he was sipping coffee through the space left by two missing front teeth. He was assuring her that he was all right. There was nothing to be done before the already arranged dental appointment for Monday morning. Mary Mallet knew of something. Before noon, she piled her children at home that weekend into her old Buick for a trip to Atlanta and "The

Greatest Show on Earth"—The Ringling Brothers, Barnum and Bailey Circus.

The end of that school year was more satisfying. On a May morning, Mary was seated in the auditorium of Old Wesleyan Conservatory on Macon's College Street where she had been graduated thirty years before. Her second daughter, with her liberal arts class, was there from the suburban Rivoli campus to receive a bachelor's degree conferred by "New" Wesleyan. In the evening of the same day, Mary joined in the applause as Hugh Mallet Jr.—valedictorian and president of the class of 1947—received a diploma from Jackson High School.

Hugh's college years coincided with those of three of his sisters. In 1947, he arrived on the Emory campus as a freshman. The same September I was there as a graduate student, and Emily returned to Wesleyan for her junior year. When Hugh graduated with his Emory Class of 1951, Marcia had just completed her Wesleyan freshman year.

If family friends marveled at how Mary was managing, she probably would not, could not have counted all the ways. Her son had himself been responsible for most of his college expenses. He received a sizable scholarship for a start. Then joining his father's Alpha Tau Omega Fraternity had helped. Hugh Sr. had been an ATO at Emory before the college moved from the campus at Oxford, Georgia, to Atlanta to become a great university. Hugh Jr.'s management of the fraternity house in Atlanta paid for housing and meals while surrounding him with congenial companions.

The beginning of the Korean War in 1950 meant that his senior year would be tinged with the knowledge that he and his classmates would be subject upon graduation to military draft. The last year of his undergraduate work at Emory had also been the first of his study of law. In January of 1951, after Christmas holidays at home, he wrote his mother:

> . . . I still am basking in the light of recollection . . . how much I enjoyed just being home. It seems about the happiest place I've ever seen . . . soaking up the atmosphere makes me feel revitalized, rejuvenated, and very glad and proud that I'm your son and a part of the Mallet household . . . School got off to a rather slow start. Most of the boys were much more concerned about getting into some branch of the service . . . five brothers over the holidays to the army . . . Most of us though believe we can wait until summer. I'm enjoying Dr.

> Bryan's course in criminal law. He's an excellent teacher tho some of the 2nd and 3rd year students say that he's extremely obstinate and dogmatic, and I've been warned not to disagree . . . I listen with quite an acquiescent ear. . . . heard about Lucia's earache. Tell her to get well and stay that way—directions from Uncle Hugh. Give lots and lots of love to Janie and Lane, too, for me. Keep the girls in line and write me more news of our "little" family . . . take very good care of the Mallet Matriarch cause, funny, but we kinda love you."

Four months after the "Matriarch" received the letter, she was attending his college graduation while confronting the fact that he would be leaving almost immediately for basic training to be followed by U.S. Air Force officer candidate school.

Letters kept with his mother's treasures record Hugh's selection for her from his experiences, reactions, and opinions during his participation in the last two years of the Korean War. He had spent the 1951–52 holiday season at home when he wrote of his arrival in January at an officer candidate school in Texas.

> . . . trip out was nice, since I had time to see Mobile, Biloxi & N.O. . . . The Upper Classmen have been very helpful in getting the neophytes adjusted and after a couple of weeks it's rumored that we'll feel right at home, which personally I rather doubt . . . being at home was all I needed to prepare me for this, and seeing you renewed my resolve . . . Time is truly precious (No more so than usual . . . just more apparent). We even have "minute calls" to tell us how long we have to get ready for this or that. Well, enough for now. Thanks for a wonderful, restful, inspiring holiday . . .

A letter written a few weeks later lets his mother know that he's receiving letters from his sisters and aunts as well as Emory's alumni news and the *Jackson Progress Argus*. He wrote that he was enjoying OCS more than he had thought and that his classmates "in the flight have a wonderful time among themselves." Mary must have been pleased to read that her son had used Sunday of an "open port" weekend to go into town to hear a concert production of *Faust*, with the Metropolitan Opera's Bjoerling singing the title role. He pronounced it "thrilling, and a very good break in the routine." He wrote about finances, too. While at OCS, he would be paid $139 a month. He was also having $37.50 deducted each month for U.S. bonds. Settling in and a new pair of shoes had further depleted his first pay. "So I didn't send any home. I know I'm not doing my share but now I'm all square here so I can begin sending some regularly the last of this month."

As for his class work, he wrote: "I'm still number one, but the new grades come out in a few days so I might drop a few places . . . " More than a page of the nine of that long letter described his daily schedule: ". . . don't get up till 5:45," he wrote. Then most of the day was spent in

> "classes from 8 to 4:30 with 45 min. for lunch, then details till supper at 5:19 . . . Before each meal, we stand in formation for scrupulous inspection, so we press our uniforms two or three times a day . . . sundry jobs till 8:30 when we have one hour all our own . . . At 9:30 we have half an hour to bathe and do our laundry . . . ready for lights out at 10:30 and I sleep like a log."

Perhaps he read the preceding pages before he wrote the conclusion: "This letter must sound awfully disconnected and our correspondence instructor would no doubt flunk me on it, but I guess I can write my own mother without regard to regulations." Then he added one more bit of information: "Our public speaking course is more fun every day."

A subsequent letter reported: ". . . after the first 11 weeks, I was number 2 in my class, less of a drop than I expected . . . School is still fine. Military Law has been very interesting. I've met many Georgia boys here and several ATO's." The day after moving into the just completed new facilities for the Officer Candidate School—separate from the rest of the base—he wrote of further satisfaction. "Our upper class will be commissioned and leave Friday . . . I'm in command of the flight now and enjoying it very much . . . a huge ultra modern academic building makes our OCS group very collegiate . . . My roommate is a boy from Harvard with a master's in political science and very pro-Roosevelt so we get along fine . . . "

In the same letter he wrote that most of the class just commissioned had received the assignments they wanted. ". . . so I believe I've got a good chance of getting assigned to the Office of Special Investigation."

Throughout his military service, his letters included questions about home, family, and friends, and often sent messages to be relayed. "When is Mary's baby expected to arrive? Seems to me it would be sometime soon. I'm pretty sure I'll have a new niece, but now I'm partial to girls . . ." Of the news that Mary and her children would follow Ralph to his assignment in postwar occupied West Germany, he wrote, ". . . beyond our reach for a while, but they will enjoy Germany tremendously and of all overseas assignments I'm sure that's the best."

His own "good chance" of getting an assignment he wanted became fact when officer candidate school was followed by duty at Lowry Air Base in Denver, Colorado. There his first experience as an Air Force intelligence officer was accompanied by experience of a different kind. One of his letters to his mother from OCS had ended with "Don't worry about me losing my head and falling in love with some Texas gal; I'll just wait till I can settle down in Jackson, which will be some time, I'm afraid. I plan to spend my service days in the BOQ." Alterations in that plan seemed to begin in Colorado.

No Colorado letters from Hugh to Mother have been found, but he described his time there in the first letter he wrote from California's Camp Stoneman, his last station in the United States before leaving for Korea:

> First my trip out here. We left Denver Monday morning, John and I, and we both rather hated to go. We were really in the clouds while we were there. John was dating a girl out at Fitzsimmons Hosp., a WAC Lt. I had introduced him to, and was really crazy about her, and I had dated Millie, whom I met almost my first day in Denver, practically every night. She was really the sweetest girl I've known in a long time, and made my few months in Denver seem like just a few days.

Hugh had driven from Denver to the West Coast with John," the OCS classmate who had become his friend. After two days and nights enjoying San Francisco together, they separated for John to drive to his nearby assignment and Hugh to take a plane for Los Angeles and duty at Camp Stoneman. From San Francisco on October 1, he mailed Mother a postcard showing a sunset aerial view of the Golden Gate Bridge. On the back he wrote ". . . still having fun . . . I'll write you all about the trip. I just wished for you every time we saw something beautiful. Guess we'll have to take a trip out here one of these days."

The long letter he wrote a few days later from Camp Stoneman included a request he deemed urgent. He had not received the absentee ballot for which he applied in July. "Mother, please go up to the courthouse and ask Mr. Head to send me a ballot, on the double quick, so I can vote."

For years to come, Hugh's letters to Mother would include his views on political issues and events—local, national, and international. After the general election of November 1952, he wrote from California where he awaited orders for Korea.

> . . . I did get my ballot in plenty of time and I'm proud I voted for Stevenson despite his loss. I'm glad you all voted . . . I was deeply disappointed over the election since everyday I had come to respect and admire Stevenson more. I don't think I missed a major speech of either side. The program and the nominee of the Democratic Party seemed to me to offer the people a remarkable and rare opportunity to choose a splendid direction over the next years. No doubt the prestige of Ike was just too great—I hope he lives up to the faith of the nation . . . Several of my old favorites in the Senate were beaten . . . if McCarthy had lost I would feel pretty good.
>
> Truman I know did a lot of things we all objected to, but someday I hope the country recognizes the magnitude of the accomplishments of his administration. So the New Deal comes to an end—
>
> Well, enough of politics—

Just before Thanksgiving, his letter home was an expression of gratitude, seemingly written without the embarrassment that speaking them might have entailed:

> . . . I've been listening to the Telephone Hour and they just sang one of my favorite hymns, "We Gather Together To Ask The Lord's Blessing." I do wish I could be there with you to thank God for all the blessings that have been ours over the years. I know that few men have had the blessings that I have: such a happy youth, so fine a family, and so many opportunities. I'm all humility, and not just on Thursday but every day, I do thank the Lord. I think I've inherited quite a lot of optimism from you, too, for despite all the trouble in the world, I feel enthusiastic about the future. I look forward to coming home for good someday, finishing law school, and taking my place as a citizen . . . Write me the news.

His next letter told her his application for a Christmas leave was approved. He would arrive in Jackson on or about December 23 and could remain for two weeks. ". . . I'll have to hurry these two weeks . . . "

The plans materialized. Christmas was another of the kind he knew well, with his family gathered around the table for meals prolonged not so much by eating as by conversation. Friends dropped by, informally joining any of them in progress in the dining room or sipping coffee ever ready to be served in the parlor. Marcia and Emily were home for the holidays, too, with their Jackson friends—often Hugh's, too—adding to the company. Mary and Ralph and their little girls were in Germany, so "Uncle Hugh" had fewer nieces vying for his knees and attention, but three-year-old Janie Settle was more than glad to claim them.

Returning to the West Coast by train made possible a stop-over in Denver for a visit with Millie, the outstanding feature for him in that city of his first assignment as officer and gentleman of the U.S. Air Force.

In his first letter home after arriving again in California, Hugh devoted only one sentence to what was perhaps the first "serious" romance of his twenty-two years. The first paragraph thanked Mother for her telephone call to him and assured her he was "getting along fine . . . have met a couple of fellows I know and plan to go with them to an officers dance in Oakland." The Millie sentence fit into the second paragraph.

> The trip out was wonderful all the way. Thru the South, the Midwest and the far west I thrilled to the beauty of America. It was snowing when I arrived in Denver early Thursday. Millie met me at the station and we had three perfect days together.

Hugh dated the last letter he wrote his mother before leaving for Korea via Japan only "Thursday." Mother dated it parenthetically in her handwriting (January 10, 1953) before placing it with his other letters.

> Dearest Mother,
>
> The days have hurried by and I'm about ready to go. Preferring sumptuous luxury to speed, I'm going by boat to Japan, (and had no choice anyway.) I've had such sweet letters from my sisters the last few days. I wrote to Marcia and Em, and tell Jane Anne for me I'll write her soon. Mother, again let me say how nice it was at home. I just loved every minute of being with you, and it won't be long before I'll be back again. I'm sure you know of the deep love I have for my home and family without my telling you. It's just as warm and sunny today as spring. There is a ridge of beautiful rolling hills

> right behind the camp, and they are really spring green. So perhaps it's as nice in Jackson. We deserve it more there. Take care of yourself.
>
> Love,
> *Hugh*

Hugh served in Korea as second lieutenant assigned to Special Intelligence throughout the winter, spring, and summer of 1953, the last of the three years of the Korean War, the conflict during which the United States was foremost in the forces of the United Nations supporting South Korea against communist North Korea supported by communist China and Russia.

Seven of his letters home were found in the contents of the big desk in the library of Heritage House. (The massive piece had once been the desk in the Macon office of our grandfather lawyer, Major Lane. Then it had been in the office of his lawyer son, our Uncle McKibben. After his death, his wife had sent it to Jackson for our mother to keep until her lawyer son Hugh could use it.)

The first of Hugh's wartime letters was only a note dated February 25, 1953, which told his mother he was about to leave Japan by plane for Korea. ". . . I'll write you about my stay in Tokyo . . ." He sent his new military address with the request ". . . have the paper sent there and thanks." The paper would have been the *Jackson Progress Argus.* The second was dated March 7:

> I am doing fine; springtime seems just around the corner, and the news of Stalin's death has been a boost . . . by now most of us realize that there are many more like Josef, and that this occasion has been waited and prepared for over many years. Just the same it was big news and set us all talking . . . I know spring is being greeted with open arms at home . . . once again we have a new season with new hopes or maybe new strength for a few old hopes we left lying around. I send all my love to you and thoughts turn as often homeward.

Disillusionment was the somber tone of the letter he wrote his mother in early June. "Cease-fire" negotiations had begun, been halted, and begun again.

> These are probably the last days of the war in Korea—for a while. When, and if, the cease-fire is signed, I can imagine no rejoicing

> even back home. For I think people must realize that this is only respite; somewhere soon, maybe here, this will have to begin again. Ending the war accomplishes many things, good and bad. I know it ends the fighting and dying and certainly that's a worthy purpose, but somehow I know this isn't right . . . somewhere we lost sight of the goal we had, and rather than a unified Korea we demanded once, we're willing to let things be as they were before the war started . . . There are many things about this I can't know . . . one thing I do know, the truce will break the heart of this courageous nation. I guess more is at stake than what happens here; our leaders have such tremendous problems, the awful burden of decisions is theirs and certainly they deserve much more than back-biting from me . . . just my first thoughts . . . I know when I speak them to you that they won't go any further . . .
>
> . . . I'm very glad about recent events at home and know how happy you all are with the new Miss Puss . . .Take care of yourself and write me about the new addition . . . I'm fine and miss you all.
>
> Your son
> *Hugh*

Beneath the signature, he had written two lines of Korean characters, probably as evidence that he was working to know and understand more about the people with whom he was living and fighting.

"The new Miss Puss" was a reference to the birth of another daughter for the Settles and niece for himself. She had been named Nancy Elizabeth for her paternal great-great-grandmother, a tiny woman who had lived for more than ninety years with the family nickname of "Miss Puss."

His next letter, dated June 24, 1953, began with other home happenings. He was concerned about the dental surgery Mother was undergoing while he was glad of the prospect of "fun" while Marcia and her friends were home for summer vacation. "Your letters," he wrote, "are always perfect and carry home to me better than a thousand pictures."

Most of the long letter, however, expressed his current political thinking:

> . . . Of course I always support U.S. policy . . . In my last letter those thoughts were just for you . . . .The need for solidarity is tremendous and I would never want to be anything or say anything that would hinder the efforts of my country . . . I'm aware of my inability to understand all the reasons for much diplomacy and realize that

> Rhee's actions in releasing those prisoners indicate very well I think the desperation of Korea now and the depths of feeling about the proposed armistice. No doubt he has aroused great disfavor and killed the sympathy many held for him, but he is not thinking in terms of the United Nations or geopolitics, just in terms of his own little battered country. I cannot agree with his latest tactic, his attempt to fill his inside straight as it's been called, but I marvel at his courage and tenacity. I highly approved of the column of Ralph McGill you sent me in which he gave great credit to Truman for making the armistice possible, should it be successfully concluded. He is really the finest editorialist I have ever read, and I don't think I say that because his opinions are mine also . . . my thinking has been largely formed by reading Ralph McGill since I was twelve or so . . . He is the perfect example of a straight thinking Southerner. He understands Georgia and the South with its countless problems and peculiarities. But beyond that he has a wonderful grasp of national and world affairs . . . Over here now, I keep as well informed as I can, but I know that in uniform I am always peculiarly representative of the U.S. . . . History is being made now and I feel the thrill. . . . The news from East Germany is tremendous . . . All over the world a war is being waged with words mostly, but often with strikes, riots, organizations—even ballots. And it will continue after open hostilities cease here. I think at last our nation is awake. Eisenhower is fine and might well be a Democrat. I notice most of his opposition comes from his own party. Democracy is about to take the offensive, it seems, and the years ahead should be momentous, exciting, and rewarding.

The letter ended with remarks about home. "I'm very interested in Jackson's participation in the Better Home Town Program. As far as I'm concerned there couldn't be a better . . . "

Almost two months elapsed between dates on that letter and the next one. During that time, truce negotiations moved in and out of deadlock positions. Hugh's intelligence assignments at the edge of North and South Korean demarcation had evidently pre-empted writing letters. Mary finally received a letter dated August 12, 1953, which began with appreciation for mail he had recently received from sisters, an aunt, and the Methodist minister's wife who lived across the street from the Mallet Heritage. Next, he asked Mother to relay his news to Onie—cook, housekeeper, nurse, and more for our family since before his birth.

> . . . Do give Onie my love and tell her that I think of her often and look forward to seeing her again. I always thought that Onie's cooking was the best in the world (next to yours of course!). And after sampling a little of the fare served up in other parts of the world, I'm sure that she is the best. The truce is signed now and things have quieted down considerably. Tho it's not the best we might have hoped for it will be a challenge. This peninsula, cut in half, each part representing and practicing theories vastly different, existing side by side for the world to see the results. Write me . . . I miss you and try to speed the days by until I am home again.
>
> All my love,
> *Hugh*

The following letter was dated August 21:

> I'm in Tokyo again for an R & R and enjoying every minute of it . . . went down to the beach at Ito and have been soaking up the sun and really taking it easy. It is wonderful to relax completely. So far I've seen no other Americans down here. We're staying in a Japanese Hotel, eating Japanese food and expect to be completely rested when we go back. . . . As I'm writing this, I'm sitting cross-legged on the floor while a girl dressed in a beautiful kimono cooks the suki-yaki right in front of me. I'm even doing pretty well with chopsticks now. . . . There is a chance that I might get to come home earlier than expected. I'll let you know . . .

That was indeed the case. Because Hugh's mission had placed him above the 38th Parallel, which the Armistice designated as the line marking the northern boundary of South Korea, American troops could no longer be there. The Korean War, which left both North and South Korea devastated, was over. Korean and Chinese military casualties numbered in the millions. There were millions, too, of Korean civilians killed as well as thousands left homeless. Included in United Nations casualties were more than twenty-five thousand dead from the United States of America.

But at 12:40 p.m. on Saturday, September 19, 1953, Mary Lane Mallet was standing at the edge of the concourse of the old Atlanta airport, awaiting the safe homecoming of Lt. Hugh Mallet Jr. Immediately upon receiving Hugh's telegram from Portland, Oregon, just hours before the scheduled arrival of his plane, Mother notified Wesleyan student Marcia, Atlanta librarian Emily, and Jackson housewife me. All three of us were standing with her, not minding at all the drizzling rain, as we watched the landing of Eastern Airlines Flight 163 from Chicago. As the passengers deplaned, we recognized Hugh immediately—the young man in uniform holding an umbrella over a small Asian woman carrying a baby in her arms.

Whether or not we three sisters gasped aloud at that first sight of our brother since his leaving for wartime service in Korea, we later admitted to each other that surprise and bewilderment at his travel companions came almost simultaneously with the joy of seeing him safe and well and as good looking as ever. As Hugh embraced us separately and together, the young woman—holding the baby tight against her breast with one arm and a small bag with the other—mumbled something and walked toward the terminal.

"I'm not exactly sure who she is," Hugh explained. "When we introduced ourselves on the plane, she said she was coming here for the first time. She was having a time getting off with all the baby stuff and the rain, too."

Mother denied to her daughters any concern at all as to the identity of the Asian woman and baby. "Of course I knew it was something like that. Hugh can be counted on for help when it's needed."

That September day in 1953 was the third time in the twentieth century—only three years into its second half—that Mary had greeted family members on their return from foreign wars. The first had been her brother McKibben. Columbia student Mary Lane had been on the New York pier in 1919 when he returned with thousands of other American soldiers from fighting World War I in France. In 1945, she had joined in Jackson's welcome to servicemen and women coming home from the far flung battles of World War II. Two of them would soon be her sons-in-law. Lt. Ralph Carr had crossed the desert sands and heat of North Africa to be part of the invasion at Anzio of Nazi-Fascist held Italy. Pvt. John Settle, near the ancient German city of Aachen just before the Battle of the Bulge, had been wounded by shrapnel. Only eight years later, she could feel around her the arms of her only son—whole and safe and home from war in a country about as far from his native Georgia as a land can be.

Taking the Baby to Europe and Coming Home Alone

MARCIA'S GRADUATION FROM COLLEGE in May of 1954 was as much an achievement for mother as for daughter. Seeing her baby receive a liberal arts degree from her own alma mater meant that all her children were college graduates—the goal Mary and Hugh had set together for their five little Mallets. A widow for fifteen years, she had reached it alone.

Mary could not give her youngest what her older children possessed—memories of a childhood within the security of a close family headed by both parents. Even son Hugh had three more years of a father than Marcia had known. Mary, though, would see to it that Marcia would benefit from whatever advantages might derive from being youngest.

There were some. First, Marcia's graduation meant that Mary no longer was wide awake in pre-dawn hours scheming ways for September college fees to be met. Still with a few dollars from her share of her mother's estate and without bills hanging over her head, Mary had been planning throughout Marcia's last semester the graduation gift she could not have given any other child—European travel.

The time was right. From Germany, daughter Mary was writing glowing letters. Her husband Capt. Ralph Carr, as part of the post World War II Allied occupation of West Germany, had been assigned housing for their family in the town of Zirndorf, near Nuremberg, the scene of the Nazi war crime trials. The Carr home, appropriated from its former

German owners, was a large, well built and furnished residence, which came with the services of gardener-furnace-tender and a housekeeper. The latter was already becoming a member of the Carr household while supplying the young American mother with domestic and childcare help—the best she was ever to know.

The Germany described in Mary's letters was more than the location of Ralph's military assignment or the living arrangements for his family. It was a land of beauty and fascinating culture and history. The itinerary mother Mary planned for herself and her youngest would have her oldest in Germany as destination with London and Paris as significant stopovers.

Additional travel advice came from one of Marcia's history professors. Dr. Florence Sherriff suggested that stays in both London and Paris could be economically arranged by taking advantage of convenient lodgings made available by the American Association of University Women. Mary did so and also booked passage for two on a ship sailing for England from Quebec at considerably less cost and little more complication than one sailing from New York.

Before sun-up on a June morning, twenty-year-old Marcia and fifty-seven-year-old Mary were ready to turn plans into action. The days since Marcia's graduation had been as tightly and carefully packed as their suitcases. Mary had seen to business matters and care of the homeplace during her absence. Marcia had accepted her first teaching job in nearby Griffin, which would begin only a few days after their planned August return. Finally—with tickets, passports, travel checks, and cash securely handy—Mary could watch Hugh load the luggage into the automobile in which he and Emily had arrived the night before. The duty of those two young Atlanta professionals was to get their mother and their sister to the Atlanta airport. There they would be joined by Mary's youngest sister Virginia and her husband, artist George Beattie, for the first leg of their journey, the flight to New York where the Beatties were headed for a special gallery show. (Several generations of both Lanes and Mallets were accustomed to the participation of numberous friends and relatives in activities that other families more often leave to those immediately involved.)

I was then a Jackson wife and mother. Leaving my husband and children sleeping in our little house on McDonough Road, I was at the homeplace to play a minor role in the family send-off production. My part was limited to admittedly jealous farewells, delivered with hugs and advice to enjoy every minute and followed by waves and kisses blown toward the passengers squeezed with their bags in the moving car headed up Third Street. I received the first news from the travelers in the following letter:

> Monday a.m. June 21, 1954 — Crosby Hall, Chelsea—London
>
> Dear Jane Anne,
>
> It's a big town, London: And a quaint place, Chelsea! We are most happily situated at Crosby Hall and awed that Carlyle's House is in the next block and that Sir Thomas Moore is buried in the churchyard of Chelsea Methodist Church next door. I am up and waiting for breakfast to be served in our room as usual. Marcia continues to doze altho the sun is pouring in. At four I was up and it was daylight and the big moon was reflected in the Thames shimmering water just over the embankment park across the road. A short 5 cents bus ride takes us into the heart of London proper, only a square mile area. This is the artists' delight, much more so than Greenwich village. And yet if you say you live in Chelsea, you are regarded as a millionaire—I love England and its people. Every contact has proven them to be friendly and helpful, courteous and polite, and each person never fails to say a good word for the wonderful young queen. No wonder they are considered deliberate or slow since they take time for the niceties of living. We are to meet a 72 year old man today (a friend made returning from services at St. Paul's) who will introduce us to the Mallets a block away on Kings Road.
>
> "Lucky you were to be greeted by the sunshine," said the warden when we were greeted by your letters. We enjoyed the boat trip up the English channel from Le Havre to London . . . interesting sights . . . Cliffs of Dover, with Dover Castle clearly seen and a windmill topping the bright green mountains . . . delay upon arrival . . . carried ashore at Tillsbury in a tender and another wait for a special train into London . . . taxi ride here . . . deposited suitcases and continued our taxi ride over the city in a 1937 Austin with a Cockney driver who pushed down a "plank" in the top so we could enjoy the spires and domes as well as the sunshine—shrubbery here much like yours . . . daisies, geraniums, pansies, nasturtiums, lilies luxuriant with the

brightest green grass due to fertilizer and dampness in the air . . . all bombed out areas are flower gardens while rebuilding goes on.

Families filled the many parks yesterday . . . Everybody walks. Miniature cars of many makes and plenty of double decker buses. We saw a Cadillac yesterday and Marcia became ecstatic. Statues everywhere. We are most familiar with Eros, god of love, in small octagonal Piccadilly on whose steps lovers forever crowd. Trafalgar Square has beautiful fountains. Big Ben is on Parliament Building across from Westminster. Clocks everywhere! We saw colors on parade & changing of the guard in Whitehall.

It's Monday so we must "hang out" here. Not a word yet in my diary.

Sat. night we enjoyed a play, a comedy about income tax, "Both Ends Meet." Last night a movie, "No Way Out" about an ambitious Negro doctor's life. A visit to St. Paul's made a full Sunday morning . . . Thence to dinner and the entire afternoon at Tate Galleries where we had tea before entering Westminster Abbey . . . plan on remaining four days in London before we leave for Edinburgh Friday when we will stop over at Stratford for a Shakespeare play and on to Warwick Castle, etc.

I am writing Reid House in Paris to expect us there on June 30th and we will meet Mary July 2nd. A welcome letter awaited us here from her. All is happiness, and coffee and toast and fruit are on the table. Another sunny day but cooler. Janie will get more tales of my trip than anybody but Nancy may listen in.

Love,
Mother

Activities reported in that letter were followed by those anticipated. The visit to Edinburgh included a surprise addition—tea in the home of a family connection there.

Then on to Paris, arguably the most beautiful of all the great cities of the world. There, as planned, the Mallets were joined by Ralph and Mary with their seven-year-old daughter Lane. There, besides the usual sightseeing, Mary Lane Mallet, in the company of her youngest and oldest adult daughters, attended a performance of the Follies Bergere.

The next message received in Georgia from the travelers was a postcard addressed to the Atlanta apartment of Emily, who was planning a European vacation of her own. Although mailed from Amsterdam, the picture side of the card was a colorful map of the English Lake District recently visited by the mother and daughter pair. Ralph, chauffeur and tour director for the long drive from Paris to the Carr home in Germany, had decided to give his passengers a swing through the Low Countries.

> July 9, 1954
>
> Keep this card. We took the morning tour and are now ready for the afternoon tour here in Amsterdam. We did the Hague yesterday with a guide in our car. Ralph thinks you should come directly to Zirndorf from London and take tours everywhere from there—Paris, The Netherlands, etc . . . You will have enough time to see everything.
>
> *Mother*

What Mary and Marcia saw in their first glimpse of the Carr residence was a doorway draped with a banner proclaiming WILLKOMMEN! in enormous letters. Beneath the welcome sign stood its creator, housekeeper Ruth, and the Carr children left in her care—five-year-old Lucia, and toddler Emily.

In the days immediately following, the Georgia visitors adjusted quickly and easily to the German–American lifestyle. The presence of three grandchildren was daily joy for Mary. Already, the automobile trip from Paris had given her and little Lane opportunity to feel again the ties that bound them. Grandmother Mary Lane Mallet discovered that her bright namesake Mary Lane Carr was rather proficient in colloquial German. In fact, she often was a convenient translator for her mother, who had not picked it up so rapidly. The adult Carrs were good guides for nearby points of interest, including the old city of Nuremberg. When Ralph was away from home "in the field," Mary seemed to have little difficulty driving German roads that led to the American post exchange, commissary, officers' club, chapel, and quarters of other U.S. personnel.

Soon after the arrival of the Mallet kin, U.S. Army Second Lieutenant Leroy Ades began making calls to see Marcia. Her mother knew about him. As a recent West Point graduate, he had met and dated Marcia while he was stationed at Fort Benning, and she was at Wesleyan College. After his transfer to Germany, they had corresponded and intended to see each other when Marcia came to Germany. Mother Mary, however, had not anticipated that his visits from Munich would begin so immediately and be repeated so often.

Ralph, familiar with the ways of young Army officers, was the first to attach special significance to the frequent visits of Lt. Ades. Ralph shared his opinion with his wife and his mother-in-law that the young officer was "serious" about the relationship that was obviously rapidly developing, adding his approval of the suitor.

The travelers had return ocean liner tickets, booked months before so that sailing dates would allow Marcia to be in Georgia in mid-August in plenty of time to begin the fall semester of her first teaching job. They had no fixed European travel itinerary beyond their primary destination—the Carr home. They were expecting to visit Garmisch in the Bavarian Alps with their hosts, and the mother-daughter pair would like to get a glimpse of Northern Italy on the Adriatic side.

Conveniently and surprisingly, Lt. Ades said that he would like very much to drive them there and that he believed he could arrange the leave that would allow him to do so. The result was a sightseeing expedition for three—two young people with eyes for each other as well as Italian vistas and a mother–chaperone who could focus simultaneously on scenic wonders and her daughter. Back at home, the mother repeated the daughter's reaction to one experience: "Just think—here we are in a gondola in Venice! And I've never even been to Florida."

The brief trip to Venice supplied Mary with evidence that her baby and a good-looking young Army officer were, as Ralph had observed, "serious" about each other. As to her son-in-law's approval of him, Mary was forming her own opinion. She might know little of specific requirements for success in a military career, but she appreciated his impeccable good manners and concern for her comfort and pleasure. She saw admirable competence as he drove miles of unfamiliar, precipitously steep and curving foreign roads.

At necessary rest and gasoline stops, they might or might not find English-speaking attendants. Claiming no formal study of Italian, he managed to communicate questions and turn responses into usable information. Mary's Italian vocabulary was limited to words she had learned years before in voice and piano lessons. Lyrics such as "O sole mio" or "Funiculi, Funicula" were as little help as sheet music directions to play a passage *forte* or *pianissimo* when she needed assistance with map-reading or making change in thousands of liras. She was thankful again and again for the creatively practical communication skills of their driver-companion.

As his conversation continued to reveal a wide range of interests and knowledge, Mary's respect for a West Point education, already high in her esteem, grew with every day she spent in his company. She especially liked his sense of humor, doubtless because it reminded her of that of her son. Both young men enjoyed word play and seemed unable to avoid liberally sprinkling their talk with puns sure to bring on grins or groans or both. When the travelers returned to Germany and the Carr household, the senior Mary confided that Marcia's choice of favored boyfriend showed that her youngest, her baby, was an adult with mature good judgment.

However, neither her liking for Lt. Ades nor her enjoyment of a sample of Italy in his company could prepare her for the announcement she received shortly after their trip together ended. As far as family members homebound in Georgia ever knew, our mother was neither consulted nor her permission asked when Marcia and Roy told her that they had decided to be married—not merely engaged—as soon as a wedding could be arranged. Mother and daughter would not go home together as they had come. Marcia would remain in Munich as the wife of U.S. Army 2nd Lieutenant Leroy P. Ades.

Only Mary could know what she felt as she accepted Marcia's unshakable decision with little opposition. Circumstances had been different in the post-World War II 1940s when her two oldest daughters had wed returning hometown soldiers, well known by family and much of little Jackson and surrounding Butts County. They had encountered their mother's strongly expressed reluctance to favor marriage at twenty-one—the age of both when they confided marriage plans. Each of them had heard "You're too young . . . so much still to see and do before . . . no need to rush . . . why not wait until . . ."

Besides those well practiced arguments, which applied even more to Marcia—her twenty-first birthday yet two months away—there were heavier concerns. Leroy had spent his growing-up years in California and Oregon, across a continent from Marcia's native Georgia and in circumstances even further from her experience. His parents were divorced when he was quite young. He and his younger brother had known a series of living arrangements that included relatives and foster homes. By young manhood, Leroy had found his best resources to be his own abilities, which would have to be developed with his own self-directed energy and determination.

Perhaps mother Mary's romantic heart, seldom far beneath its necessarily practical surface, beat the message that real love could surmount background differences. Perhaps Mary was remembering that she had told her mother of her marriage plans only three days before she and Hugh were wed. Perhaps she knew that arguments for postponement would be as ineffective with Marcia as with herself and her two oldest daughters. For twenty-one years Mary had attempted to satisfy her baby's serious desires as well as harmless whims. Marcia had ways to match her will. So it was that Mary found herself in the summer of 1954 about to play for a third time the part familiar to women the world over. This time, she could not set the stage in the sanctuary of the Jackson Methodist Church. Marcia's wedding would take place in the chapel of a U.S. Army post in a foreign land.

Arrangements involving family, friends, and many kinds of professional and personal commitments began immediately and proceeded as rapidly as was possible for mid-twentieth-century trans-Atlantic communication. One letter from Marcia dated August 22, 1954, referred to a delay in the telegram she had sent to the Georgia school superintendent to notify him that she was withdrawing her acceptance of the teaching job she was scheduled to begin in a matter of days. " . . . I don't understand about that telegram . . . I hope Mr. Cheever didn't have too much trouble . . . I can't believe today was the day for me to start to work . . ."

". . . you have really had to go to a lot of trouble . . . " she wrote, referring to what she called "a progress report" of matters the stay-at-home siblings were handling for her. Emily, planning a September European vacation with a congenial Jackson family friend, Lucile (Mrs. John) Hutcheson, had been notified first. Marcia and her mother wanted the Georgia travelers to arrange to be in Zirndorf for wedding festivities and the ceremony in which Em would be maid-of-honor.

Imbedded in jumbled sentences mixing accounts of trying to assemble a trousseau and wedding "necessities" while attending military social functions with Leroy were these lines: "What in the world did the relatives say? Especially Uncle Kib! I know everyone feels that he is a foreigner since he comes from California—so far from Butts Co's borders. Let us hear from you when you can rest from all these errands and duties."

Writing on the backs of the big sheets of onionskin paper Marcia used, the mother-of-the-bride added her messages before the letter was posted "Via Air Mail." More than fifty years later, all the pages are intact and the words legible.

> Dear Jane Anne,
>
> Please get Emily off in safe manner! Can hardly wait for her to get here altho we figure she will only be in the house three or four nights. I do want everything perfect for Marcia's wedding and plans are being perfected gradually. . . . Chaplain, Capt. Ray Roland of Tennessee . . . has given us three copies of "recommendations" (couple mature, mentally, morally & physically o.k. etc.) in German which we must have along with 3 copies of birth certificates, license . . . civil ceremony and then the real marriage at the chapel with maid-of-honor and best man and ushers, reception following the wedding with wedding cake and everything Marcia wants. So you see this marriage is not entered into in haste. Only one month from tomorrow and Mr. and Mrs. Ades will be on their honeymoon in Switzerland.
>
> . . . I will not be home until after the Nov. Garden Club meeting so I can't entertain this year. My trip home on the Christopher Columbo sailing from Genoa will be a marvelous Mediterranean cruise. Don't think I'm forgetting Janie and Nancy, just busy with my baby. We are sending the announcements of the engagement to Sacramento, Atlanta, Macon, and Jackson papers . . . We plan to address invitations this week before going to Garmisch in the Alps.

A letter dated September 20, 1954, began "My dearest daughter, The Only One who stayed at home and looked after our interests, I do thank you." In snatches, written over a period of several days, the mother-of-the-bride related more nuptial developments. On their way to Switzerland, Emily and Lucille had flown in ". . . much to our joy at noon Saturday and delivered the beautiful trousseau. Everything fits to a T . . . " (Em and I had been designated Atlanta shoppers for Marcia's wedding suit and accessories.) The letter continued with a description of the Sunday afternoon tea hosted by guest Lucile for the bride and her family. The site had been a famed inn located in the nearby ancient walled city of Rothenburg. " . . . most fun we've had anywhere with gay spirits predominating and Lane and Lucia on their best behavior."

The letter continued with the comings and goings that began early Monday morning. "The girls boarded the train under escort of Ralph and me at 6 a.m. and . . . will return from Lucerne next Thursday aft. in time for the rehearsal and to help us get the Officers Club ready for the reception before the entire wedding party goes to Nurnberg for dinner."

The next part of the letter, written a day or so later in different ink, began "We did everything today—put on the finishing touches." The "everything" had included placing orders for wedding and reception flowers—Marcia's white orchid, maid-of-honor Emily's bouquet of yellow roses, yellow rose corsages for herself, daughter Mary, and guest Lucile, as well as palms, tall brass vases of chrysanthemums and low bowls of white flowers. "All of that," she wrote, "will only cost me 40 DM." Forty Deutsche marks would mean about ten American dollars, the surprisingly low price reflecting current rate of exchange. The U.S. Army hotel bakery would supply wedding cake and refreshments for the reception.

She had already filled front and back of a large sheet of the thin paper recommended for air mail, but she had more to write. The page was turned sideways, and "Keep account of how much I owe you" was scribbled on one narrow margin. On the other, our mother finished the letter. "You and Hugh will be with us in spirit and in our prayers on Friday at four o'clock. Love, Mother."

All reports of the wedding festivities—including those given at the Ades's fiftieth anniversary celebration in September of 2004—confirmed that plans and preparations culminated in joy-filled style.

Mother remained with the Carrs throughout October, stretching the two months she had intended to be away to five for herself and "indefinite" for Marcia. Together they had experienced more miles of geography and centuries of history than they had planned and expected before a wedding engulfed everything else on their schedules altered those of all family members.

During her final extra month in Europe, Mary accepted the Ades's invitation to visit them in their Munich apartment. She sampled, enjoyed, and admired Marcia's early cooking experiments and saw the beginning of her married life and homemaking. She may have tried not to make too many suggestions.

More time with the Carr family gave the two Marys more opportunity to be together and to go together to Beyreuth and hear Wagner opera in the city of its birthplace—a special treat for the mother Mary—music lover and singer since her childhood.

The last letter we Georgia "children" received during Mother's 1954 travels bore Italian stamps and was addressed to my Settle family.

> Dearest Children,
>
> I'm just floating on this palace down where the mountains meet the sea, with the Apennines rising above the Mediterranean or I should say the Bay of Naples as they tell me these little islands are the outskirts of Naples where we will anchor in twenty minutes for the day. I've already purchased my sightseeing bus ticket for about 1000 lires. Yesterday sightseeing boats brought visitors out to see us when we were anchored at Cannes.
>
> Ralph brought Lane and Lucia (splendid travelers), Mary and me to Munich last Thursday where we left little Emily with Marcia and Leroy until they return Monday. We had lunch at Garmisch at the Zug Spitze, the highest of the German Alps, and on into Austria to the Innesbruch Bridge over the Innes River where the Twelve Apostles are the highest peaks of the Austrian Alps and on down the Brenner Pass high up in the snow-topped mountains where Mussolini and Hitler met on the border . . . little time was lost at Mittenwald where we entered Austria or at Brenner Pass for the inspection of passports. We had a good hotel at Bologna and came on to Verona where we enjoyed our picnic lunch before arriving at Genoa a little after dark. Ralph did magnificent driving in the faithful old Dodge which has held up so well for our many trips. The Dolomites were high and the roads as corkscrew as possible . . . I was so lucky to get another trip to Italy and Ralph stopped everywhere and I saw much more of that part of Italy than I did with Marcia and Leroy. Naples is too beautiful to miss a minute looking now . . . We will have bus trips at Gibralta Wednesday and then across the broad Atlantic to New York by nine o'clock Tuesday morning, Nov. 9th. A representative of the Pennsylvania R.R. will meet me at the boat and I have my R.R. ticket to Washington . . . I'll

> see Washington before leaving for Atlanta at 8 p.m. and expect to arrive there Wednesday at 8 a.m. . . . Don't try to meet me. I'll call you from Emily's or Virginia's.
>
> Little boys the ages of Janie and Nancy are having a good time here on deck with their parents. So many interesting people, and oh! the food! Can hardly wait to see you all—Thanks for your wonderful letters—my greatest joy abroad.
>
> Much love,
> *Mother*

Before Mother left Germany, Marcia wrote a long letter to Georgia with special messages addressed to each of her siblings there: Emily, Hugh and I. We were each assigned one or more tasks relating to what she needed from home. New marital bliss was reflected on every page. "I can hardly wait for you all to get to know Leroy better. He really does get more wonderful every day. I trust Em has given a good report of him." Just after they had settled into their new apartment, Leroy had been "sent to the field for three weeks." Marcia was looking forward to the arrival of her mother, whose visit of several days would help ease the loneliness of the first separation from her newlywed husband. "I do hate for her to be leaving so soon . . . Mother really hates to go home to an empty house so I'm hoping somebody will show up to live with her."

An empty house is what she would find waiting for her. In the thirty years since Mother had been given the house built by her grandparents, it was first time it was home only to her. For much of the last half of the fifties decade she lived there, usually alone, through the changes and crises dealt her by those years.

The comings and goings of her grown up children could shake the old house to life again for a few hours or a few days. My family and I were in and out almost daily, and Em and Hugh came often from Atlanta on weekends. In early 1955, daughter Mary and her Carr brood returned from Germany with a Georgia assignment to Fort Benning for Ralph, which made fairly frequent visits to the Jackson homeplace possible. Marcia's first year as army wife ended with the arrival of daughter Leah, born in Munich. Soon after her birth, the little family of three were flown back to the States for Leroy's next assignment—advanced language study (Arabic) in California. After landing on the East Coast, they drove west across the nation, stopping in Jackson to give all family members who could assemble there opportunity to welcome home the parents and admire little Leah as the newest family member.

In 1956, McKibben, Mary's beloved, depended-upon brother, died of cancer. With their oldest brother Andrew, Mary and Kib had enjoyed a happy childhood threesome and mature adult friendship encompassing their adult families. Linda, Kib's wife, was as truly a sister to Mary as were blood-kin Margaret and Virginia. Kib and Linda, together and separately, especially since the death of Hugh Sr. in 1939, had been both rock-solid support and fountain of pleasure for Mary and her children.

Virginia, youngest of the Lane children, had perhaps depended upon McKibben even more. He and Mary had played almost parental roles since her childhood. Soon after her brother's death, torn and grieving Virginia left Georgia with artist husband George Beattie and their two little boys to live for a year in Florence, Italy. Through a Fulbright Grant, George found means and opportunity to paint, study, and gain recognition. There, wife and mother Virginia—herself a creative woman—found emotional healing along with intellectual stimulation. Mary remained at home, where attic and basement of her house, her Heritage, became storage space for Virginia as well as her own on-the-move children.

She was alone again in the family homeplace when she became seriously ill. We five young adult children, for all our lives, had taken our mother's health and strength for granted. Her daily display of energy gave us no reason not to do so until symptoms of severe pain and nausea could not be ignored. In a Macon hospital we learned that a life-threatening gall bladder condition required immediate surgery. The operation was performed successfully, but there were complications. For several days, singly or with partners, we offspring in Jackson and Atlanta and her Macon kin kept vigil until we heard a positive prognosis from her doctors.

We were told that although she was showing definite improvement, she would still need hospital care for at least another week. Back at home, she would require bedrest, a special diet, and constant care. I was then the only daughter living in Jackson and was not "gainfully" employed. Chuck and I decided to close our little house on McDonough Road and move temporarily into Mother's big one on Third Street.

There, for two months, I was nurse, care giver, housekeeper, dietitian, and supervisor of second-grader Janie and preschooler Nancy. Our just-across-the-street Methodist minister's wife, an experienced registered nurse as well as good neighbor, "dropped in" almost daily. When we could see that Mother was finally on a good road to recovery, Janie assured one of our visitors, "You don't have to worry about Grandmother anymore; she's getting all welled-up."

As she regained health and strength for her unquestioned position as family matriarch, Mother's major concern may well have been one she seldom discussed. Only son Hugh Jr. was in the process of seeking a career distant and different from what he had talked about since his high school years—practicing law in Georgia.

Returning to Emory's law school soon after his Air Force service ended with the Korean "conflict," he continued his practice of self-support, begun in boyhood. He financed that phase of his continuing education by working in the legal department of the Atlanta based Coca-Cola Bottling Company. He passed the Georgia bar examination before graduation from Emory's law school. (After a list of those passing the test was printed in the Atlanta newspapers, Hugh found another announcement—this one unique—waiting for him when he next drove down to Jackson. Tacked to a front porch entrance post was a wooden roof shingle on which Ralph had painted "HUGH MALLET, ATTORNEY AT LAW.") When court next convened in the Butts County Courthouse, with his mother and me seated in the courtroom, Hugh was formally admitted to the Georgia Bar. Before leaving that scene, Mother told several of the group offering congratulations that her son was following the professional path already marked with footprints of his great-grandfather Van McKibben, his grandfather Andrew Lane, and two of his uncles—Joel Mallet and McKibben Lane.

Their way, however, was not to be that of young Hugh. After weathering upheaval of personal plans during his last months at Emory, he was seeking another direction. When Mother and Marcia left for Europe, his fiancee had been present at their departure. The Mallets approved his choice and liked the attractive, intelligent, popular young woman who was daughter of a dean respected throughout the Emory scholarly community.

Mary had given her son the diamond that she had worn since 1922 when Hugh Sr. placed it on her own finger.

But in the fall of 1954, the events of homecoming did not include the anticipated marriage of her son. Just days before the couple were to announce the date for their wedding, the bride-not-to-be cancelled it and returned to the would-be groom the diamond reset for her.

We sisters were never told reasons for the break. Neither did we learn our brother's reasons for changing his professional plans. Perhaps he wished to leave the scenes of his disappointment and hurt. Perhaps his job as an Air Force intelligence officer in the Korean War had introduced him to work he found interesting and challenging. Whatever his motivations, he applied for, received and accepted admittance to the program requisite for becoming a special agent for the Federal Bureau of Investigation. Before the 1950s ended, he had successfully completed that intensive, rigorous training conducted in the Washington, D.C., area. There he also met, fell in love with, and married a bride unlike any of us or the other girls and women we knew to have inhabited his past.

Tiny, soft-spoken Cathy Levecque seemed to us tall, big-boned Mallet women like a lovely, fragile French doll. She obviously returned his lasting affection, making him the definite center of her life for all the rest of his. Adapting to his ways and choices, she left the Catholicism of her family to join Hugh in his family's Methodist Protestantism. Accepting the demands of his work—long, usually uncertain hours as well as the more dramatic dangers—she seldom made plans for herself because she wanted to be available whenever he had free time to spend with her and their children, all three of them born during his first assignments, in Detroit and Chicago, before transfer and promotions brought him to the Washington, D.C., FBI headquarters where he quickly rose to the position of chief of legal counsel.

Knowing that her husband and his mother would ever be close, Cathy became a model daughter-in-law—selecting gifts for special occasions, writing letters with the family news when Hugh's letters were apt to be brief and hurried, welcoming and caring when her mother-in-law visited, and quietly fitting into many kinds of big family doings when the Hugh Mallets visited Jackson and the homeplace. Mother never told us daughters her deepest feelings about Hugh's work or his wife. She did say when he chose the FBI over practice of law in Georgia and again when he married someone she had never met that she trusted his judgment completely and that she was sure he was making the right choices, choices perfect for him.

As the fifties ended, Mary Lane Mallet and all her children could look back over another decade of change. The five little Mallets of the thirties and forties had become five young adults, still deciding and changing into who they would be. Their mother, with more gray in her hair and more pounds registering on her scale, seemed, through all the changes, to be sure who she was. She bragged that she was "grandmother of seven." (That number would double during the sixties.)

The old house, her Heritage and her home, had stood solid and tall through more change than she or her children had known. Except for white paint instead of its original grey, it looked much the same on the outside as in the early 1890s. Inside, running water for the kitchen and four bathrooms and electricity for lighting and appliances were twentieth-century improvements. It was still serving the purpose for which Van and Janie McKibben had built it—to be a comfortable family home where the pineapples carved into the entrance gingerbread woodwork promised as well as symbolized hospitality—beginning always with family.

The 1950s had begun with a full house: one Mallet daughter writing her master's thesis at home, another daughter with her husband and baby waiting to move into their own recently purchased house, son and youngest daughter returning often for weekends away from college, and also three boarding teachers. The prospect Mary had dreaded as she returned from Europe in 1954—an empty house to be lived in alone without her last baby—was not to be her permanent reality.

When the decade slipped into history, Heritage had been filled again—this time just with family members. Oldest daughter, Mary, and youngest, Marcia, were both married to the U.S. Army officers who were subject to assignments that did not allow family accompaniment.

Daughter Mary, with three children mother Mary had so enjoyed in Germany, arrived to live temporarily in the Jackson homeplace when Ralph left Fort Benning, for his next duty, South Korea. While he was part of the American troops in the occupation coalition with the task of keeping the uneasy peace there, his wife and children would be occupying the upstairs bedrooms and baths of the house where Mary Mallet Carr had grown up. Her task was keeping peace there. Carr daughters Lane and Lucia were enrolled in the public grammar school just a block away, the same one their mother had attended.

In the same timeframe, Leroy completed his assignment to California for study of Arabic. While they lived there, he and Marcia became parents to another baby. Their Leah, was given a baby sister they named Mary Elaine, to be called "Elaine." When Roy left for assignment in Saudi Arabia, the best living arrangement for Marcia, two-year-old Leah, and the new baby seemed to be the home Marcia had left just after college graduation. The Carrs were already upstairs there, but the downstairs back bedroom with its own bathroom and cedar-lined closet was still vacant. When Mary and Hugh Mallet were given the house by her mother Hattie, they planned that space adjoining their bedroom to be "the nursery." Marcia and her little girls made the name appropriate again.

As for mother and grandmother Mary, for a while she was the owner and central figure of a house offering shelter to eight distinctive females whose ages ranged between her sixties and Elaine's six months. She could rock and sing to another baby, play and read with pre-and-school-age children, and enjoy adult give-and-take with her grown-up daughters. Of course there were times of stress, but the senior Mary and her house gave more evidence that together they could accommodate needs of the fifth generation to call the old place home.

With Onie's Hope

THE STORIES OF MY MOTHER, MARY LANE MALLET, during the 1930s, the 1940s, and most of the 1950s are not complete without the inclusion of Onie tales that tell at least something of her part in our life then. Onie's role defies classification. I suppose she could be called domestic "help." She was certainly our cook and sometimes housekeeper or nursemaid or laundress or all or none of these. She helped us, and we helped her. Mallets taught, and she learned; then the roles might be reversed. Sometimes she leaned on us—even while she was our prop. Onie could see and participate in Mary Mallet's development from young, cherished wife and mother through grieving widow and on to financial and operational manager of a changing household and family in which she was the social, educational, and spiritual center. Onie was one reason our center could hold.

I cannot remember my childhood before Onie came to our house. I cannot picture our life then without her huge, dark, splendid presence, but I know how Onie came because our mother seemed determined to make her memories ours.

In 1928, when Emily was a baby, Mary faced a new situation—three little girls and no household "help." Since she and Hugh had moved into the McKibben–Lane house and added "Mallet" to its designation, a series of cooks and young nursemaids had helped her keep the early years of marriage smooth and bright. But the experienced, skilled, and aging cook retired to live with a daughter, and young Margaret Scott went North. No one, especially Mary herself, expected Hugh Mallet's wife to manage a big house, a big yard, and three children without "help."

So Onie came, as she said, to "hope" us. She and her husband, Jack Grier, had moved into the tenant house at the edge of the home farm. Jack was already too old to work, but his two adult sons could make a crop. Onie came from the cotton field to our kitchen, and it became her domain.

It was a big room, one end dominated by the black, wood-burning stove, itself a taskmaster. Daddy usually made a fire in it very early in the morning before Onie came to cook breakfast. Under the window, opening onto the high, screened back porch, stood the woodbox. Its legs wobbled only when it was empty. Every morning, before they left the barn lot for the fields, the farm hands clumped up the steep back steps, their breath making puffs in winter weather, and filled the box from the woodpile in the yard. (Mrs. Smith, the teacher who later boarded with us said that our big woodpile was a sure sign of prosperity.) As the hands dumped their armload of firewood, they gave deferential greeting: "Mawnin', Miss Onie." She knew them all and their families, too, and understood their morning grumbling and news sharing. The hands, including our father's right-hand man Es, respected her.

The stove was a black beast, but Onie had it tamed. With just the right feeding and control of the damper, she could get the burners red hot for fast breakfast cooking. Her tools and symbols of authority were an iron poker and an iron handle for removing the cooking "eyes" from the stove surface so that a skillet or kettle could be more directly heated. She could later calm and steady the fire for oven baking. When our mother cautioned Onie about burns and suggested more use of pot holders, Onie's reply was, "I got asbestos hands." The stove knew its mistress. Spreading and sharing its warmth in winter, glistening from its heat in summer, Onie was in control.

How she nourished us! Daddy liked his coffee and breakfast brought to his bedroom, but we children began our day in the kitchen and breakfast room with Onie. In coldest weather we often finished dressing there because we did not often have fires in our bedrooms. Breakfast was hearty—always plenty of eggs, and the milk and butter delivered every morning from Uncle George's Willow Valley Dairy. In winter we had grits with smoked ham, sausage, or "streak-of-lean" bacon from our hogs.

Every morning Onie made either biscuits or the pancakes we called "batter cakes." We had our own cane syrup and apple jelly or blackberry jam. In summer there were peaches and melons and berries and wild plums. When we had company or on special occasions when we all ate breakfast together in the dining room, we might have beefsteak and gravy served on toast.

As soon as breakfast dishes were washed and beds made, Onie began working on our mostly vegetable midday dinner. Green beans had to be strung and snapped, peas shelled, turnip greens washed and washed and washed. In warm weather, Onie sat on the back porch by the wooden ice box, peeling vegetables, shucking fresh corn, and talking to any of the hands who might be out of the fields to work in our yard. She greeted the iceman and any tradesman who came to the back door. It was Onie, too, who assessed the need and the honesty of the occasional ill-clad stranger asking for something to eat or a few coins before he made his way back to the railroad tracks to climb into another freight train car. Onie gathered the eggs from the few chickens we had in the lot and killed and dressed the ones we ate. I hated the neck wringing and the final headless flapping, but I watched in fascinated horror.

After our noontime dinner, Onie washed the dishes and walked home toting any leftovers. During spells of cold or rainy weather, either Mother or Daddy went for her in the morning and drove her home in the afternoon. She preferred walking, maintaining that in light showers she "jes' stepped between the drops."

Onie did little housework outside the kitchen.Younger housemaids came and went. Onie stayed, directing any other household help and us, too. As we first three little girls grew and our family expanded, so did her influence and authority.

Experienced in midwifery and infant care, Onie proved her dependability where babies were concerned during Emily's first year and Onie's first with us. While Daddy was on a business trip to Savannah, baby Emily developed a severe case of croup. The doctor came and went, but Onie remained hours after her usual afternoon departure. Mother never forgot and told us how she had reluctantly urged Onie to start her walk home before dark. Mother related Onie's response. "I ain't fixin' to leave you here with this chile sick and Mr. Hugh gone. I'll jes' set here by the fire and hold her."

Hugh Jr. was born in that same room two years later, and as at Emily's birth, a nurse was brought from Macon. That white-uniformed professional, with Onie in the nursery, was given the task of supervising my fourth birthday celebration when my new brother was four days old. Hugh's birth, followed so soon by my birthday cake and ice cream served in our play area by the side steps, is foremost in my earliest memories. I remember, too, my feeling of relief when the stiff-starched nurse went back to Macon and left our baby with us.

The family handful of little Mallets was complete when, three years later, Marcia was born. For her birth there was no imported nurse. Mother and Onie had become a team.

Together they got us through scrapes, bruises, fusses, and tantrums; through coughs, fevers, chicken pox, measles, and mumps—which we passed on to Daddy. Usually, however, the whole family was well. Mother said children could thrive on sunshine, good food, lullabies, and laughter. Health and strength were natural states. With Onie's help, she maintained our Natural State, and we seldom crossed its borders.

Onie always knew more about us than we did about her. She knew exactly what we ate and whether our farm produce was supplemented sparingly or occasionally lavishly by purchased items. She took our laundry home every week, boiled our linen in a black wash pot in her yard, and brought it back in a long woven straw basket with Daddy's white shirts and our dresses starched and ironed and placed on top of sheets and towels.

She knew the personality and peculiarities of each of us. She could and did trace every trait or quirk to its genetic source on Mother's or Daddy's "side." She knew "Miss Hattie," our Grandmother Lane, and her Butts County roots and connections. Grandmother Lane was also the actual owner of the fields and the tenant house where Onie lived.

She knew all the Mallets. She recognized the contrast between the booming voice and military style of Uncle George's farm management and Daddy's quieter but equally responsible and effective methods. With us, Onie accepted the brusque manner of our Aunt Pauline, as thin veneer for solid family loyalty and love. It seemed to us children that Onie and

Sister must be in some conspiracy that kept one or the other ever on guard to keep us from the prohibited pleasures of skating or riding a bicycle in the street and opening the lot gate to play in one of the barns.

Onie's younger sister, Eulah, worked for Uncle Joel, who was living in Jackson again with his second wife, Maria. Eulah was their cook and afternoon nursemaid for their Billy, just a year younger than my brother Hugh Jr. Onie knew the special bond between Daddy and brilliant, lovable, flawed Uncle Joel. She knew the telephone calls that meant Daddy would leave our house to find Uncle Joel and take him home.

Onie was at our house, too, on the Sunday morning the telephone call to Daddy brought news more tragic than another of Uncle Joel's drinking binges. The body of Es, the top black worker in our father's farm and farm-related enterprises, had been found by the railroad tracks. He had been beaten to death with brass fist knuckles.

Es had worked for our father some years before our parents' marriage. He paid "Miss Mary" dutiful respect, but even when he worked around our house, where she directed the "help," Es took his orders from "Mr. Hugh." He called us children "Mr. Hugh's chillun." If Es was holding the mule reigns, Daddy might let us ride in the wagon the short distance between the barn lot and the home farm. One Christmas we rode in the wagon with Es all the way out to the Mallet farm where we selected our Christmas tree. In memory I still smell the cedar branches beside us on the wagon floor as we rolled and bumped home.

On the Sunday morning we learned of Es's death, I saw my father cry. Onie had to have seen the tears in his eyes, too. And she and the other hands must have known of his and our lawyer Uncle Joel's efforts during the following weeks to bring justice to the prosecution of the white boys who had perhaps seen in Es—probably on his way home after a Saturday night of crap shooting and moonshine—a vulnerable, inferior black being whose beating would show "white supremacy." I was a child, and I never learned all the facts; I do remember that the Mallet family believed the punishment for Es's killing was far too light. Today it would be called a hate crime.

Although our knowledge of Onie was more limited than hers of us, we had glimpses into her private life and world. She told us that she was descended from African royalty. We never doubted it. She wore enormous aprons made of bleached flour and feed sacks over the dresses she sewed for herself. The regular women's sizes of dresses from a store could never have accommodated her frame. She was usually shod in men's shoes. On the fourth Sunday of every month she left our house early to go to the Negro Macedonia Baptist Church. Then a snow white dress and a royal blue banner across her bosom signified that she was an usher and a member of the prayer band. She was clothed in dignity and honor.

We had no genealogical table to trace Onie's roots back to Africa. Even her more recent background was vague. We did know that her surname was Grier, both before and after she was Uncle Jack's wife. In the 1930s, elderly black men were often called "uncle." Ignorant and innocent of the opprobrium the term carried in later years, we called Jack Grier "uncle" to announce respect and affection. The Griers had been a pioneer family in the county. Jack, born a slave, may have belonged to them. He was much older than Onie, who was probably his cousin.When he was left a widower with small sons, Onie had moved in to care for them.

We also knew Mandy, Onie's mother. She was even older than Uncle Jack and lived with Onie's sister Eulah. Eulah and her husband owned their own house and a little store in Darktown, an area across the railroad tracks from the depot. Mandy was blind. On rare occasions Onie relieved Eulah of the care of their ancient parent by bringing Mandy with her to our house. She could sit on the back porch or in the backyard while Onie worked.

In the summer, Uncle Jack often came. He liked children, and we liked him. He didn't mind giving a push to get a swing started or making simple repairs of a scooter or little wagon. In the early fall he sometimes peeled sugar cane and cut it in chewing size strips for us. Mother liked him, too, and said she knew we were safer when Uncle Jack kept an eye on us.

Besides Jack's sons, Onie had two of her own. Ralph still lived in the county, but Dick, her pride and joy, worked for the railroad and lived in distant, fabled Cleveland, Ohio.

One summer Dick's two little girls came to visit Onie. They were about the ages of Em and me, and Onie brought them to play with us. Onie received the news a year or so later that one of them had died. She could not go to Cleveland, but she shared her grief with Mother. Onie's saying for pain and disappointment was "We jes' got to wear this world like a loose garment."

Onie was mother-proud of Dick. She could paint his life and accomplishments in far-away Ohio in whatever hues she chose. It was a fact that the railroad paid him more money than any Butts County farmhand ever saw. Wearing a dark suit, a white shirt, and a tie, Dick could come home on the train and tell of a city that must have seemed to his mother both Babylon and Promised Land.

Dick had used the little schooling he had scrounged in Butts County. He had added literacy to the survival skills Onie had taught him. She had a word for common sense and confident ability to cope with whatever life served—"mother-wit." She passed hers on to Dick. He could make changes; he could see and seize opportunity.

So could Onie. "See Dick. See Dick run." One of the New Deal programs was an adult literacy class. Onie must have been in her fifties when she enrolled. She brought her books and her tablet to our house where Mother encouraged her.

We children knew that some of the older hands could not read or write. We were familiar with the "X" they made when a signature was required. We knew Onie never consulted the cookbooks and printed recipes our mother often used. We accepted her declaration, "I don't need no book to make vittles fittin' to eat," as genuine contempt. It had never occurred to us that Onie, all-knowing Onie, could not read before her ongoing education spilled out onto our kitchen table. After she had mastered reading, as she seemed to master most adversaries, she said that she was proud she could learn but that Jack was just too old for it.

As Uncle Jack became older still, he became senile and sometimes wandered away if he were not watched. Onie said he was trying to "go home." If Onie and her family could not find him, she called on us. Then Mother or Daddy would take Onie in the car and search the red, rutted, narrow roads near the Ocmulgee until they found him.

After Uncle Jack's death, Onie came to Mother with a problem. Although Onie had cared for Jack Grier and his sons, borne him two of her own, worked with him in the fields, and brought home cash, too, for working in white households, she and Jack had never been formally married. It had just seemed natural, she said, to live with him when he needed somebody. Onie was a respected member of the Negro Macedonia Baptist Church. As a Christian, she knew her job was to fight sin. "I'm worried, Miss Mary," she confessed. Mother listened. She told Onie that she understood and believed God understood, too. He had surely blessed her long union with Jack Grier whether a paper license and a ceremony had been part of it or not. Relieved and satisfied, Onie took off guilt and again wore this world like a loose garment.

The reading class was not the only New Deal program directly to affect Onie's life. Mallet property had been the site of a CCC camp. During those Great Depression years of the 1930s, young men who would otherwise be unemployed could find work and small wages as part of the Civilian Conservation Corps, a regimented, army-like labor force for public projects related to the environment. Nearby Indian Springs State Park qualified as one of them. When the improvements there had been completed and the camp closed and abandoned, Hugh Mallet had a section of the barracks removed and set up again behind Onie's sister Eulah's house in Darktown. Onie had her own house.

Looking back, I see that my perception of Onie was complex and changing. But most of the time, we Mallet children simply accepted her, neither questioning nor appreciating. I remember my hot blush of embarrassment when I called my first grade teacher "Onie." Miss Annie Lou, however, seemed not to be insulted. She knew who Onie was, and she doubtless knew that both she and Onie were authorities in my life that must be obeyed.

We toyed with rebel desires, but we "minded." When Onie told us to bring in more wood for the stove, we did. When she was in a bad humor and told us to get out of her kitchen, we did that. If we asked her to do something—pour a glass of milk, tie a knot, locate a toy—that she knew we could do for ourselves, she asked contemptuously, "Is you pair-lyzed?"

We thought sometimes that Eulah gave our cousin Billy Mallet better treatment that Onie gave us. Eulah let him decide what to wear and helped him get dressed. She walked with him wherever he wanted to go in the long summer afternoons. She seemed to cook desserts everyday. What he had called allergies must confer distinction and privilege, I decided. Yet Onie baked tea cakes for us on those days when she felt good and sang a lot. She might let us roll out the dough or cut the cookies and eat the scraps. And she kept peach puffs warm for us until we got home from school.

Onie would not put up with our fussing and fighting when she was in charge. Hugh was more rambunctious than we girls were. Onie shared the family knowledge that Hugh was indeed special, a special, a natural source of pride and joy. She called him "Sugarfoot" and let him drink milk flavored with coffee with her, but he still couldn't get away with "No foolishness." He liked to chase Emily and her best friend Libby, the youngest daughter of the Methodist preacher. (It was always our hope that any new preacher the bishop sent us would have children with ages to match ours.) Part of Em's and Libby's delighted terror as he pursued them up and down the steps and around the house was squealing, "Run for your life!" On one such occasion, a car filled with visiting Macon relatives pulled into our yard just as Onie, arms akimbo, was massively blocking the path of the rampaging Hugh and forcefully delivering her ultimatum: "You cool off fo' I cools you off." Actually Onie never laid a hand on us for discipline; she didn't need to.

Onie could be an embarrassment. I hated for my friends to see how Onie bossed and criticized. "You ain't about to walk to town lookin' like that." I envied the perfect household of our Macon Lane cousins. Their Iona seemed ever quiet and respectful, never intrusive. She wore a black dress and little white apron and called our cousin "Miss Linda." She never talked or grumbled while she served meals. I never heard her tell Linda, "I ain't studying' you," which meant that under no circumstances would Onie grant what I thought a reasonable enough request. That paragon Iona would never have come out of the kitchen to sing for company seated at the dinner table. But when our cousin Billy Lane asked her, Onie wiped her hands on her apron and sang "Swing Low, Sweet Chariot," her voice rising and falling and weaving the familiar melody in and out of her own richly embroidered variations. It seemed to me that the tune was all but lost until the final exaltation of "Comin' for to carry me home!"

There was a worse company occasion, at least for our mother Mary. When Aunt Margaret and her husband—a successful, midwestern, Yankee engineer—came from St. Louis to visit Georgia relatives, Mother made special preparations for their dinner with us. Uncle Earl did not come often, and Mother may have felt that not only the family but the entire Southern way of life was being inspected. After eating the best dinner Mother could provide, Uncle Earl complimented Onie, who had come from the kitchen to clear the table. Mother could only gasp when Onie's response was, "I don't see nothin' under yo' plate." The episode became a favorite Lane tale retold at family gatherings and guaranteed to bring on laughter. The best Mother ever managed was a sick smile.

Mother often maintained that she believed that children required a certain amount of "wholesome neglect." Actually, she knew—at least approximately—where we all were and what we were doing. We were not allowed to handle knives or matches. When fireplaces were in use, there were always screens. Mother did not like to leave us for very long and did not unless Onie was left in charge. But Daddy liked for Mother to go with him on short business trips to Atlanta or Macon or the nearby rural towns and communities. He said that it was fine for her to keep house but not for the house to keep her.

One rainy spring day she drove with him across the Ocmulgee River to adjacent Jasper County. The distance was less than twenty miles, but that trip could offer a bit of excitement. There was no bridge across the river, and a ferry transported cars and passengers. The roads were unpaved and rain turned the red clay into slick, soggy mud. When afternoon became twilight and our parents had not come home, we began to feel uneasy. Even "Little Orphan Annie" on the radio failed to command our attention. It only made matters worse because we knew the time was five-forty-five. Late!

At the first ting of the telephone in the back hall, we dashed to it. Mary answered, but all of us could hear Central Operator announce a long distance call from Macon. It was Mother. She talked to Mary first and then to Onie explaining that the ferry had stopped operation because of high water. They decided to drive home by way of Macon. Arriving there later than they anticipated, they discovered the unpaved road to Jackson too muddy to risk getting stuck on it after dark. If we were all right and Onie could stay, they would spend the night with Grandmother Lane in Macon. We did not think anything was all right, but with Mother and Daddy, at one end of the telephone line and Onie with us at the other, we knew we could get through the night.

The ties between Onie and Mother were the strongest and most intricate, tightening and loosening to accommodate mutual dependence and mutual respect for independence. Onie had come when times were good, when Mary and Hugh Mallet were in the "high cotton" of youth and prosperity. Our house, especially in summer, was right for easy Middle Georgia hospitality. Besides big, close families, both Daddy and Mother had valued friends throughout the county and state. They might visit for an hour or a day or so or just stop by on their way between Macon and Atlanta. Highway 42, which connected those two cities, went right by our house once the state highway became Jackson's main street, Third. Mother soon discovered that Onie could be counted on to make our simple meals tasty enough for guests. Our mother Mary could add flourishes—a carefully set table, her own mayonnaise, peach pickles in a cut crystal dish, and roses for a centerpiece. Onie's skills were best exercised behind the dining room door.

Mother's respect and appreciation for Onie grew as prosperity shrank into the Great Depression. Mother put on her whole armor for a long battle with hard times: cheerful optimism and intelligent adaptability. She rented two of our upstairs bedrooms to young, fledgling teachers. Daddy was on the board of education when Massie Lane, Mother's pretty cousin from Americus, and Jim Etheridge, son of a former Jackson resident, were elected to fill vacancies on the Jackson High School faculty. For several years, Massie and Jim were more than boarders; they were lively, interesting additions to our household.

Onie supplied her tested tactics. She could stretch a single chicken into a family feast by cooking an abundance of rice, glorified with egg and giblet gravy. Then she used the broth and any leftover bony pieces for a soup that could be supper. One day during a siege of rainy weather, she looked out the kitchen window to see a huge turtle proceeding ponderously down the little unpaved road that separated our side yard from the Redman's. Onie saw more than a turtle; she recognized our dinner. Her turtle soup was gourmet fare.

Christmas was never skimpy even when buying had to be. Mother proudly gave her brothers and sisters the big dark fruitcakes she and Onie made. In November Mother would say, "We've got to get started on the fruitcakes." Onie's comment was, "Lincoln done freed the slaves. I ain't got to do nothin' but be black and die." Then they went to work.

There was no recipe for the cakes, and they differed from year to year. The ingredients cost little. Throughout the summer, Onie had turned fresh fruit, especially the figs that grew in the corner of our backyard into preserves. As soon as citrus fruit from Florida became plentiful, Mother and Onie candied the thick grapefruit and orange peelings. The nuts came from the pecan trees that provided summer shade. Soon after Halloween, we began to shake their branches and pick up the nuts. Shelling pecans after supper was a family project as we sat around the fire in the library and listened to "Fibber Magee and Molly" or "Fred Allen" or "Lux Radio Theater."

Mother and Onie later worked side by side measuring out the spices and preparing mounds of nuts and fruits. Onie's powerful hands squeezed and mixed it all together into a heavy batter. Then the cakes baked in the slow oven of the wood-burning stove as the whole house was filled with fragrance. Fruit cakes took all day.

Confidence and self-esteem went into the cakes. Mother's were rooted in education and the security of unquestioned family approval and support. Perhaps Onie's resulted at least in part from long experience with meeting and managing almost daily crises. Both women possessed some fathomless well of strength. Neither would have understood nor had much patience with a quest for identity. They knew who they were, and they liked themselves. As they worked together, they liked each other.

My father's sudden death shattered it all—all our little glass bubble world. The year was 1939, and the great world outside our little one was never to be the same again either.

Even Onie, whose health and strength we took for granted, was subject to attacks of what she called "the High Blood." She didn't exactly "get down" with it, and she didn't "quit" us either. She just wore us and our demands looser because, as she said, "she didn't have to do nothin' but be black and die." She didn't come to our house so early in the morning that some of us could be still in bed. She might not come at all for days at a time. She went to see Dick in Cleveland. Babies were her specialty, and she sometimes accepted other temporary, higher paying jobs of a week or so taking care of new mothers and their babies. We knew she had not abandoned us; she came when she "felt like it." When we needed her, Mother drove down by the depot and over the tracks to Darktown to bring her to our house from hers, the old CCC barracks now in Eulah's brush-broom swept backyard.

Onie often helped with our invalid Grandmother Lane's care. She was already at our house when Mother's first grandchild was brought home to Jackson from the hospital in Athens. When she strode up the hall with a filled coal scuttle at the end of each powerful arm, our household was in her care again.

Mary told me of waking up during one of the long nights. Firelight revealed Onie, sitting near the hearth and holding the baby. "Put her down, Onie," Mary directed. "It's all right for her to cry a little. You need some rest." Onie's reply was "Ain't studyin' you. I'm too old for sleep." And she cradled little Lane in her arms and continued to rock forward and back.

When a college friend of mine stopped by the next weekend, she found all of us—especially Mother—eager to show off the first representative of our new generation. Onie assumed detached objectivity. "It's jes' a baby; ain't nuthin' but a baby. Can't make it nuthin' but a baby."

Onie was soon to give up regular work with us or anybody else, but she continued to come to our house for special events—my wedding, Grandmother's death and funeral, summer reunion celebrations in the backyard. In the mid 1950s, Onie was part of our welcoming group clustered in the front walk when Marcia and Leroy returned from Europe with infant daughter Leah. Roy, knew about Onie from descriptions by the Georgia home folks he had met. Holding out his first born to her, he said, "See, Onie, we've brought you our new baby."

Onie, with a surge of her old strength, took not baby Leah but grown-up Marcia in her arms, actually lifting her off the ground. "This here's my baby."

On the morning Marcia was to leave with her new family for Roy's assignment in California, Onie, unbidden, was again in Mother's kitchen before daylight. She had come to cook breakfast and fry chicken for the travelers' lunch. She would see to it herself that her baby did not get in a car headed for the other side of the country without something "fittin' to eat."

A few years later when I returned to Heritage with Chuck and our young children to provide post-surgical care for Mother, I had plunged awkwardly into a swamp of responsibilities, taking care of bedridden Mother and keeping up with two active children, cooking for all of us while following the restrictions imposed by Mother's diet, and keeping the house presentable for the steady stream of visiting friends. One afternoon, as I was catching my breath, I glanced through the screen door to see Onie coming up the front walk.

I hurried out to meet her on the front porch, but, panting from the walk beneath the September sun all the way from Darktown, Onie scarcely acknowledged my welcome. "I come to see Miss Mary," she said as she pushed by me into the hall and through the door to Mother's room.

"Onie!" was what I heard, the old lilt back in Mother's voice. What I saw was Mother sitting up in bed with arms out-stretched and Onie bending to embrace her. "Miss Mary," she proclaimed, "if you was colored, I'd call you cud'n." That was Onie's and our own Southern pronunciation of cousin, the term of address for many adult relatives. In our family its use stood for respect, sometimes love. It meant we were proud to claim kinship, which could be stretched from first cousin to fourth or fifth and beyond actual lineal tracing.

Time was squeezed out in days and weeks and months and years. In another summer, Mother got the news that Onie had "passed." Emily, who happened to be at home on a break from work at Georgia Tech where she was a librarian, accompanied Mother to Eulah's house to express our family's respect and love for Onie, our sense of loss, and our sympathy for all the Grier family. Mother and Em gave evidence of the latter in the case of cold Coca-Colas they brought for the mourners.

Onie was laid out in Eulah's front room. Just as on all those fourth Sundays when Onie left our house early to attend her church, she was wearing a white dress with the royal blue banner across her bosom as her final announcement to the world she was leaving that she had served the Negro Macedonia Baptist Church as faithful usher and Prayer Band member.

Eulah said that Onie had wanted to go out in style. We knew Onie had life insurance; she always had her money tied up in her apron, ready for the "Polish Man" when he came every week to collect the premium on her policy. Eulah told Mother that she was spending every cent of that "polish" with Abe Trimier, the local colored undertaker. "Onie didn't want no fussin' 'bout none of her money," Eulah said.

The funeral, of course, would be held at Onie's beloved church, which was out in the country and some distance from town. We were not urged to attend, and none of us went. Mother said that we might seem to be intruding. We heard, though, that it was grand. The church was full, and the eulogies were testimonies from men and women, young and old whom Onie had "hoped." She had hoped at births and at deaths. In times of crisis or just plain tough times, she had shared her food and roof. She had given boosts with encouraging words; and if she thought a "blessin' out" was needed, she gave that, too. More than once, she had taken an unwanted, neglected child into her home.

And she didn't "have to do nuthin' but be black and die."

I hope they sang "Swing Low, Sweet Chariot."

Emily's Time: A Love Story

EARLY IN JANUARY, 1961, MOTHER RECEIVED A LETTER that was to mark the beginning of an entire year when the focus of her life would be her third daughter Emily.

> This is a quick note to let you know my schedule for coming home. I will leave Frankfurt on Sunday, 8 January 1961 at 2:30 p.m. and arrive in New York at 5:00 pm. Seems impossible doesn't it. I have reservations on an Eastern Airlines flight leaving NY at 9:45 pm and arriving in Atlanta at 11:45 . . . If I don't see a familiar face at the airport I'll call . . . Looking forward to seeing you soon.
>
> Love to all,
> *Em*

Familiar faces throughout at least a hundred miles of Georgia began wearing smiles as soon as the news spread that Emily, after an absence of more than a year, would soon be home. At the age of thirty-two, she could count ten post-college years spent quite differently from those of her sisters. Mary, Marcia, and I had each married at age twenty-one. Our brother Hugh, with perhaps more lifestyle opportunities, still chose marriage over single life at twenty-eight. By the time of Emily's homecoming announcement, her four siblings had made possible her continuing performance in the role of doting, beloved "Aunt Em" for eight nieces.

As a toddler, Emily was described by her mother as "most winsome." Entering her thirties, she was enriching the meaning of a relatively new term for a single, working woman—"Bachelor Girl." She had earned part of her tuition at Wesleyan College by working as one of the student assistants to the much admired and respected head librarian. Then and there she chose her profession.

After graduation from Wesleyan, she entered Emory University Graduate School. After earning a master's degree there, she accepted her first job as a professional librarian at Lockheed, the aircraft manufacturing corporation, which had been located since World War II in Marietta, an Atlanta suburb. There she set up a technical library before taking her education and experience to Georgia's Institute of Technology.

Em's living arrangements proved to be as satisfactory as did her jobs. With two other librarians and close friends, her Wesleyan roommate an Emory classmate, and another mutually chosen young woman, she rented an apartment in "Colonial Homes," a recently constructed complex on north Atlanta's Peachtree Road. Before such popular television sitcoms as that in which Mary Tyler Moore introduced many unsophisticated Americans to ways of life not only possible but becoming common for career women, real-life Emily and her companions were practicing their chosen profession and enjoying youthful independence as they selected leisure activities. Common interests in books, the arts, and travel had brought them together; flexible, tolerant sharing of domestic chores and responsibilities took care of different attitudes and habits regarding housekeeping. They assembled furniture from many sources—including the homes of their parents—and created a comfortable apartment for themselves and welcoming space for their friends of both sexes. Among Em's male friends were several engineers met while she was at Lockheed.

In combinations with each other and with their current "boyfriends," the young women attended movies, plays, concerts, exhibitions, and sports events—the number and quality of them increasing with Atlanta's growth. Two or more of them sometimes shared vacations at beach and mountain resorts. Several of them traveled together to Mexico, to South America, and to Europe.

As could have been anticipated, their close, congenial, all-female group living could not be permanent. The friends who comprised it never surrendered individual options. While marriage was pulling two of them from the menage, Emily was also considering a move. Sidney Thomas, a friend from Emory student days, had taken a government position as civilian director of the library for U.S. military and civil service personnel assigned to the NATO (North Atlantic Treaty Organization) Air Force Headquarters in Ramstein, West Germany. He was offering her a job as his assistant, and urging her to seize such an opportunity for broadening professional experience in a location that could be a hub for travel throughout Europe and farther. Emily remembered how much she had enjoyed being in Germany when she visited that country to be maid-of-honor in her sister Marcia's wedding. Five years later, an appealing job beckoned maiden Emily back. She took a leave of absence from Georgia Tech and took the job.

Just before leaving her mother and the family home, she received a hastily penned note addressed to Miss Emily Mallet, Jackson, Georgia, from her soon-to-be-boss postmarked October 2, 1959, by Army Air Force Postal Service.

> . . . your toes must be tingling with excitement by now and no doubt you're experiencing a little nervous apprehension. Right? Well just relax and come on over. I expect to be there to meet you next Thursday with a bundle of welcome.
>
> *Sidney*

From mid-October of 1959 through December of 1960, Mother, siblings, and nieces received cards and letters from Emily postmarked the same way. Mother collected and saved as many as she could. Travel was a primary motivation for Em's taking the job in Germany; almost all her family correspondence detailed impressions of what she saw and did in the Europe of 1960, divided by an "Iron Curtain."

Em's first letters reported Sidney's warm welcome and the library work as he had described it—interesting, demanding, and often hectic because of under staffing. He had arranged her housing—a suite in a government facility for civilian women employees, conveniently near the library. Intending to spend most of her free time traveling, Emily wrote her mother that her quarters were "adequate."

In his Opel automobile, Sidney introduced her to the Rhineland-Palatinate area surrounding the Ramstein Air Base. He also drove her across the nearby French border to sample sights and cuisines in Strasbourg and Dijon. (Em had never before pondered the origin of the mustard she preferred.)

Mary Lane at age four, December 1900.

Mary Lane stands behind her grandmother Janie Fletcher McKibben and her mother Hattie McKibben Lane, c. 1910.

Mary Lane graduated from Wesleyan at age 20 in 1917. This photo was probably taken while she was a student there.

Hugh Mallet, c. 1920.

Mary Lane a year or so before her marriage, c. 1921. On the back of the photo she later inscribed a message: "Remember me! When Mother and Father returned from a visit to Kib at Yale and brought me that pointed Fox Fur from the furriers in New York where Hugh later purchased my fur coat on our honeymoon in Nov. 1922."

Mary Mallet holding her fourth child, her son Hugh, c. 1930.

The first four of the five Mallet children pose for a traveling photographer in the summer of 1933, leaving a space on the settee for their sister Marcia who was to be born in the fall of that year.

Emma Nutt Mallet (right of center) stands behind her young grandchildren surrounded by her children and their spouses on the front porch of the Mallet home on Covington Street in the fall of 1937.

Mary with her five children in the mid-1940s.

Hugh Mallet, c. 1951, just after graduating from college and joining the Air Force.

Mary Lane Mallet with her five children in the 1960s. Left to right: Mary Mallet Carr; Jane Anne Mallet Settle; Hugh Mallet; Mary; Emily Mallet Johnston; Marcia Mallet Ades.

Mary Mallet stands on the front porch of her house on Third Street with her five children and their spouses, thirteen of her fourteen grandchildren, and her first great-grandchild, 1971.

Mary Mallet on Thanksgiving 1972, shortly after her retirement.

The Mallet and Lane families gathered in 1984 for a family reunion in Jackson. Attending were Mary's children, grandchildren, and great-grandchildren who came from all over the country.

Also present were many of Mary's Lane relations, including her sisters Virginia and Margaret. This photograph was posed on the front porch of Heritage house.

The author at the front door to Heritage house in 2005. Jane Anne Settle is the fifth woman to own the house built by her great grandparents Janie and Van McKibben.

Suite-mate Marie, whom she was finding easy to live with, also owned an Opel. Emily was pleased to accept Marie's invitation to join her on an autumn weekend trip to Bavaria, the southern Alpine region of Germany. The letter telling Mother all about the trip began with "My stay here would be perfect if you were here, too."

Their first overnight stop was the old mountain town of Oberammergau, famed for its woodcarving and even more for the all-day amphitheater performance of the Passion Play. Since the 1600s, when the village was spared during an outbreak of the plague, its citizens, usually once each decade, have re-enacted the crucifixion of Christ as expression of gratitude. With the picturesque villages dotting the natural scenery of mountains, lakes, and streams, the young women also toured one of the "Renaissance" castles built in the nineteenth century by "Mad" King Ludwig of Bavaria—a much smaller copy of Versailles set in magnificent gardens but classified as "his hunting lodge."

The next automobile trip with Marie began with a two-hour drive to Paris. Within one weekend, Emily and her new friend and companion crammed sightseeing and shopping, spectacular musical theater, and Sunday hours in the Louvre. On a postcard showing the Arc de Triumph, Em summarized it all for Marcia and Roy, then stationed at Fort Benning.

Em spent her first Thanksgiving in Germany in the divided city of Berlin with Sidney and his American teacher friend Jim. They had managed the red tape permitting an American owned car to drive through the hundreds of miles of then separate communist East Germany in which Berlin—before World War II the capital of a united Germany—was located. The Peace Treaty had divided the city as it had the nation: one part occupied and dominated by communist Russia and the other by the Western democratic Allies.

The three Ramstein-based Americans were invited to Thanksgiving dinner in the flat of Jim and Sidney's friend who taught in the American school in Berlin. She, like everyone seated at her table for traditional turkey and all the trimmings, had taken her job qualifications to Europe in exchange for travel opportunities and a taste of another lifestyle.

The entire holiday weekend was described in Emily's letter to her mother on stationery from the West Berlin Hilton Hotel, where her room was "small but elegant." The experience gave her a first peep into communism when that form of government could be seen side by side with capitalist democracy.

> . . . you just drive through the Brandenburg Gate and you're in East Berlin . . . cars with U.S. forces plates are waved through . . . difference between East and West Berlin is amazing. West Berlin . . . completely rebuilt, modern . . . shops as pretty as the ones in Paris . . . . you wouldn't believe German women could be as stylish . . . In East Berlin . . . few people on the streets, few cars, whole streets of buildings that are just empty shells . . . seems pretty grim . . . went to ballet in State Opera House in East Berlin—one building completely restored . . . Khatchaturian music and dancing good . . . ballet about collective farms . . .

The travel that had lured Emily from Georgia Tech to the Ramstein Air Force Base library had just begun, and she could already feel her eyes and mind opening wider in new surroundings. She appreciated every mile Sidney and Marie introduced to her in their automobiles, but she decided she wanted neither the responsibility or expense of owning one herself. Train service was better than any she had ever known. She could reach Paris by train in three hours. London was accessible, too, by plane or train and ferry. Tours, which could be fitted to match time-off from the library, further expanded travel opportunities. There were Service club jaunts within Germany and into neighboring Switzerland and Austria. Highly recommended tours throughout Western Europe and the Near East were conducted by American Express, Swiss Hotel Tours, and other firms. Emily became a potential customer of them all.

She wrote her college roommate that she had dreaded her first Christmas away from home and family. But she continued with ". . . everything was so different and so beautiful that actually I had a very happy time." She had taken a service club tour planned to show Americans picturesque towns where old customs were observed and traditional holiday fare served. On Christmas Day she was in the Austrian village chapel where "Stille Nacht" ("Silent Night") was written. Of the day spent on skis, she wrote " . . . had a wonderful time—fell down only 12 times."

In February she sent the Carrs a postcard showing scenes of a prestigious ski resort with the message, "This grand trip to St. Moritz seems like a dream."

All her letters to family and friends (especially the detailed ones to Mother) along with picture postcards and carefully selected gifts reveal Emily as enthusiastic, adaptable traveler. ". . . can't believe it's really me seeing so many beautiful sights . . . What a life!" She was describing a weekend trip to Vienna via train with a Swiss Hotel Tour as "one of the nicest I've had . . . We arrived on Sat. morning ready to see everything—and we succeeded . . . I was so impressed with the way they (Swiss Hotel Tours) operate I'm thinking of going to the Near East over Easter . . . I want to go to Scandinavia this summer and with a few trips to Paris and around here. I believe I'll be ready to come home . . . Anyway I think I get my love of going and doing from you . . ."

Maybe she did. And maybe love of home came from mother Mary, too. On Leap Year Day, February 29, 1960, her letter home included the admission that she was not indefatigable. She was seriously considering the possibility of cutting short the assignment she had accepted with the Ramstein Air Force library and returning to the one she had left at Georgia Tech. ". . . .a nice job and congenial working associates. Life is so strenuous here with hard work and travel that I don't know how I can hold up physically much longer . . ."

She weighed her options. She was enjoying traveling even more than she anticipated. She appreciated her professional association as well as personal friendship with Sidney. The work was what she knew and could do, but she missed wider and more professional ties. Making up any hours that travel took from her library schedule meant that she had little time to relax in her own living space—which she never called "home." And home, family, and "old" friends were what she missed most of all. Realizing, too, that her library position at Georgia Tech could not remain open indefinitely, she decided to submit her resignation to be effective at year's end.

For the interim of late spring, summer, and fall she determined to give her best to the hard job that was hers in the Ramstein library and still find time for more travel. She did both.

On May 11, a five page letter to Mother described the Near East trip as "perfect." After Cairo, the Nile, and King Tut's tomb, she had flown to Israel—by way of Cyprus. Israel, in 1960, would not permit a plane to enter from an Arab land. Emily had looked forward to seeing the places known to her since childhood Sunday school. She did visit a number of them, including some where "they think" some Biblical events may have occurred. "I'm glad I went to Israel," she wrote. "The Jews have worked hard and have done a lot with the country, but they never let up telling you about it." A day and night in Istanbul gave time to shop in the Grand Bazaar and to visit the Blue Mosque and St. Sophia. She wrote, "I began to feel at home in a mosque by the time we left."

By the time she mailed the letter, two weeks had elapsed since her flight back to Germany from Istanbul. The added last paragraph mentioned an overnight "grand trip to Holland" while the tulips were blooming. She had ordered bulbs to be sent her mother and promised to write more about that trip later.

Summer and fall letters tell how and where Emily squeezed more travel into the remaining weeks of the time of her life spent as young American single woman, living and working in Europe. One of them was begun as she sat under a hair dryer in a Stockholm department store beauty salon. She was midway through a tour of Scandinavia with major stops in Copenhagen, Stockholm, and Oslo. The letter, giving her impressions of all three, was concluded in her hotel room in Oslo, where she was anticipating a two night boat trip through Norway's fiords.

She had enjoyed Copenhagen and its surroundings—Hans Christian Anderson's "Little Mermaid" as a statue in the harbor, Tivoli amusement park, and Hamlet's Elsinore Castle. She remembered them only vaguely from a shorter trip made several years previously with a Georgia friend. She thought Sweden very much like America, and found Stockholm's biggest store comparable to Atlanta's Rich's. Oslo was her favorite city—perhaps because there had been less rain during the sightseeing. She had a fine view of the city from its ski jump before being inside museums that stretched maritime history from the Vikings to polar explorer Amundsen. She liked the food so well that she determined to get up earlier on the last morning to have plenty of time for the smorgasbord breakfast before leaving for the fjords.

Back at work in Ramstein, she wrote us Settles a late August letter declaring her "major" travels over. But even laboring under an increasingly heavy workload, she seized every opportunity for shorter journeys. A September letter to the Carrs, described a leisurely one-day drive with a friend. They began by following the Rhine where castle ruins seemed like illustrations for fairy tales. At the great cathedral city of Cologne, they turned back to Koblenz, where the Mosel River flows into the Rhine, and then traced the Mosel to the tiny country of Luxembourg. Em found the Mosel valley even prettier than the Rhineland. Just inside the border, Trier—Germany's oldest city—deserved a stop. There they could see Roman walls and mosaics remaining from the time of Emperor Constantine.

After Thanksgiving she wrote Mother about a weekend outside the democracies of Western Europe. Hoping to visit historic Prague, she had applied for documentation then required for entry into Czechoslovakia. With little time left before her return to the States, the long awaited papers finally arrived. Immediately she found a place on a tour to Prague. She would have at least a peep behind the Iron Curtain that during the Cold War so separated and hid a country and its capital only a few hundred miles distant from where she was living and working that they seemed to be in another world. She described the trip as "impressive and depressing," as she wondered why "they" let "us" in the country at all.

A guide had joined them at the border and was with the tour "every minute . . . no opportunity to talk freely with anyone . . ." Excerpts from her impressions included ". . . people in Prague look very drab . . . not much in the stores . . . appliances look old-fashioned . . . many wood-burning stoves . . . nicest thing is the Bohemian crystal, beautiful but very fragile and impractical to consider shipping any home." A Saturday morning tour showed her the Prague she had heard and read about: "a beautiful city." It reminded her of Vienna. Saturday night was spent in a nearby town, "gayer" because it had once been one of the most popular European spas and could still boast fine hotels and a pavilion. The long drive back to Germany more than filled Sunday, especially since leaving Czechoslovakia, like arriving there, meant several hours of delay at the fortified border. Shortly after 2:00 a.m., Monday, she dropped onto her U.S. government issued bed at Ramstein Air Base.

She had promised herself one more trip to London—just for theater. With colleague Virgil as her companion, she made it. They shared many of the same interests although he was a much less experienced traveler and had never before been to England. For this trip, an outstanding asset was his automobile. He drove them to the airport of neighboring Luxembourg where the two boarded a Wednesday afternoon flight to London. The car was left in the airport parking lot to be ready for the drive back to Ramstein on Sunday after their return flight. Emily had been invited to stay in the flat of an American teacher who had been transferred to London from Germany. Virgil had reservations at the London Air Force Hotel. On Thursday morning, the pair were standing at the hotel's travel desk selecting and buying all their theater tickets.

That very afternoon they would see a Chekov play with Rex Harrison, and that evening, "My Fair Lady." (Em said it was "perfect" seen in London.) On Friday, while Virgil took a London sightseeing tour, Emily shopped at Selfridge's ("even bigger than Rich's"). Friday evening they saw the famed acting couple Alfred Lunt and Lynn Fontanne in "The Visit." She judged them "very good" and the play "very strange." The tireless pair packed Saturday with a guided tour of Westminster Abbey in the morning, followed by three more plays. At two o'clock, they were in second row seats to see Alec Guiness (whose performance Em rated "excellent") play the role of T. E. Lawrence of Arabia. They had only to cross the street to be on time for a five o'clock showing of an American production of "West Side Story," which was "making quite a hit in London." There was time for a bite of supper before another curtain rose at eight-thirty for "Passage to India."

Before their Sunday afternoon return flight to Germany, Virgil had a short visit to the National Gallery while Emily crossed the street to Hyde Park, where anyone can speak about anything and possibly attract listeners. Em heard snatches of several: one about communicating with the dead, one about English politics, and another about American politics.

Ten days later, Emily wrote her mother ". . . I've wanted to write you every day—before I forget the details . . ." Probably she did forget many of them, but she was to remember and confront for the rest of her life the theme unifying three very different plays crammed into one 1960 London Saturday.

> . . . The day's theater going brought to mind almost too vividly the world's greatest problem today—different nationalities getting along together and understanding each other. Though the Arab-English, American-Puerto Rican, and Indian-English problems were all well presented, no solutions were offered. The day was really too much for me . . .

Had the entire stay in Europe been "too much" for Emily? As other family members and friends joined and prolonged her welcome home, Mary wondered. Should she simply accept the differences she saw in her daughter—fatigue, weight loss, distraction—as natural results of stress, which should be relieved when the process of returning to the Georgia Tech library and residence in Atlanta was complete?

Another situation could not escape a mother's notice—the constant attention her daughter was receiving and apparently enjoying from Bill Johnston, an aeronautical engineer at Lockheed. Before Em's move to Germany, Mary had met and briefly known him as one of the men she liked well enough to bring with her to Jackson occasionally. If Mary knew that he had also sought her out in Germany when he was traveling there on vacation, she attached little importance to his visit. No mention of it has been found in any of the copious mother-daughter correspondence of late 1959 through 1960.

Mary remembered Bill as older than her daughter by ten years and established and respected in his profession. She knew that he was a Georgia Tech alumnus whose friends often shared his hobby—flying. Mary found "Emily's Engineer" to be pleasant, well-mannered, and quiet—especially when surrounded by her numerous, diverse, and voluble relatives. She had yet to change her assessment.

When Emily was ready to confide, perhaps Mary was not completely surprised by what she learned of the two matters that had concerned her most since her daughter's homecoming—her health and her relationship with Bill.

As to the former, Em admitted that she had not felt really well since before leaving Germany. She had assumed that she was merely feeling the effects of doing too much in too little time. At Bill's insistence, she had already seen a doctor. After a preliminary examination, she had scheduled a hospital stay for several additional tests.

As for the relationship with Bill, there was no need for further tests. Their diagnosis of mutual desire for a life together was complete. The brief time they had spent together in Germany had resulted in far more than renewing their Atlanta friendship. In fact, Bill was one of the reasons (although not expressed) that she decided to cut short the time she had originally planned to be in Germany. Back in Atlanta, Emily was making new discoveries about him. She liked what she was finding: the active, thorough way he examined and dealt with problems; the genuine affection and sense of responsibility he showed for his widowed step-mother; the practice of his chosen Christian religion—Episcopal—not very different from her own and her family's Methodist faith. Her mother could believe Emily's mature values were well matched by those of William Marshall Johnston.

Bill had proposed marriage, and he wanted it to take place as soon as they could arrange it. Emily insisted that any definite wedding plans wait for medical tests to affirm her general good health. The test results, however, indicated that her return to good health would take time, care, and modern medicine. The diagnosis was tuberculosis—doubtless contracted during the past year spent overseas.

The distress felt by Emily, Bill, and those who cared about them was somewhat counteracted by additional information. The "consumption" Em associated with the death of Beth, the third of the *Little Women* sister heroines in a favorite book all the little Mallet sisters had read, and also with that of the young Romantic poet John Keats—all that was in the past.

The prognosis for Emily was excellent. Following doctors' directions and responding to medicines recently developed specifically for tuberculosis, Emily could realistically anticipate complete recovery and cure by the end of 1961. There were options for where she could receive the required supervised care. There were state and private sanitariums. There was also the possibility that home care could be arranged.

Bill urged that she accept his repeated proposal of immediate marriage so that he could supply the home care. Emily refused. She did want to be his wife—but not until she was well.

Mother Mary ended the discussion, not with a proposal but with a pronouncement that could not be refused. The best place, she said, for her daughter's recovery was where she was born—the downstairs back bedroom and "nursery" of the Jackson homeplace. The caregiver would naturally be herself.

Mary left Emily's Atlanta hospital bedside almost immediately for Jackson and the preparations to be made there. Needed professional assistance was waiting in the person of family friend Lucille Hutchinson. Eager for the latest news of Emily, she was ready to act in her capacity as registered nurse in charge of the Butts County Health Department.

She was one and the same as the Lucille who had been Em's travel companion. Six years had passed since the two of them added Zirndorf, to their European itinerary so that they could attend the wedding of Marcia and Leroy. Lucille had hosted one of the parties and taken the opportunity to tell the bride of her lost hope that romance might develop from the high school and college friendship and fun her son Richard had enjoyed with Marcia. Indeed, the Hutchinson-Mallet family ties were almost as complicated as they were strong and lasting.

Before Emily was brought to Jackson, Lucille had directed the transformation of a bedroom, a bath, and kitchen facilities to conform to every regulation and recommendation for the care of patients with communicable disease. She also instructed Mary in helpful, practical procedures for personal care of a patient for whom almost complete bedrest and isolation would at first be required. Mary's caregiving experience had piled high from years as oldest sister, mother of five children, and daughter of a stroke-impaired mother, but she had much to learn about new techniques of sterilization and medication as they applied to Emily's bout with tuberculosis.

Meanwhile, Emily and Bill were stars in a romantic drama in which white costumes and hospital paraphernalia dominated the set. Bill, wearing a mask covering his nose and mouth, slipped the engagement ring on Em's finger in her hospital room. She later said that the song "A Fine Romance With No Kisses" should have been playing as background music for that scene although she considered "Along Came Bill" her theme song.

Within a few days after Em's transfer to Jackson, a workable, not unpleasant patient-caregiver routine was established. Nurse and friend Lucille made frequent check-up calls, but visitors were prohibited. Even immediate family members were allowed only to peep in for a very few moments. In recent years, Mary had seldom driven to Atlanta, but she seemed to have experienced no difficulty in getting Emily to her doctor there when her driving was necessary for meeting scheduled appointments. (Anyone questioning her coping with increasingly challenging highway and city traffic would likely hear Mary's boast that she had been driving an automobile since she was twelve and at twenty-one was certified to be a World War I volunteer emergency ambulance driver.)

Bill Johnston remained a vital part of Emily's recovery. As fiance, he was granted exception to visitation regulations. He was in Jackson every weekend and sometimes appeared during the business week. He co-owned a small airplane that he occasionally piloted to a landing field in Griffin—twenty miles from Jackson. Arrangements could be made for a friend or relative to meet him there and after his visit with Em in Jackson return him to his favorite means of transportation.

As spring became early summer, Emily's health was obviously much improved. She said that she felt better, and her voice sounded stronger as she said it. She was out of bed for longer periods of time. She walked out to the side porch to sit in a rocking chair. With visiting rules somewhat relaxed, I often joined mother and daughter there for a sip of something (served, of course, in disposable cups or glasses) while my little girls played in the tree-shaded area beneath us just as Em and I had when we were children. Aunt Pauline made it her habit to stop by for just a few moments after she left her work as librarian at Hawkes Library for Children on College Street. Doctors and laboratory tests confirmed our observations that prescribed treatment and medication were producing desired results.

Bill had a motorized two-wheeler, portable enough for him to stash in his car or airplane. On one beautiful afternoon Emily felt so well and ready for adventure that with her arms around Bill's waist, she rode behind him for a spin around the neighborhood. The son of a College Street neighbor yelled to his mother, "Look quick! Mrs. Settle is on that funny motorcycle with some gray-haired man."

Em and I had long been accustomed to being mistaken for each other. Those who knew who we were but never bothered to learn who was who referred to us as "just those Mallet sisters."

At last, she was ready and able—as well as willing—for "wife of Bill Johnston" to be added to any identifying introductions that could be hers from heredity, achievement, or chance. Bill had long been ready, willing, and able to hear and participate in such presentations. With the full approval of Emily's doctors, the couple began attaching more specific dates, places, and people to their vague, general marriage plans.

An early December date for a small but traditional wedding would allow plenty of time for simple arrangements to be made for a happy, not hectic occasion. They definitely wanted family and close friends to be present while they knew that the December date right for them presented problems for Marcia and her family in Milwaukee and Hugh and his in Chicago. Brand new baby Mark Ades had arrived in July. Hugh and his wife Cathy were expecting a brother or sister for one-year-old "little Cathy" in October. Emily did hope that somehow her brother Hugh could walk down the church aisle with her as he had older sisters Mary and me. Both of us also chose a December wedding date in the same church, just across the street.

As Emily's return to good health gained momentum and more people and activities gradually re-entered their daily lives, which were dominated more and more by wedding plans, the hours Mother and Em spent together changed. For months, they had made time (beyond that required for routine giving and receiving personal care) for looking through windows and seeing the outside world, reading aloud or separately the same books, newspapers, and magazines, watching television, perhaps playing Scrabble; but—most of all—time with each other had meant talking, talking about *everything* and laughing about much of it, sometimes through tears. As their unique year of companionship moved toward its end, both mother and daughter admitted in different ways and words their desire, their need to preserve it as privately owned memory treasure. So they carefully wrapped it up in a few vacation days on St. Simon's Island.

In a ceremony in which both the Methodist minister and Bill's Episcopalian priest participated, Harriet Emily Mallet and William Marshall Johnston were married on December 9, 1961. She did walk down the aisle of the church where she had been baptized on Hugh's arm. (He had managed to leave Chicago for a long weekend.)

The bride, according to everybody present, was lovely in a wedding dress of pale beige lace. Em was to smile every time she remembered selecting it from several choices. The saleswoman with her in the fitting room had been quite helpful but not especially tactful when she said, "This one is perfect for an older bride." As Em later recounted the events of that day, she said her comment should have been at youthful thirty-three, "Maybe I'm too young for it."

Mary sat proudly composed in her mother-of-the-bride front pew. She had every reason to be satisfied with the wedding itself and her part in the storybook happy ending of her "winsome" third daughter's love story.

The groom radiated happiness as he introduced his best man to his bride, her relatives, and her homeplace. He had chosen Johnston Avary, his first cousin and nearest male relative for that role. Also representing the Johnstons was Allie, his stepmother and real friend since his father's marriage to her. In fact, he shared with her the house his father left. However, Bill and Em had already decided that as soon as possible they would locate their own house near Allie's in the Sandy Springs area of North Atlanta.

The house would have to wait, though, until they returned from the honeymoon Bill had planned. The day after the wedding, they would climb together into his plane for flight to their Caribbean Island destination. Already packed in the plane was the familiar two-wheeler, ready to be convenient land transportation.

Ten years later, Bill and Emily, with their children—nine-year-old William Marshall Jr. and seven-year-old Mary Gage, were again in Jackson for another happy occasion—the celebration of Mother's Day, May 14, 1972. The Johnstons joined the group gathered at my house for a backyard picnic, the honoree was, of course, mother Mary. As many of her children, her grandchildren, and other kin who could possibly attend were there for hours of fun and food. Before the Johnstons left for the return to their Atlanta home, Emily gave her mother this carefully handwritten message:

TO MOTHER

Your eldest daughter's beautiful;
Your second's might smart.
Your youngest is your "baby;"
Your son has claimed your heart.

But I know that I'm special
Because you've given me
Life and love and laughter
In a wonderful family.

Emily

Professional Woman

AT THE AGE OF SIXTY-FIVE, Mary Lane Mallet for the first time in her life, became an employee working regular hours for a specific monthly salary from which taxes—including those for Social Security benefits—were deducted. She was more, however, than another mere working woman. Never "mere" anything, she entered a profession that utilized and expanded her education, abilities, and interests. Her job also required that she conform to rules and performance routines set by authority outside herself—not easy for strong-willed independent Mary. The change and challenge of her late-in-life career began with a death in the family.

In late summer of 1962, Mary, describing herself as "footloose and fancy free," was visiting in the Atlanta area where daughters Mary and Emily and sister Virginia were then living. There she received the telephone call from Jackson with shocking news that sister-in-law Pauline Mallet was dead, apparently from a heart attack preceded by little or no warning.

After a full day's work as librarian at the Jackson-Butts County Library (by then the official designation of the old Hawkes Library) Pauline returned to her home, the Mallet house, and lay down on the couch in her bedroom. There she was found by her tenant and friend, Miss Grace Garlington, who lived in the apartment made from the downstairs rooms across the hall. Miss Grace had anticipated a late afternoon chat as soon as Pauline returned from her first day back on the job after a vacation spent driving her older brother George to and from Florida and visiting with cousins there.

Soon after learning of the death of her sister-in-law, Mary, accompanied by her daughters, was on the road back to Jackson. It was time for mixing memories with grief. With Pauline's death, only George remained of the big Mallet family that had welcomed her forty years before. And he was far from well. Since his wife Minnie's death, he continued to live in the house they had built on the dairy farm property after World War II and happily named "The Mallet Shack." There, assisted by Pauline and the Burfords, who had long lived on the farm and managed operation of the dairy, George coped with loneliness and the worsening effects of the diabetes, which had already caused near blindness. There he cherished memories, especially those of a military past that had begun in the local National Guard and included officer service in both World Wars. He could pin a star on his dress uniform signifying that he had achieved the rank of brigadier general in the U.S. Army. Mother never imagined that George would outlive Pauline. He did so by only two months.

For every one of the years since she and Hugh had returned from their New York honeymoon to the Mallet house, her first Jackson home—Pauline had remained a significant presence in the lives of Mary and her children. With the rest of her sister-in-law's family and friends, they knew Pauline's ways—honest, direct, dependable, intensely loyal—and her opinions, usually expressed, and sometimes not completely grounded in fact or logic. Pauline made no attempt to wrap her ways or opinions in tact or to cushion them with the charm often expected of Southern women of her generation.

"Sister," as she was called by nieces and nephews, seldom missed a piano or "speech" recital or any other school, church, or community production involving them. If scheduled events required transportation to out-of-town locations, she and her automobile could be counted on. She was practical and economical, but those virtues were outweighed by generosity at Christmastime when she seemed to disregard price as she chose gifts to fit the age and current enthusiasm of each niece and nephew. We children grew up but never out of our relationship with our aunt. Through all the stages and changes of our lives, unmarried, aging Pauline remained ever-ready "Sister" to us all.

If Mary had been a blood sister, perhaps Pauline could not or would not have requested her assistance in a matter Mary never divulged until after the main characters in the little drama were dead. Some years before her death, Pauline had asked Mary to go with her and an old friend for dinner at a Macon restaurant. Her "old friend" was Henry H., scion of a once prominent local family, who was back in town for a few days to attend to family matters.

Somewhat amused, Mary realized she was being asked to be the chaperone Pauline evidently thought proper even for an "older adult" unmarried couple. Pauline's carefully detailed planning resulted in neither brother George nor friend Grace having to know about her dinner date. Henry was to meet her and Mary at Mary's house and leave from there for Macon. My mother told me years later that "Sister" looked very nice, even wore a bit of lipstick with her best outfit, and was ready and waiting with her when Henry arrived. The evening progressed as planned; in fact, it was so pleasant that it became an annual, although completely unpublicized, occasion.

It would probably not have been included in this memoir had I not, a few weeks after my aunt's death, met Miss Lois Biles in the Mallet plot at the Jackson City Cemetery where she was carefully reading the tombstones. Recognizing me, she began to talk about my aunt Pauline. Miss Lois had returned as a frail old lady to the town and family roots from which she had sprung before branching out and away. Lodging near a niece, she gave piano lessons to a great-niece while renewing memories and friendships among the living and the dead. I listened while she told me that she and Pauline had been schoolmates before World War I. She wondered if I knew that my "old-maid aunt" had quite a romance with Henry H. "Everybody," she said, "expected to hear that they were engaged to be married." She really did not know the reason for the break-up, but she would tell me the gossip she had heard: Pauline's brothers were much opposed to the match and adamant in their refusal even to consider the idea of her marriage to Henry. Maybe they preferred that she remain single to care for their mother . . . they may have depended on her, too.

I left Miss Lois identifying my Mallet kin who lay beneath granite slabs. I needed to join my very much alive mother Mary in the Land of the Living where she was taking on a new identification.

Appointed to fill the position held for many years by my husband's grandmother (another Mrs. John Settle), I was a member of the board of trustees of our local library. I had attended the recent meeting called to select a new librarian from applicants for the job left vacant by the recent death of my aunt. There the regional director of the Flint River Library system had advised us board members to employ the applicant with the broadest educational background and the most successful experience in "dealing with people of all kinds and ages." Then he had gestured toward the applicants waiting on the other side of the librarian's desk and work area. I gasped. There was my mother. She had not mentioned to me or her other children—as far as I knew—her intention to apply for Sister's job. This was no time for a mother-daughter confrontation. I asked to be recused from the scheduled procedures. I said not a word during any of the interviews and took no part in the selection. Following the recommendations of the regional director, so they told me, the other members of the library's board of trustees employed my mother to be librarian of the Jackson-Butts County Library.

No job could have better suited Mary Lane Mallet at that time in her life. Physically well at sixty-five, she enjoyed walking familiar ways, such as the three Third Street blocks that separated her house from the town square. The walk to Hawkes Library was shorter and even more satisfactory. She could exit her side door, walk down the wide, high steps and across her side yard to the unpaved sidewalk (little more than a path), along McKibben Street, which ended at College Street. Just around the corner was the library. Only on rainy or very cold days did she drive the black Chevrolet, formerly Em's, which had replaced her old red Buick.

Walking past the four tidy houses lining McKibben Street, she could remember when the entire block had been part of her family's barnlot and pasture, separated from her backyard by a fence and high crepe myrtle hedge. After her mother's death, Mary had divided the property into building lots and sold every one.

The library property, however, had been donated by her mother in 1924 when Jackson received money from the Hawkes Library Foundation to build the columned, classic red brick building. With every step of the way between locking her side door and unlocking that of the library, Mary could feel supported, confident, and at home.

Inside, the job that awaited would bring together two of the great joys of her life—books and people.

Librarian Mary soon came to know—occasionally to her surprise—the avid readers who comprised the bulk of the patrons she served and the kind of books they most enjoyed. Although book selection was handled primarily at the district headquarters in Griffin, Mary's requests for specific titles and more books of all kinds did not go unheeded.

Mary also had ways for inserting her own opinions and preferences into regular duties. She became known for almost forcing books on readers when she thought they were perfect fits. And more than once she had declared an acquisition "temporarily unavailable for check-out" when she deemed a young reader not yet "mature" enough for its contents.

Her natural and cultivated people-handling skills could be challenged by complaints. One situation involved a local, rather "fundamentalist" minister who charged through the open library door one afternoon clutching a book, which Mary herself, along with much of America had judged excellent—*To Kill a Mockingbird.* Not he! Opening it, he pointed to lines and entire passages he had highlighted with a yellow marker because he considered them profane, obscene, or heretical and certainly unfit for circulation by a public library.

The librarian of our town and county's public library listened attentively and politely to every accusing word spoken by the unauthorized, self-appointed censor of community reading. She took the book from his hands, closed it, and laid it on her desk. "I'm sorry you checked out a book from this library that you found so offensive," she said. "If ever you do so again, please stop reading the book and return it as soon as you can to this desk—right here."

Throughout the 1960s, Mary was happy in her library work and in the home she had created for her family. She learned that she and her Heritage House could contract and expand to satisfy requirements of her simple lifestyle when she was alone or to make possible the more complicated arrangements necessitated by the comings and goings of her children and their progeny.

In 1966, Lt. Col. Ralph Carr retired from the Army. He and Mary, and their four daughters—then ranging from college freshman to kindergartner—returned to their hometown and the homeplace. They would share Mother's old house until they could buy their own.

Until the Carrs' return to Jackson, only the big, empty house awaited librarian Mary's return from work. She never complained of loneliness.

She saw me and my family almost daily and often enjoyed visits with Emily and her Johnstons either in Atlanta or Jackson.

Less frequent but always eagerly anticipated were the letters, calls, and visits from Hugh Jr. in Chicago. On his visits, whether alone or accompanied by Cathy and their children, his mother's gladness seemed to radiate. Hugh seemed to need to assure himself that his mother lacked for nothing he could supply, whether it was help with household maintenance—occasional improvements as well as repairs—or a new television set. My sisters and I knew that our brother gave our mother what only he could—his presence: his feet under her table again, his laughter, his awful puns, his good talk.

In a letter Mary wrote Hugh in January of 1965, she has just watched President Lyndon Johnson's inauguration on the television set that was Hugh's gift. These excerpts still seem true reflections of our mother's characteristic attitudes.

> Dear Son,
>
> I'm warm here by your TV and your big gas grate enjoying the inauguration and praying that Johnson's "Splendid Society" with justice, peace, and liberty may come to pass. Our family has always, as far back as recorded, enjoyed the benefits of "The Splendid Society" to which all should aspire. "As a Man thinketh, so is he." You, too, in your own generation have earned your place of trust all by yourself, and I'm just as proud of you as if I were a president's mother. I will admit that from the day of your birth I believed you might become president just as I imagined as a girl that I might be the president's wife. I aimed high and have been rewarded far more "greatness" than I ever dreamed of. As life goes on, I'll expect not only my grandsons but also my granddaughters to achieve "greatness." My ideas of greatness probably never included great public recognition so I have never been disappointed as all my dear ones developed greatness of soul . . . Each one has what it takes to live a rich, full life and adjust to the needs of each new day.
>
> I Love Life!
>
> . . . I listen to Radio Chicago every night when I retire and am sure we are in close touch . . .
>
> Love to you and your dear family,
> *Mother*

Letting Go

"I LOVE LIFE!" MARY HAD WRITTEN HER SON. But loving life had not and would not shield her from the common ailments of aging flesh and blood and even mind and certainly not from losses of what and whom she loved.

On the front page of the July 15, 1971, issue of the *Jackson Progress Argus,* her picture appeared beneath the headline "MARY L. MALLET RETIRES AS LIBRARIAN." The article beneath restated the news: "Mrs. Mary Lane (Hugh Sr.) Mallet, librarian at Hawkes Library for Children since August 1962, has retired at her request, it was announced this week by Richard W. Watkins, Chairman of the Board of Trustees . . ."

Since Mother began her late-in-life career, my husband and I had also made changes. His civil service career with the Department of Defense had prompted our move in 1969 from the heart of Georgia, U.S.A. to the heart of Frankfurt, Germany. It was there that I received our Jackson newspaper and read from the first word to the last the news item about my mother, which the hometown readers had perused a week earlier.

Further paragraphs provided more information: "During her term of service, Mrs. Mallet gave unselfishly of her time, knowledge, and energy, to the 'library family,' as she fondly refers to those who use the library's services. The circulation of the library increased from 11,792 books a year in 1961–62 to 13,481 in 1970–71. Through Mrs. Mallet's interest the Vacation Reading Club for students out of school during the summer was continued and developed . . ."

The article continued with the new retiree's personal plans: "She leaves this week for a visit with her son Hugh, of the FBI, assigned presently in Washington, D.C. . . . Mrs. Mallet has four other children, Mrs. Mary Mallet Carr, Mrs. Jane Anne Mallet Settle, Mrs. Emily Mallet Johnston, and Mrs. Marcia Mallet Ades, as well as a large family of grand-children and great-grandchildren, all of whom, she says, are now the center of her interest."

Indeed, we were, and spending time with us, so scattered then, meant travel. The visit with Hugh and his family in Alexandria, Virginia (where he was in commuting distance of Washington), was first on her itinerary.

She was at home when I visited Georgia in late summer to attend the college graduation of our older daughter. She would hardly need to re-pack, she said, to be ready to return to Germany with me.

She insisted that she was up to anything, including the Scandinavian tour we had booked some months earlier with old friends from college days. So the name (Mrs.) Mary L. Mallet was added to our tour director's roster, and she met very well the demands of traveling with new compan-ions for glimpses of Denmark, Sweden, and Norway—with the add-on of an overnight sail through the fjords.

In Frankfurt, my music loving mother enjoyed several concerts with us. I was her guide for the history laden city itself, not yet completely rebuilt from World War II bombing. Saddened that only exterior walls remained of the once imposing opera house, she was glad to learn that ongoing money-raising projects would soon result in rebuilding the grand structure.

In the midst of German culture again, she remembered and talked often of her visit to Bavaria, in southern Germany, where in 1954 she and Marcia had visited Mary—and where she had left Marcia as bride of young Lt. Ades. So, in 1971, my husband drove us to Nuremburg and sur-roundings for another visit. Since the first visit, much had changed. She recognized almost nothing. We found the little village of Zirndorf, but we could not locate the house where she had been daughter Mary's wel-comed, honored, and pampered guest.

"Good traveler" was a description my mother had earned and could still claim. From our Frankfurt apartment, the two of us made a one-day train trip to Heidelberg. Arriving in that old city on the Neckar River, we joined other tourists strolling through picturesque, historic streets that included Germany's oldest university. She knew about it primarily from the musical play, "The Student Prince." There we saw the inspiration for its setting and songs as well as evidence of actual student pranks and serious scholarship of by-gone centuries. After lunch at an outdoor café near the river, we managed to reach the wooded hilltop location of Heidelberg's huge, well preserved medieval castle. Feudalism was on display within its walls, and from its high look-out positions, we had a spectacular view of the city below.

The late afternoon train returned us to our own times and lives. It had been a long day for both of us.

"Homesick" was not a word she admitted to her travel vocabulary. However, her conversation with us in Frankfurt, turned every day more and more to what she had left in Jackson: kin and friends, her own house, her own daily doings and responsibilities. Yet talking about the fast approaching date of her departure was not received with unalloyed joy. Could the prospect of flying across the wide Atlantic by herself be eroding her characteristic self-confidence?

As we gathered together her scattered belongings, including the gifts she had selected and bought for special recipients, I assured her that I would be right with her from the time she left our apartment until she was actually boarding the plane. Then Hugh would be waiting for her when she landed in Washington. It was the mention of her son's name that seemed to obliterate further uneasiness. She rejected my offer to help her with packing. "I really need to do it myself to know where my things are," she said.

Leaving her in the jumbled midst of them, I knew my mother, at seventy-five, was herself. I closed the door, but I could not shut in or shut out my memories of years of other confrontations and challenges she had met head on. More than once, I had heard her declare, "I'm bigger than this is."

Back in Jackson, Mother found her house lively again but different. When daughter Mary, with Ralph and their four daughters returned to Jackson, the old homeplace became their home, too. The Carrs took care of most outdoor maintenance and made improvements inside, too, including remodeling and modernizing the kitchen. While she worked as librarian, mother Mary had enjoyed the excellent meals daughter Mary prepared in it.

When the Carrs moved in, little Kibbie (Carolyn McKibben) was about to enter elementary school. A gap of ten years separated her from Emily (named for her aunt), the youngest of the three older sisters whose interests and activities were high school, college, boyfriends, and marriage. Their parents were each beginning new careers of their own—Ralph's requiring commuting to Macon daily and Mary's in local public education.

Returning from visiting other children, Mother did not know her role in the house she no longer headed. Whose house was it? Whose and what authority was whose? The situation demanded tolerance, acceptance, and constant adjustment. Not even family love could ease all the tension or smooth rough spots where so many conflicting interests collided.

The Carrs bought and moved into their own house, a substantially built brick home, conveniently located near both the homeplace and schools. It was part of Garden Hills, a development created from what had been cotton fields on the "home farm" of the estate Hattie McKibben Lane inherited from her parents. Little more than twenty years had elapsed since the "big land auction" resulted in that post-World War II stretching of little Jackson's residential limits. Again alone in her Third Street homeplace, Mother often suggested to me or any other visiting kin that we "go over to the farm and see Mary."

For a while, she seemed to manage "aloneness" very well. She arranged her rooms and their furnishings as she desired—as she did her routines and social life. She played canasta with old friends, some of them "the girls" of the past garden club years. Of course, she attended worship services in the church across the street; it had been central in her life since coming to Jackson as a bride. She spent hours in what she called "going through" old papers, letters, and photographs.

She never lost interest in the doings of her children and grandchildren. She visited them when possible, and they "dropped in" on her. She was in daily contact with her Mary, who had become a curriculum director in the central office of the county education department. (Who could have imagined that Butts County's education would be administered from a building occupying the same space that had once contained her husband's office—a walled off front section of the corrugated metal warehouse for his seed, feed, and fertilizer business?) Emily came often from Atlanta. In the early-to-mid-1970s, we other three children—located in Pennsylvania, Virginia, Louisiana—depended on the telephone calls and letters, supplemented by reports from our Georgia sisters, to keep us aware of our mother's well-being.

Her physical health was usually rather good. She had prescribed medication for high blood pressure. However, maintaining that she knew when she needed it, she refused to take it daily as directed. She was persuaded—much to the relief of her children and doubtless of many townspeople—to give up driving. Daughter Mary kept the keys, and the old car remained in the old garage on the east side of her front lawn. Giving up driving meant giving up part of who she was or considered herself to be.

So did other adjustments. She admitted that she needed part-time help for house and yard maintenance. Such workers, even those with minimal qualifications, were hard to find and harder for her to supervise. What had happened to her "executive ability"?

Money matters often necessitated calls for daughter Mary's assistance. Monthly check-writing for routine utility bills and infrequently used charge accounts became dreaded tasks. Simple cash transactions—buying a few groceries or paying for a meal in a café on the square—could conclude with her at the cashier's corner pouring the contents of her purse, along with bills and coins, on the counter.

Sometimes she mentally withdrew from frustrating attempts to cope with present daily life. Memory could transport her to pleasures of the past where people she loved still lived. I surprised her one day with an unannounced visit. In her parlor, standing by Grandmother's old piano, she greeted me. "I've just had the best time talking to Andrew . . . wish he was still here to sing while you're here, too."

I had no comment. I had been with her at Uncle Andrew's funeral several years previously.

There was no question that she was already "failing" in 1976 when tragedy again invaded the life she loved. In March of the bicentennial year of the country, Hugh Mallet Jr.—having served as an Air Force officer in the Korean War and in far more stressful and demanding assignments for the Federal Bureau of Investigation—suffered a fatal heart attack in his Washington office.

After the initial shocking blow, Mother rallied her strength for the long automobile drive with her daughter Mary and Ralph to Alexandria, and the Mallet home. Chuck and I, on vacation with his sister and her husband, received the terrible news in Madrid, Spain. We were able to secure one seat on a flight leaving Madrid within hours for Washington. I was on it. In fact, I was already in Alexandria when my mother arrived from Georgia with the Carrs. Before the next day ended, Emily and her family from Atlanta and Marcia with some of hers from Louisiana had joined family members already there. We shared our grief, and perhaps found in familiar family togetherness some measure of strength. My sisters and I felt real empathy for our brother's three children; we had experienced losing our own father when our ages ranged from five to fifteen years.

The Mount Vernon Methodist Church could not hold the throng attending Hugh funeral. All the parking spaces were filled, and automobiles lined the street. Some of them were long black official limousines. Inside the church, I saw my mother publicly mourn the second Hugh Mallet she had loved and lost. Erect and composed, behind her son's wife and their three children, she walked down the church aisle leading to her son's coffin, placed before the altar. The March day was cold, and she wore a cape I had brought with me and insisted that she wear. It became a robe for the grieving mother who wore it with the dignity of a queen.

Back at the Mallets' home, I heard Hugh's widow talk to his mother. The tiny, seemingly fragile "little French doll from Maine" (as we Mallet sisters may have so mistakenly assessed our sister-in-law) was showing her strength. She said to our mother, "When your husband died and left you with five children to bring up, you did it. Now I'll have to do it with our three." In the years that followed, she showed us that she could.

Three years after her son's death, Mother—we daughters knew—was becoming increasingly unable to cope with daily life, either in her own house or with one of us. In January of 1979, she became another confused resident with impaired memory at The Living Center, a personal care facility some twenty miles from the Jackson homeplace that had been hers for sixty years. She took little with her besides several indestructible elements of her being.

On one of our visits to see her there, she pointed out another Living Center resident who appeared to be both glum and hostile. “You can see that she’s really unhappy,” Mother whispered. “Before this day’s over, I’m going to see her smile.” Mother kept her love of music and could often be heard singing in her trained mezzo soprano. When I visited, we were encouraged to use the Center’s dining room piano if she wanted accompaniment for singing hymns or old remembered songs. Often, other residents joined in. If I played a wrong note, she immediately reached over my hand to strike the right key. I might hear, “It’s a sharp.” One of the staff members who seemed really to understand—even like her—told us how she helped our mother on the bad days when she was agitated and disoriented. “I ask her to sing a hymn to help all of us feel better.” Then, so she said, her strong voice might ring through the halls with “I sing because I’m happy; I sing because I’m free. His eye is on the sparrow, and I know he watches me.”

After our mother’s death, we sisters gathered at the homeplace. We could not miss seeing a book on the table in the side hall. A message in Mother’s handwriting, “FOR MY FUNERAL,” protruded from a collection of verse. It marked the place of Victorian novelist George Eliot’s poem, “The Choir Invisible.” The poem begins:

> “O may I join the choir invisible
> Of those immortal dead who live again
> In minds made better by their presence . . .

And it ends:

> “So shall I join the choir invisible
> Whose music is the gladness of the world.”

What Happened to the Things

"*It's terrible that things outlast people . . . these things of Mama's and Grandma's . . . I'm tired of things . . .*" —Mary Lane Mallet (1896–1985)

We just had to do something about Mother's things. It had been a year since her death, and her house and her things—furniture, china, bric-a-brac, clothing—were almost as they had been seven years before when, reluctant and confused, she had left them for residence in The Living Center. Our practical husbands urged us to action, warning of the risks of leaving so much in an unoccupied house. We agreed with them, of course, but we knew, I believe, that there was more to our delay than the difficulty of juggling schedules and arranging to get together.

The three Georgia sisters—Mary, Emily, and I—agreed to meet at Mother's house on an April Saturday to do at least a bit of outside maintenance, pruning, and spring neatening. My husband and I were the first to arrive. I saw that there was plenty to keep us busy. The front walk, first of all, needed attention. Many of the octagonal paving blocks were broken, and grass and weeds were pushing up in the cracks.

I was on the steps before I saw that what our husbands had warned about, what we had feared had happened. The big beveled glass pane in the front door had been smashed, and shiny slivers lay all over the porch.

Careful not to be cut by the jagged glass remaining, we pushed the dangling curtain aside and peered through. The front hall seemed as we had left it last except for glass on the floor. When Mary and Ralph arrived with the key and Em, almost simultaneously drove in from Atlanta, we inspected further and called the police.

What a stupid, bungling burglar the intruder had been. We were very lucky that he or she or they had not stolen or damaged more. After we noticed blobs of wax on the floors and rugs all over the house along with the remains of decorative candles Mother had placed on tables and mantels, we knew we were fortunate that the house had not been burned down. Evidently the breaker-and-enterer had come at night and was afraid that turning on the lights would attract attention to the usually dark house.

Actually, very little had been taken. If the burglar had been looking for modern television and stereo equipment, he had come to the wrong place. Although Mother had squirreled cash away throughout the house (we continued to find it for a long time), he had not taken the time to look in tiny desk pigeon holes or the bottoms of vases or between the pages of books. He had dumped the contents of a metal strong box on the back hall floor only to be disappointed that it yielded long-cancelled checks and scraps of trivial correspondence. We felt rather gleeful as we pictured his frustration.

Draperies had been yanked from a parlor window, and one panel was missing. So was a little Dresden figurine, a dainty dancing girl who had graced a marble topped table. It had been one of the few souvenirs Mother had bought for herself when she visited us in Germany. Gone, too, were six porcelain angels, each playing a different instrument. We had sent those to Mother as Christmas decorations. She liked them and kept them out all year on the dining room mantel. The drapery had been used to wrap up and carry out the pretty, if not particularly valuable, loot. The finer, older pieces, which we loved and valued much more, had been left—probably considered as just dusty, out-of-date junk.

Still, we were angry—Mother's *things*! We knew we could not keep putting off; decisions and divisions had to be made.

So on a humid July morning, there we all were, together in Mother's cool, high ceilinged musty parlor. Mary and I had only to come from our own houses, each less than a mile away. Em had driven down from Atlanta. Hugh, whose death ten years before, Mother had never really been able to accept, was represented by two of his three children. Young Hugh, a college senior, and Cathy, Georgetown graduate and Washington working girl, had arrived from Virginia very late the night before. Marcia and Roy had also just had a long drive, their's from western Louisiana. There we all were, ready to get on with the task.

Mother had left a will stipulating that everything she owned was to be divided among her five children or their surviving children. Her surviving children were to be joint executors. Some years previously Mary and I had also read a letter to us that was in her lock box at the bank; it also stated that, although her desire was not legally binding, she hoped that her house could remain in our family.

The will made only one specific, individual bequest. Mother's crescent diamond pin, a sixteenth birthday present from her grandmother Janie, was to go to Marcia. It was the only piece of truly valuable jewelry Mother still possessed. Although we had seen it only on those special occasions when it was taken from the bank box, the pin was a significant factor in our lives. We knew why Mother wanted Marcia to have it.

She had already parceled out to us older children what she held most dear of her personal possessions. Mary had received her sterling silver tea service and tray as a wedding gift. She gave me her silver pitcher and goblets, the pitcher her own wedding gift from her brother Andrew. Grandmother's lovely old piano from Boston still stood in the parlor, but Mother had given it to Emily. She gave Hugh her diamond solitaire engagement ring to give to his own bride. Mother held on to the diamond pin; it had been her security, our ace in the hole. Marcia had been five years old when our father died suddenly of a heart attack. Mother was trying finally to leave her youngest some substitute for the security that had been snatched from her childhood.

Mother had been a widow for forty-six years, every one of them presenting financial hurdles. Land was important in Mother's Southern background, but more important, real estate was expendable. She sold off most of her heritage, foot by square foot, at cheap forties and early fifties prices. The diamond pin never was sold. If some money problems seemed to be insoluble, Mother could announce in a positive, confident tone, "Remember we still have the diamond pin. We always have that to fall back on."

It was beautiful: big diamonds at the center of a gleaming crescent taper to smaller ones at each end. I remember wondering if that single piece of gold-set glitter could really secure our future. As far as I knew, we never had it appraised. Mother just said that it was "very valuable."

I wore it one time. The occasion was my college senior prom. I had a new dress—simple, black, sophisticated, I thought. It had been bought on sale, but it had not been worn previously by sister or cousin; it was chosen by and for me. Mother said that the diamond pin was just the right accent for the boat shaped neckline. I agreed. But I have seldom experienced relief so complete as that when, after a quite satisfactory prom weekend, I returned our family security to my mother.

Forty years later it had again been taken from the bank. This time Mary placed the pin in Marcia's hands. Assembled in her parlor, Mother's children had begun to carry out her final wishes.

The house, itself—slate roof leaking, chimneys toppling, balcony sagging—was the next consideration. Here Emily supplied the happy solution. She would buy our shares, repair and restore, and return on her retirement to the house where she had been born. The house could be kept in the family.

Em had an idea, too, for how we could fairly distribute the contents of the house, all the amazing accumulation of four generations. She had read how Franklin Roosevelt had directed that his belongings be distributed among his children so that each could have the best chance of receiving what he really wanted. Beginning with the eldest and going down to the youngest, each child chose one item. On the second round, the second child had the first choice, and so on until all the belongings were distributed. We agreed unanimously to accept and follow the Roosevelt procedure.

Through hours of July heat the distribution continued either by drawing or by taking turns at choice. Books, pictures, lamps, personal effects seemed to multiply. Emily claimed the gold and pearl pin that she had designed for us five to give Mother in 1972 the year of the fiftieth anniversary of her marriage to our father. Em had replaced one of the five pearls actually lost from the pin the same year Hugh died.

What we accomplished took three days. Of course we did not finish. There were and are still diplomas, books, family pictures, letters, dangling decisions still to be disposed of. But all of us had overdrawn our time and energy and will for the task, at least for the time being.

Before we separated to return to our present and waiting lives, we celebrated together at a kind of dining room picnic at our house. We were in a gala mood, each of us confident of receiving the best. There had been more laughter than tears.

Setting the table, I needed a small spoon for the relish tray. Reaching into the silver I had just brought from Mother's house, I saw it—a fanciful silver coffee spoon, engraved CONEY ISLAND. Mother and Daddy had gone to New York in the fall of 1922 on their honeymoon. She had told us that they spent one day there at Coney Island. So before we shared the ham and chicken and potato salad, we drank a toast in iced tea or wine from the Piggly Wiggly to Mother and Daddy, to us children, and to Coney Island.